# The Patient Factor

## Volume II

T0315347

# The Patient Factor
## Applications of Patient Ergonomics

## Volume II

Edited by
## Rupa S. Valdez and Richard J. Holden

CRC Press
Taylor & Francis Group
Boca Raton  London  New York

CRC Press is an imprint of the
Taylor & Francis Group, an **informa** business

Cover illustration by Michael Morgenstern

First edition published 2021
by CRC Press
6000 Broken Sound Parkway NW, Suite 300, Boca Raton, FL 33487-2742

and by CRC Press
2 Park Square, Milton Park, Abingdon, Oxon, OX14 4RN

ISBN: 978-0-367-24564-1 (hbk)
ISBN: 978-0-367-72089-6 (pbk)
ISBN: 978-0-429-29300-9 (ebk)

Typeset in Times
by codeMantra

*To our Wisconsin mentors, Bentzi, David Z.,
Mike S., Pascale, and Patti*

*To the mentors we gained along the way, Dan C.,
Judy H., Malaz, Matt W., and Peter B.*

*To all the other unnamed mentors, who were there for us*

*To the secret mentor, who knows who they are*

# Contents

## SECTION I  Introduction to Applications of Patient Ergonomics

## SECTION II  Patient Ergonomics Settings

# SECTION III   Patient Ergonomics Populations

# SECTION IV   Conclusion

# Foreword

Patients and healthcare consumers are becoming more involved with their own health care. This trend has highlighted the central role of patients and the need for new ways to apply human factors and ergonomics to improve and optimize their experience as well as healthcare outcomes. This includes ways of improving patient access to and effective use of healthcare information, technologies, and resources. With these changes, patients are taking greater charge of their own care. This has included diabetic patients using sensing devices to provide real-time information about their own blood sugars, monitoring of chronically ill patients using sensor devices at home to improve patient safety and to enhance independence, patients' accessing health information using mobile apps, and patients directly accessing hospital-based electronic record data from home (Tang et al., 2006). Along with these trends is the need to better understand the information needs of diverse patient populations in order to create tailored care and management approaches for a wide range of patients including children, older adults, the disabled, and the underserved. The importance of health promotion and prevention for the health of individuals has also come to the fore with the advent of social media and online communities, which have radically changed the role of the patient (Eysenbach, 2000). Furthermore, integrating patient-generated information in health records with conventional hospital-based healthcare processes is radically changing health care by increasing availability of personal health data to patients. This had led to consideration of a broader range of participants in health care, including patients, their families and caregivers, the general public, and the various health professionals interacting within a more collaborative healthcare system.

Along these lines, health care is fundamentally shifting from a hospital-based physician-centric approach to a more distributed healthcare system, where the patient moves to the center of the "healthcare work system" (Holden, Cornet & Valdez, 2020). This emerging work system is supported by the ever evolving and rapidly changing healthcare technological ecosystem. Developments spurring this shift include but are not limited to the following: the greater use of health information technologies by consumers of health care; the move to mobile health and smart home technologies; greater online access to one's own health information; and an overall greater involvement of patients in their own decision-making (Eysenbach & Diepgen, 2001). Along these lines, the field of *patient ergonomics* has emerged as the application of human factors and ergonomics to study and improve patient work (Holden & Mickelson, 2013). The key concept here is of "patient work," which underlies and highlights not only the role of the patient but also the centricity of the patient at the heart of the efforts of the healthcare system (Valdez et al., 2016).

Human factors and ergonomics work has long focused on ways of improving the processes and decisions of health professionals in traditional healthcare settings (e.g. hospitals) (Carayon, 2016). In contrast, the focus on applying a human factors lens starting from the perspective of patients and other nonprofessionals (e.g. family members) represents a newer perspective from which to view healthcare processes and the healthcare technology ecosystem. Volume II of *The Patient Factor: A Handbook on Patient Ergonomics* is an important follow-up to Volume I on patient ergonomics, which represents a groundbreaking approach to considering human factors and ergonomics in health care. Topics covered in Volume I include theories of patient ergonomics, the domains of patient ergonomics, and patient ergonomic methods. Volume II focuses on applications. Applications range from patient ergonomics approaches to improving care transitions and optimizing healthcare in home settings to community pharmacies and supporting online social networks. The objective of better understanding the patient journey through the application of methods from human factors and ergonomics forms a common thread of the authors of the various chapters in both Volumes I and II. By better understanding the issues, challenges, and gaps in health care, from the perspective of the actual consumer of health care, considerable light will be shed on where improvements can be made so health care can become more efficient and effective.

This new second volume uniquely brings together a range of international experts from varied fields to provide an interdisciplinary approach to considering how human factors approaches can be applied to optimize health care. A commonality of the chapters in this volume is the focus on the work of the patient. One of the strengths of the research presented is the use of a range of methods, borrowed from human factors and ergonomics literature more broadly. The settings described, by the very nature of patient ergonomics, are also varied. Chapters 1 and 12 describe the importance of attending to this variation, arguing for why context matters and summarizing key takeaways about patient ergonomics applications across contexts. Chapters 2 through 6 include specific "patient ergonomics settings" where patient work takes place (e.g. in the hospital or at home), whereas Chapters 7 through 11 deal with "patient ergonomics populations." The book deals with patient work in the context of a variety of domains and contexts, ranging from conventional hospital-based locations to virtual patient work.

The substantive chapters in this volume cover a range of applications:

- *Chapter 2: A human factors and ergonomics approach to understanding the patient experience in emergency medicine.* It has been widely reported that patients are often frustrated by wait times and issues around processes in emergency department. The authors focus on applying human factors and ergonomics approaches to better understand patient needs in the emergency department to lead to patient-centered solutions for more efficient and safer health care in that setting.
- *Chapter 3: The patient ergonomics approach to care transitions: Care transitions as a patient journey.* Care transitions are a critical and challenging aspect of health care. As patients and caregivers do much of the work during transitions of care across health settings, greater emphasis is needed to understanding transitions from their perspectives. In this chapter, challenges specific to patient work during transitions are discussed and two case studies are provided to illustrate a patient-centered approach.

- *Chapter 4: Patient ergonomics in the wild: Tailoring patient ergonomics models and methods to home and community settings.* This chapter provides an overview of frameworks that can be used to understand patient work in home and community settings. The objective is to allow human factors and ergonomics researchers to conduct cross-study data sharing and synthesis. The chapter also describes practical considerations for analyzing patient work-focused activities in both the home and community, along with two case studies to illustrate the approach.
- *Chapter 5: Community retail pharmacies: The incipiency of patient ergonomics research in the retail pharmacy setting.* Despite the considerable body of literature indicating that patients often do not take medications optimally (leading to errors, morbidity, and mortality), the focus of much human factors and ergonomics work has typically been on the pharmacist and pharmacy work system. In this chapter, a different perspective is taken where patients are considered as being active and equal team players. The chapter discusses approaches to improving the usability and patient understandability of medication instructions, prescription labels, and over-the-counter medication packaging.
- *Chapter 6: Online communities and social networks: Considering human factors and patient ergonomics.* Patients, caregivers, and clinicians increasingly use online communities and social networks (OCSNs) as they are becoming an important vehicle for patient work. OCSNs are increasingly used for many tasks, including making sense about health information, healthcare management, and coordinating resources. This chapter discusses key considerations of OCSNs as a vehicle for patient work; the value, quality, and interpretation of information; participation in OCSNs; and privacy issues. An example of an OCSN intervention focused on older adults is described, along with an example of a non-interventional OCSN.
- *Chapter 7: Designing for veterans: A participatory ergonomics approach to design a mental health self-management tool.* There are a range of physical, cognitive, and ergonomic issues facing returning combat veterans. In this chapter, a veteran-centered approach to designing mobile technology-based mental health interventions is described. These interventions are designed to allow for continuous monitoring of physiological and emotional states and to provide self-care alternatives. Experiences using the approach and issues unique to this population are described, along with veteran-specific design guidelines.
- *Chapter 8: Patient ergonomics in pediatric settings.* Patient ergonomics is particularly important in the area of pediatric health care. As compared to adult populations, pediatric patients often rely on their nonprofessional caregivers (e.g. family members or legal guardians) to make decisions, and they are an integral part of the patient's healthcare management. This chapter discusses differences between adult and pediatric populations, the relevant sociotechnical system context, and the various different roles and settings that pose challenges in this domain. Four case studies are presented

to demonstrate the complexity of patient ergonomics in pediatric healthcare settings.

- *Chapter 9: Understanding the patient, wellness, and caregiving work of older adults.* This chapter provides a general overview of the older adult population and their needs. Three kinds of health-related work that older adults engage in are discussed: patient work (related to health management); wellness work; and work caring for others (caregiving work). How these activities vary by location (e.g. in the home or formal work setting) is discussed and challenges and opportunities are described in the context of technology-based solutions to help manage information, support remote engagement, and coordinate caregiving activities.

- *Chapter 10: Underserved populations: Integrating social determinants of health into the study of patient work.* Patients from underserved populations face a number of health-related disparities. In this chapter, an ergonomic perspective is taken to examine complex interacting factors that can lead to such inequity. The chapter argues for a new model integrating social determinants of health with patient ergonomics in a way that takes into consideration how work system components may interact to drive inequity. Two case studies focusing on an ergonomic approach to improving health care for these populations are described along with recommendations related to underserved populations.

- *Chapter 11: Health promotion: Patient self-management, cognitive work analysis, and persuasive design.* Patient self-management involves a variety of behaviors around planning and maintaining health promotion activities. This chapter aims to bridge the work in human factors and ergonomics with theories in health promotion and persuasive design. Specifically, the chapter explores the relation between theoretical foundations of health promotion and the use of cognitive work analysis for informing persuasive design for health promotion. Implications and recommendations for work in persuasive design for health promotion are explored.

This collection of chapters represents a unique and much needed perspective from human factors and ergonomics research and practice that puts the patient and their caregivers directly in the center of focus. This volume has been dedicated to the coverage of advances in patient ergonomics in a variety of settings and contexts. Human factors and ergonomics approaches for assessing patient experience and patient journeys will become increasingly important tools for understanding complex healthcare processes as health care moves from the hospital and clinic to a wider range of settings and contexts, particularly from the patient perspective. Approaches for characterizing and analyzing the experience of patients as they journey through the health system will need to be better understood, for example, from diagnosis of a disease such as cancer through treatment and discharge from a hospital and management at home. The human factors and ergonomics perspective or "lens" allows for in-depth understanding of the decisions, tasks, processes, and problems encountered by patients and informal caregivers in real-life complex activities as they occur over time. The objectives of understanding and analyzing how patients and their caregivers can best be supported as participants in their own healthcare process are multifold. Such analysis can point out areas where problems and bottlenecks are occurring in a process that need to be rectified. In addition, such analysis can provide strategic insight into where there are opportunities for improving key processes, for example integrating technology or automation in novel, understandable, and useful ways. This will also lead to envisaging new ways of designing and reengineering solutions that solve problems in a range of healthcare domains.

This volume describes advances and innovations in use of methods emerging from the area of patient ergonomics for improving domains where understanding complex processes from the user perspective is essential. These approaches have the potential to lead to key insights into reengineering complex healthcare processes in ways that are more effective, efficient, and enjoyable for the users of those healthcare services and processes, highlighting the critical importance of patient ergonomics.

**Andre Kushniruk, PhD, FACMI, FIAHSI**

*Professor and Director, School of Health Information Science,*
*University of Victoria, Victoria, Canada*

## REFERENCES

Carayon, P. (Ed.). (2016). *Handbook of Human Factors and Ergonomics in Health Care and Patient Safety.* Boca Raton, FL: CRC Press.

Eysenbach, G. (2000). Consumer health informatics. *BMJ*, 320(7251), 1713–1716.

Eysenbach, G., & Diepgen, T. L. (2001). The role of e-health and consumer health informatics for evidence-based patient choice in the 21st century. *Clinics in Dermatology*, 19(1), 11–17.

Holden, R. J., Cornet, V. P., & Valdez, R. S. (2020). Patient ergonomics: 10-year mapping review of patient-centered human factors. *Applied Ergonomics*, 82, 102972.

Holden, R. J., & Mickelson, R. S. (2013, September). Performance barriers among elderly chronic heart failure patients: An application of patient-engaged human factors and ergonomics. In *Proceedings of the Human Factors and Ergonomics Society Annual Meeting* (Vol. 57, No. 1, pp. 758–762). Los Angeles, CA: SAGE Publications.

Tang, P. C., Ash, J. S., Bates, D. W., Overhage, J. M., & Sands, D. Z. (2006). Personal health records: definitions, benefits, and strategies for overcoming barriers to adoption. *Journal of the American Medical Informatics Association*, 13(2), 121–126.

Valdez, R. S., Holden, R. J., Caine, K., Madathil, K., Mickelson, R., Lovett Novak, L., & Werner, N. (2016, September). Patient work as a maturing approach within HF/E: Moving beyond traditional self-management applications. In *Proceedings of the Human Factors and Ergonomics Society Annual Meeting* (Vol. 60, No. 1, pp. 657–661). Los Angeles, CA: SAGE Publications.

# Preface

For me, context is the key—from that comes the understanding of everything.

**Kenneth Noland (1988)**

In Volume I of this two-part handbook, we established the need for patient ergonomics and presented the theories and methods to guide its study. In this, the second volume, we illustrate the ways in which such theories and methods may be applied. In particular, we explore the range of settings and populations that may serve as application areas for patient ergonomics. In doing so, we emphasize the ubiquity and pervasiveness of patient work.

As Volume I illustrates, there are key underlying components of patient work that exist across settings and populations. Regardless of the specific qualities of either, patient work often encompasses information seeking, care coordination, and treatment plan adherence, among other processes. Despite these commonalities, the details of how patient work manifests vary across settings and populations. For example, the patient work performed by and for a child with medical complexity in a pediatric hospital setting may look different than the patient work performed by and for a middle-aged veteran living with post-traumatic stress disorder (PTSD) in a home setting. Given the ubiquity of patient work, it is impossible to provide an exhaustive discussion of settings and populations in one volume. However, Volume II presents a first attempt to consolidate what we know about the particulars of patient work across diverse contexts.

We would like to thank the many individuals who made this volume possible. We are first and foremost grateful to the many patients, family members, and community members who have shared their experiences with us and kept us focused on the problems that affect their everyday lives. We have also been fortunate to be part of rich professional communities in human factors and ergonomics, health informatics, and patient safety, as well as other spaces, and are grateful for the opportunities our colleagues have provided to discuss and refine the ideas contained within this book. Moreover, we are forever grateful to our first mentors at the University of Wisconsin-Madison and our subsequent mentors around the globe who first showed us how human factors and ergonomics could meaningfully improve health care, taught us to always consider context, urged us to translate our theoretical efforts into practice, and have continued to deeply influence our work. From our mentors' examples, we have also learned how to be meaningful mentors to our students and mentees, for whom we are also thankful. In particular, we would like to thank Chi Mila Ho for the many hours she has dedicated to editing this volume. Last but not least, we are thankful for our families who have provided unconditional support for our efforts to develop the field of patient ergonomics, including this handbook.

This handbook was written several months after the preface for Volume I and we continue to live in a world not only consumed by a pandemic but also increasingly aware of the differences in how such an event is differentially experienced across people and places. This pandemic has exacerbated existing health disparities across race, ethnicity, and other demographic characteristics, with Black Americans in particular being three times as likely to contract COVID-19 and two times as likely to die from its complications in comparison to White Americans.[1] Moreover, the role of settings has been repeatedly highlighted. Statistics have shown extremely disproportionate rates of infection and death in congregate living settings; individuals living in these settings comprise less than 1% of the population, but make up 42% of all deaths.[2] Thus, although everyone globally must engage in patient work of some variety during the pandemic, it is imperative that those seeking to support patients remember its differential impact. In other words, in addressing patient work in a pandemic and beyond, *context is the key.*

**Rupa S. Valdez,**
*Charlottesville, Virginia*
**Richard J. Holden,**
*Indianapolis, Indiana*

---

[1] Soucheray, S. (2020). US blacks 3 times more likely than whites to get COVID-19. Retrieved from https://www.cidrap.umn.edu/news-perspective/2020/08/us-blacks-3-times-more-likely-whites-get-covid-19

[2] Roy, A. (2020). The most important coronavirus statistic: 42% of U.S. deaths are from 0.6% of the population. Retrieved from https://www.forbes.com/sites/theapothecary/2020/05/26/nursing-homes-assisted-living-facilities-0-6-of-the-u-s-population-43-of-u-s-covid-19-deaths/#6dc718ce74cd

# Editors

**Rupa S. Valdez, PhD,** is Associate Professor at the University of Virginia jointly appointed in the Schools of Medicine and Engineering and Applied Sciences. She is also affiliated with Global Studies and the Disability Studies Initiative. Dr. Valdez merges human factors engineering, health informatics, and cultural anthropology to understand and support the ways in which people manage health at home and in the community. Her research and teaching focus on underserved populations, including populations that are racial/ethnic minorities, of low socioeconomic status, and/or living with disabilities. Her work draws heavily on community engagement and has been supported by the National Institutes of Health (NIH), Agency for Healthcare Research and Quality (AHRQ), and the National Science Foundation (NSF), among others. She serves as Division Chair of Internal Affairs for the Human Factors and Ergonomics Society (HFES) and as Associate Editor for *Journal of the American Medical Informatics Association (JAMIA) Open*. She is the founder and president of Blue Trunk Foundation, a nonprofit dedicated to making it easier for people with chronic health conditions, disabilities, and age-related conditions to travel. Dr. Valdez lives with multiple chronic health conditions and disabilities, which have and continue to influence her work and advocacy.

**Richard J. Holden, PhD,** is Associate Professor of Medicine at the Indiana University (IU) School of Medicine and the Chief Healthcare Engineer at the IU Center for Health Innovation and Implementation Science. He earned a joint PhD in Industrial Engineering and Psychology from the University of Wisconsin. He founded and directs the Health Innovation Lab and co-directs the Brain Safety Lab. Dr. Holden's research applies human-centered design and evaluation methods to improve health outcomes, especially for older adults. He specializes in research on technology for patients with chronic diseases, such as dementia and heart failure, and their family caregivers. He is a scientist in the Regenstrief Institute and in 2020 received the 2019 Outstanding Investigator Award and the Regenstrief Institute Venture Fellowship. Dr. Holden has led or played key roles in more than 20 federally funded research and demonstration projects, totaling more than $75 million. He has authored over 150 peer-reviewed works in the fields of human factors engineering, patient safety and quality, health informatics, and research methods. He is most proud of being an innovator, mentor, and connector of dots.

# Contributors

**Alicia I. Arbaje**
The Johns Hopkins University School
of Medicine
Baltimore, Maryland

**Natalie C. Benda**
Weill Cornell Medicine
New York City, New York

**Orysia Bezpalko**
Children's Hospital of Philadelphia
Philadelphia, Pennsylvania

**Catherine Burns**
University of Waterloo
Waterloo, Canada

**Annie T. Chen**
Department of Biomedical Informatics
and Medical Education
Seattle, Washington

**Jessie Chin**
University of Illinois at
Urbana-Champaign
Urbana-Champaign, Illinois

**Michelle A. Chui**
University of Wisconsin-Madison
School of Pharmacy
Madison, Wisconsin

**Andrea L. Hartzler**
Department of Biomedical Informatics
and Medical Education
University of Washington School of
Medicine
Seattle, Washington

**Richard J. Holden**
Department of Medicine
Indiana University School of Medicine
Indianapolis, Indiana

**Melinda Jamil**
Advocate Aurora Health
Downers Grove, Illinois

**Andre Kushniruk**
University of Victoria
Victoria, Canada

**Ethan Larsen**
Children's Hospital of Philadelphia
Philadelphia, Pennsylvania

**Jenna Marquard**
University of Massachusetts Amherst
Amherst, Massachusetts

**Ruth M. Masterson Creber**
Weill Cornell Medicine
New York City, New York

**Enid Montague**
DePaul University
Chicago, Illinois

**Ashley Morris**
University of Wisconsin-Madison
School of Pharmacy
Madison, Wisconsin

**David Mott**
University of Wisconsin-Madison
School of Pharmacy
Madison, Wisconsin

**Albert Park**
Software and Information Systems
University of North Carolina-Charlotte
Charlotte, North Carolina

**Siddarth Ponnala**
Children's Hospital of Philadelphia
Philadelphia, Pennsylvania

**Arjun H. Rao**
Collins Aerospace Cedar Rapids, Iowa
Texas A&M University
College Station, Texas

**Mitesh Rao**
Stanford University
Stanford, California
and
OMNY Health

**Wendy A. Rogers**
University of Illinois at
    Urbana-Champaign
Urbana-Champaign, Illinois

**Rachel A. Rutkowski**
University of Wisconsin-Madison
Madison, Wisconsin

**Farzan Sasangohar**
Texas A&M University
College Station, Texas

**Rupa S. Valdez**
Department of Public Health Sciences,
    Department of Engineering Systems
    and Environment
University of Virginia
Charlottesville, Virginia

**Nicole E. Werner**
University of Wisconsin-Madison
Madison, Wisconsin

**James Won**
Perelman School of Medicine
Children's Hospital of Philadelphia
Philadelphia, Pennsylvania

**Abigail R. Wooldridge**
University of Illinois at
    Urbana-Champaign
Urbana-Champaign, Illinois

**Jie Xu**
Zhejiang University
Hangzhou, China

# Section I

Introduction to Applications
of Patient Ergonomics

# 1 Patient Ergonomics
## *Attending to the Context of Settings and Populations*

*Rupa S. Valdez*
University of Virginia

*Richard J. Holden*
Department of Medicine
Indiana University School of Medicine

## CONTENTS

This book, Volume II of *The Patient Factor: A Handbook on Patient Ergonomics*, is predicated on the motto, "patient ergonomics for all—now!" (cf. Holden, Toscos, et al., 2020, p. 58). Such a motto recognizes that patient work is neither performed by a select few nor performed in only a handful of settings. Rather, it emphasizes that patient work is performed across demographic characteristics and physical and virtual locations. Consequently, improvements to patient work—the end goal of patient ergonomics—should be distributed equitably, including in marginalized settings and populations, and that neglected contexts must be prioritized now rather than set aside out of convenience. As stated in Volume I, Chapter 1 of this handbook, *patient ergonomics* is the science (and engineering) of patient work. More formally, patient ergonomics is the application of human factors and ergonomics (HFE) or a related discipline (e.g. human–computer interaction, usability engineering) to study or improve patients' and other nonprofessionals' performance of effortful work activities in pursuit of health goals (Holden & Valdez, 2018). Embedded in this definition are three core assumptions of patient ergonomics:

1. Individuals who have no professional health-related training—including, for example, patients, families, and community members—nevertheless perform goal-driven, effortful, health-related, and consequential activities called patient work.
2. The theories and methods of HFE are applicable and useful for studying and improving patient work.
3. Studying and improving patient work requires adapting existing and developing new HFE approaches to suit the specific characteristics of patient work and the various contexts in which it is performed.

Although historically less recognized by those seeking to improve health and health care, patients and others in their social network (e.g. family members, friends, community members) may engage significantly in the patient's health management, a phenomenon we call "work" (Skeels et al., 2011; Valdez et al., 2015; 2017a). This "work" of nonprofessionals, or "patient work," consists of preventing disease, treating health conditions, and keeping the conditions from worsening or causing undesirable life outcomes such as life disruption and death. In other words, patient work consists of a wide range of tasks, ranging from those which may be considered physical and tangible (e.g. visiting a healthcare facility) to those which may be considered psychological and social (e.g. forming coping strategies) (Yin et al., 2020). This work is: (1) effortful, (2) goal-driven, and (3) consequential, meaning it results in something important.

## 1.1  INVISIBILITY, VISIBILITY, AND IMAGERY OF HEALTH-RELATED WORK

Elsewhere we have described our cursory Google Images search of the terms "health" and "health care," as an exercise in examining the public mental model of these concepts (see Chapter 1 in Volume I of this handbook and Holden & Valdez, 2019b). The returned images were largely of healthcare professionals, wearing professional garb, holding professional tools, and doing professional tasks. Patients and other nonprofessionals were rarely seen, but when they were, they were slim, young people jogging or in yoga poses. The typical setting was a hospital room or hallway for "health care" and sunny, outdoor settings for "health." As we prepared to write this chapter, we expanded our Google Images search to focus explicitly on the word "patient" and the dominant imagery associated with it. Our first three searches were of the words "patient," "patient health," and "patient health care." All three searches led to similar depictions of patients interacting with health professionals, usually while lying in a hospital bed or seated in an examination room. A search using the phrases "patients at home" and "patient in home" predominately resulted in images of individuals in middle-class homes interacting with formal health professionals or a spouse. These patients were often older adults, passively lying or sitting. In an attempt to find images illustrating more active patient participation, our final searches employed the terms "patient engagement," "patient participation," "patient self-care," and "patient self-management." These searches returned a preponderance of infographics either in isolation or embedded in other media such as flyers or slides. The few pure images included in the results, once again, focused only on patients interacting with health professionals or even just health professionals on their own. The results of these searches repeatedly underscore our culture's ingrained imagery, which highlights the work of the healthcare professional in health and health care rather than the work of the patient.

As such, the search lends further support to a key concept in the patient work literature, the invisibility of both patient work and the patient work system in which it is performed (Star & Strauss, 1999). As defined by Star and Strauss (1999), invisible work can be seen as "disembedded background work [...] [transpiring] where the workers themselves are quite visible, yet the work they perform is invisible or relegated to the background of expectation" (p. 15). In Valdez et al. (2015), this definition was expanded to include work processes that are "taken for granted by others and thus implicitly valued less" (p. 3). With these definitions in mind, Gorman et al. (2018) extended the concept of invisibility from processes to structural elements and by doing so expanded the concept of invisibility to also include "undervaluation, misinterpretation, or lack of detail concerning the patient work system" (p. 1576). Although invisibility is often discussed in reference to work being invisible to health professionals (Ancker et al., 2015), it may also be considered invisible to the general public, as illustrated by the Google Images searches.

Although all patients are likely to engage in invisible patient work and to have invisible components of their patient work system, such invisibility is likely to be more pronounced for patients belonging to marginalized groups. For health disparity populations, the often invisible work of following a treatment plan may be greater in magnitude due to social determinants of health as compared to more privileged populations (Thomas et al., 2011). For example, the work of following an appropriate diet may be compounded with the work of finding affordable sources of food and finding ways to locate healthy food options in food deserts (Whelan et al., 2002). Similarly, the effort of engaging in regular exercise may be compounded with the effort associated with finding safe spaces to go for a walk or finding reliable transportation to a community recreational facility. Both of these examples also highlight the invisibility of settings that may not typically be considered sites of patient work, yet may be considered critical spaces in which such work is performed. A key goal of this volume, then, is to render visible settings and populations that may not be readily apparent as application areas for patient ergonomics because they are not those that immediately come to mind when thinking about who a patient is and where they perform their work.

## 1.2 PATIENT POPULATIONS INVOLVED IN PATIENT WORK

In contrast to the results of the Google Images searches, the reality of patient work is that it is performed by a wide range of individuals, the young and old, the privileged and the marginalized, the healthy and the chronically ill. The patient work performed by a given individual is shaped by a constellation of factors and varies by person in both quantity and quality. In other words, for one individual, patient work may consist of moderate exercise and moderate attention to diet, punctuated by yearly check-ins with healthcare professionals such as primary care physicians and dentists. For such an individual, patient work may only be perceived as substantive during episodes of acute illness rather than on a day-to-day basis. In other words, at times, patient work may be invisible to the individual performing it, that is, auto-invisible. In contrast, an individual living with multiple chronic health conditions may experience patient work as nearly continuous, wherein most decisions or actions are interrelated with considerations of health-related goals. Even for individuals with similar health conditions, then, patient work may vary in quantity and quality depending on the particular stage of the illness, the symptoms experienced, and the presence of comorbidities.

Although the experience of patient work is meaningfully shaped by diagnosis and medical condition, it is also substantially shaped by the wider contexts in which individuals are embedded. Salient contextual factors include the cultural, social, and technological environments in which patient work is performed, in addition to other forms of individual variation. Patient work, therefore, may differ quantitatively and qualitatively along dimensions such as values and beliefs (Valdez et al., 2012, 2016a), the ways in which social network members are involved (Skeels et al., 2011; Valdez et al., 2017a; Valdez & Brennan, 2015), and the ways in which technologies such as mobile health apps and wearable devices are used (Kononova et al., 2019; Peng et al., 2016). Due to the diversity of patients and patient work, there exists a need to explicitly account for this range rather than to rely on the stereotypical image of a patient. In this volume, we highlight specific populations and particular considerations that should be kept in mind when designing for individuals identifying with a given population. At the same time, we encourage HFE practitioners and researchers to always attend to individual variation within a population.

## 1.3   SETTINGS INVOLVED IN PATIENT WORK

As noted earlier, different populations may perform patient work in different settings, and these settings, by the nature of their physical, organizational, and other characteristics, may meaningfully shape the way in which patient work unfolds. For those who study patient ergonomics, patient work is often thought of in terms of the "care between the care" or the care that occurs between encounters with the formal healthcare system (Brennan & Casper, 2015). These home and community settings encompass places of residence, work, recreation, and worship, among others (Ye & Holden, 2015). Moreover, a given individual is likely to perform patient work in multiple settings across a given day and a life course.

In addition to home and community-based settings, patient work is increasingly recognized to take place in clinical and virtual settings. Traditionally, clinical settings have been conceptualized as spaces for professional health-related work. However, with recent movements related to patient engagement (Carman et al., 2013) and shared decision-making (Bae, 2017), patient work is increasingly recognized as occurring within these clinical spaces. As with clinical settings, virtual settings are also being seen as locations of patient work. These virtual settings include patient portals, online health communities, and telehealth, among others. Designing to comprehensively support patient work, therefore, requires consideration of the range of settings in which patients play an active role in their health management. This volume presents the ways in which multiple settings—those that are home and community-based, clinical, and virtual in nature—play a role in shaping patient work and how HFE researchers and practitioners should account for the unique characteristics of each. Moreover, the volume offers a discussion of designing for transitions between settings, as patients are likely to flow between multiple contexts of care over time (Ozkaynak et al., 2017; Werner et al., 2016).

## 1.4  HFE DESIGNS FOR SETTINGS AND POPULATIONS

The way HFE professionals achieve the goal of improving performance is by studying and designing interactions between humans and other elements (e.g. technologies, tasks) in the context of sociotechnical systems (Carayon et al., 2006; Wilson, 2014). A key tenet of HFE practice is accounting for variation and context. In other words, a core belief of our discipline is that one size does not fit all, but rather, one must design for the range of human diversity instead of for the average. As such, HFE professionals are well suited to systematically understanding the range of ways in which patient work is performed across settings and populations and designing for that range.

In Volume I, we emphasized the need not only to use existing methods for the practice of patient ergonomics but also to adapt them and develop new methods, as necessary. In this volume, we highlight the need for this adaptation to take multiple forms depending upon the context in which patient ergonomics is practiced. As an example, sociotechnical systems models (Pasmore, 1988), and more specifically work systems models (Smith & Sainfort, 1989), were originally developed outside the specific application area of health care. Since that time, these models have been adapted specifically for health care (Carayon et al., 2006) and, more recently, for patient ergonomics (National Research Council, 2011). Efforts to further specify patient work systems models have generally sought to find common factors of relevance across patients living with a particular diagnosis (Gorman et al., 2018; Holden, Schubert, et al., 2015) or to synthesize across patients living with multiple diagnoses (Holden et al., 2017). There is an opportunity, however, to further adapt these models to specific patient settings and populations to facilitate more targeted design efforts. For example, a recent review of systems models applied to patient work argued that these models have not been but should be adapted and applied in pediatric settings (Werner et al., 2020).

## 1.5  SETTINGS AND POPULATIONS IN RECENT CONFERENCE PROCEEDINGS

A 10-year mapping review published in 2020 provides an overview of recently conducted patient ergonomics research from 2007 to 2017 (Holden, Cornet, et al., 2020). Specifically, this review focused on research and practice published in the proceedings of two conferences associated with the Human Factors and Ergonomics Society (HFES)—the International Annual Meeting of the Human Factors and Ergonomics Society and the International Symposium on Human Factors and Ergonomics in

Health Care. Mapping reviews provide an early exploration of an emerging area of study, pointing to areas which need further exploration.

This review demonstrated that patient ergonomics was the focus of between 3% and 5% of HFES Annual Meeting proceedings and 13%–25% of Healthcare Symposium proceedings over the 10-year span. This review further illustrated that studies of patient ergonomics spanned multiple populations, but had a strong focus on older adults and individuals living with a chronic health condition. Fewer studies targeted other vulnerable populations such as racial and ethnic minorities, veterans, children, and individuals with disabilities. There is, therefore, a clear need for additional attention to these latter underserved populations. Although individuals belonging to these groups may be more difficult to access and engage in research (Holden, McDougald Scott, et al., 2015; Valdez et al., 2014a), failure to include these populations may result in the exacerbation of health disparities and differential impact of design solutions (Montague et al., 2013; Valdez et al., 2012; Wooldridge et al., 2018).

In addition, the review highlighted early attention to patient work in certain types of clinical settings, especially in outpatient care, but less attention to others such as the emergency room, inpatient settings, or community retail pharmacies. Moreover, the results demonstrated an opportunity to focus on home and community-based settings as well as transitions of care between settings. Finally, the review illustrated the need for an increased focus on health promotion and more broadly, wellness, across settings and populations. Volume 2 therefore aims to "review" the state of science as related to these opportunities and to present case studies demonstrating how such settings and populations may be addressed by patient ergonomics.

## 1.6   ABOUT THE HANDBOOK

For those picking up Volume II before picking up Volume I, we want to reiterate our motivations for organizing this handbook on patient ergonomics. This handbook arose from a collective desire among its contributors to accelerate and expand the patient ergonomics community of practice. The handbook builds on the growing parallel movements in health and health care and HFE toward studying and improving patient and other nonprofessionals' health-related activities. It also capitalizes on a growing corpus of prior work, much of which is reviewed in individual chapters and some of which has been presented as part of an ongoing series of HFES panels and town halls on patient ergonomics and the patient in patient safety since 2014 (Holden, Valdez, et al., 2015, 2020; Holden & Valdez, 2018, 2019a; Papautsky et al., 2018, 2019, 2020; Valdez et al., 2014b, 2016b, 2017b, 2019). During these sessions, we have particularly attended to the need to account for diverse settings and populations (Valdez et al., 2017b, 2019), and Volume II builds explicitly upon these discussions.

One of this handbook's objectives is to inform. The handbook, for the first time, provides a single reference for patient ergonomics, collecting in one place theory, research, methods, and applications that heretofore have been distributed across many venues and disciplines (e.g. HFE, gerontology, public health, nursing, medical informatics, human–computer interaction). As a result, much of the content of individual chapters consists of reviews and syntheses of prior work. Each chapter also presents new findings or case studies.

Another objective is to further develop the field of patient ergonomics. We have included a breadth of topics that together define a comprehensive, inclusive community of practice. Each contribution includes thoughtful commentaries on the current state of the science and expert recommendations for future work. In keeping with the themes of inclusiveness and multidisciplinarity, we are proud of the diversity of contributors to the handbook, representing different nations and regions, racial and ethnic identities, disciplines, and perspectives. Some of the contributors identify as scientists or researchers; others as clinicians, practitioners, HFE professionals, or government officials; some as patients or caregivers; and most as a combination of some of these. This diversity is a core strength of the handbook.

The handbook's final objective is to inspire and encourage others to join the patient ergonomics community—or minimally to learn from it meaningful lessons for their own work. If you are a student or professional in HFE or related fields, this handbook can be of value in future applications of HFE to patients' and other nonprofessionals' work. Or perhaps you will find the patient ergonomics perspective helpful and complementary as you study or improve the work of healthcare professionals. If you belong to another discipline or community of practice, we are just as delighted. Your expertise can help improve patient ergonomics, and we hope you obtain value from the HFE approach. Patient ergonomics is, in many ways, a multidisciplinary effort with overlap and connections with other fields, from patient- and family-centered health sciences to the social sciences to systems engineering and design and more. If you are a Hollywood producer, journalist, or entrepreneur who stumbled upon this book and are asking yourself "why does such an important pursuit have such low visibility?" then we invite you to help us get the word out about patient ergonomics through other media. If you are a patient, family member, or "just a person" reading this because you perform health-related activities and identify with the content of this handbook, then we hope we have done justice to your experiences and needs. You are, after all, the reason that patient ergonomics and *The Patient Factor* exist in the first place.

## 1.7 ABOUT VOLUME II

This volume explores applications of patient ergonomics across settings and populations. Rather than distinguishing between these dimensions of context, each chapter presents salient dimensions of each. Some chapters, however, foreground considerations of settings (Chapters 1–6), while others foreground considerations of populations (Chapters 7–10). The last chapter of the volume (Chapter 11) focuses on health promotion, including the way settings may be redesigned to support health-related goals. Settings represented in this volume span clinical, home, community, and virtual spaces with attention also given to movement between settings of care. Chapters covering populations focus on four groups that have generally been underrepresented in patient ergonomics research and practice, allowing the reader to gain a deeper understanding of how to conduct work more inclusive of these groups. Although by no means exhaustive, Volume II provides the reader with a breadth of understanding relevant to the study of patient work. Each chapter in this volume provides one or more case studies to explicitly discuss how context shapes the application of patient ergonomics.

## 1.8  PARTING WORDS

We are excited to share with you the range of ways patient work is manifested across people and places. If there is one thing to keep in mind as you read this volume, in the words of artist Kenneth Noland, it is that *context is the key—from that comes the understanding of everything.*

## REFERENCES

Ancker, J.S., Witteman, H.O., Baria, H., Provencher, T., Van de Graaf, M., Wei, E. (2015). The invisible work of personal health information management among people with multiple chornic conditions: Qualitative interview study among patients and providers. *Journal of Medical Internet Research*, 17(6), e137.

Bae, J.-M. (2017). Shared decision making: Relevant concepts and facilitating strategies. *Epidemiology and Health*, *39*, 1–5.

Brennan, P. F., & Casper, G. (2015). Observing health in everyday living: ODLs and the care-between-the-care. *Personal and Ubiquitous Computing*, *19*(1), 3–8.

Carayon, P., Hundt, A. S., Karsh, B., Gurses, A. P., Alvarado, C. J., Smith, M., & Brennan, P. F. (2006). Work system design for patient safety: The SEIPS model. *Quality & Safety in Health Care*, *15*(Suppl 1), i50–i58.

Carman, K. L., Dardess, P., Maurer, M., Sofaer, S., Adams, K., Bechtel, C., & Sweeney, J. (2013). Patient and family engagement: A framework for understanding the elements and developing interventions and policies. *Health Affairs*, *32*(2), 223–231.

Gorman, R. K., Wellbeloved-Stone, C. A., & Valdez, R. S. (2018). Uncovering the invisible patient work system through a case study of breast cancer self-management. *Ergonomics*, *61*(12), 1575–1590.

Holden, R. J., & Valdez, R. S. (2018). Town hall on patient-centered human factors and ergonomics. *Proceedings of the Human Factors and Ergonomics Society Annual Meeting*, *62*(1), 465–468.

Holden, R. J., & Valdez, R. S. (2019a). 2019 town hall on human factors and ergonomics for patient work. *Proceedings of the Human Factors and Ergonomics Society Annual Meeting*, *63*(1), 725–728.

Holden, R.J., & Valdez, R. S. (2019b). Beyond disease: Technologies for health promotion. *Proceedings of the International Symposium on Human Factors and Ergonomics in Health Care*, 8(1), 62–66.

Holden, R. J., Schubert, C. C., & Mickelson, R. S. (2015). The patient work system: An analysis of self-care performance barriers among elderly heart failure patients and their informal caregivers. *Applied Ergonomics*, *47*, 133–150.

Holden, R. J., Cornet, V. P., & Valdez, R. S. (2020). Patient ergonomics: 10-year mapping review of patient-centered human factors. *Applied Ergonomics*, *82*, 102972.

Holden, R.J., Toscos, T., & Daley, C. N. (2020). Researcher reflections on human factors and health equity. In R. Roscoe, E. Chiou, & A. Wooldridge (Eds.). *Advancing Diversity, Inclusion, and Social Justice Through Human Systems Engineering* (pp. 51–62). Boca Raton, FL: CRC Press.

Holden, R. J., McDougald Scott, A. M., Hoonakker, P. L. T., Hundt, A. S., & Carayon, P. (2015). Data collection challenges in community settings: Insights from two field studies of patients with chronic disease. *Quality of Life Research*, *24*(5), 1043–1055.

Holden, R.J., Valdez, R. S., Hundt, A. S., Marquard, J. L., Montague, E., Nathan-Roberts, D., & Zayas-Cabán, T. (2015). Field-based human factors in home and community settings: Challenges and strategies. *Proceedings of the Human Factors and Ergonomics Society Annual Meeting*, *59*(1), 562–566.

Holden, R. J., Valdez, R. S., Schubert, C. C., Thompson, M. J., & Hundt, A. S. (2017). Macroergonomic factors in the patient work system: Examining the context of patients with chronic illness. *Ergonomics, 60*(1), 26–43.

Holden, R.J., Valdez, R. S., Anders, S., Ewart, C., Lang, A., Montague, E., & Zachary, W. (2020). The patient factor: Involving patient and family stakeholders as advisors, co-designers, citizen scientists, and peers. *Proceedings of the Human Factors and Ergonomics Society Annual Meeting, 64*(1).

Kononova, A., Li, L., Kamp, K., Bowen, M., Rikard, R., Cotten, S., & Peng, W. (2019). The use of wearable activity trackers among older adults: Focus group study of tracker perceptions, motivators, and barriers in the maintenance stage of behavior change. *Journal of Medical Internet Research mHealth and uHealth, 7*(4), 1–16.

Montague, E., Winchester, W., Valdez, R. S., Vaughn-Cooke, M., & Perchonok, J. (2013). Considering culture in the design and evaluation of health IT for patients. *Proceedings of the Human Factors and Ergonomics Society Annual Meeting, 57*, 1088–1092.

National Research Council. (2011). *Health Care Comes Home: The Human Factors.* Washington, DC: The National Academies Press.

Ozkaynak, M., Valdez, R., Holden, R. J., & Weiss, J. (2017). Infinicare framework for integrated understanding of health-related activities in clinical and daily-living contexts. *Health Systems, 7*(1), 66–78.

Papautsky, E. L., Holden, R. J., Valdez, R. S., Belden, J., Karavite, D., Marquard, J. L., & Muthu, N. (2018). The patient in patient safety: Starting the conversation. *Proceedings of the International Symposium on Human Factors and Ergonomics in Health Care, 7*(1), 173–177.

Papautsky, E. L., Holden, R. J., Valdez, R. S., Gruss, V., Panzer, J., & Perry, S. J. (2019). The patient in patient safety: Clinician's experiences engaging patients as partners in safety. *Proceedings of the International Symposium on Human Factors and Ergonomics in Health Care, 8*(1), 265–269.

Papautsky, E. L., Holden, R. J., Ernst, K., & Kushniruk, A. (2020). The patient in patient safety: Unique perspectives of researchers who are also patients. *Proceedings of the International Symposium on Human Factors and Ergonomics in Health Care, 9*(1), 292–296.

Pasmore, W. A. (1988). *Designing Effective Organizations: The Sociotechnical Systems Perspective.* New York: Wiley.

Peng, W., Kanthawala, S., Yuan, S., & Hussain, S. A. (2016). A qualitative study of user perceptions of mobile health apps. *BioMed Central Public Health, 16*(1), 1158.

Skeels, M.M., Unruh, K.T., Powell, C., & Pratt, W. (2010). Catalyzing social support for breast cancer patients. *Proceedings of the SIGCHI Conference on Human Factors in Computing Systems, 2010*, 173–182.

Smith, M. J., & Sainfort, P. C. (1989). A balance theory of job design for stress reduction. *International Journal of Industrial Ergonomics, 4*(1), 67–79.

Star, S. L., & Strauss, A. (1999). Layers of silence, arenas of voice: The ecology of visible and invisible work. *Computer Supported Cooperative Work, 8*(1), 9–30.

Thomas, S. B., Quinn, S. C., Butler, J., Fryer, C. S., & Garza, M. A. (2011). Toward a fourth generation of disparities research to achieve health equity. *Annual Review of Public Health, 32*, 399–416.

Valdez, R.S., & Brennan, P. F. (2015). Exploring patients' health information communication practices with social network members as a foundation for consumer health IT design. *International Journal of Medical Informatics, 84*(5), 363–374.

Valdez, R.S., Gibbons, M. C., Siegel, E. R., Kukafka, R., & Brennan, P. F. (2012). Designing consumer health IT to enhance usability among different racial and ethnic groups within the United States. *Health and Technology, 2*(4), 225–233.

Valdez, R. S., Guterbock, T. M., Thompson, M. J., Reilly, J. D., Menefee, H. K., Bennici, M. S., Williams, I. C., & Rexrode, D. L. (2014a). Beyond traditional advertisements: Leveraging Facebook's social structures for research recruitment. *Journal of Medical Internet Research*, *16*(10), e243.

Valdez, R.S., Holden, R. J., Hundt, A. S., Marquard, J. L., Montague, E., Nathan-Roberts, D., & Or, C. K. (2014b). The work and work systems of patients: A new frontier for macroergonomics in health care. *Proceedings of the Human Factors and Ergonomics Society Annual Meeting*, *58*(1), 708–712.

Valdez, R.S., Holden, R. J., Novak, L. L., & Veinot, T. C. (2015). Transforming consumer health informatics through a patient work framework: Connecting patients to context. *Journal of the American Medical Informatics Association*, *22*(1), 2–10.

Valdez, R.S., Guterbock, T. M., Fitzgibbon, K., Williams, I. C., Menefee, H. K., & Wellbeloved-Stone, C. A. (2016a). *The role of culture and personality in health information communication with social network members.* Presented at the American Medical Informatics Association Annual Symposium.

Valdez, R. S., Holden, R. J., Caine, K., Madathil, K., Mickelson, R. S., Lovett Novak, L., & Werner, N. (2016b). Patient work as a maturing approach within HF/E: Moving beyond traditional self-management applications. *Proceedings of the Human Factors and Ergonomics Society Annual Meeting*, *60*(1), 657–661.

Valdez, R. S., Guterbock, T. M., Fitzgibbon, K., Williams, I. C., Wellbeloved-Stone, C. A., Bears, J. E., & Menefee, H. K. (2017a). From loquacious to reticent: Understanding patient health information communication to guide consumer health IT design. *Journal of the American Medical Informatics Association*, *24*(4), 680–696.

Valdez, R.S., Holden, R. J., Khunlerkit, N., Marquard, J. L., McGuire, K., Nathan-Roberts, D., Ozkaynak, M., & Ramly, E. (2017b). Patient work methods: Current methods of engaging patients in design of systems in clinical, community, and extraterrestrial settings. *Proceedings of the Human Factors and Ergonomics Society Annual Meeting*, *61*(1), 625–629.

Valdez, R. S., Holden, R. J., Madathil, K., Benda, N., Holden, R. J., Montague, E., & Werner, N. (2019). An exploration of patient ergonomics in historically marginalized communities. *Proceedings of the Human Factors and Ergonomics Society Annual Meeting*, *63*(1), 914–918.

Werner, N. E., Gurses, A. P., Leff, B., & Arbaje, A. I. (2016). Improving care transitions across healthcare settings through a human factors approach. *Journal for Healthcare Quality*, *38*(6), 328–343.

Werner, N. E., Ponnala, S., Doutcheva, N., & Holden, R. J. (2020). Human factors/ergonomics work system analysis of patient work: State of the science and future directions. *International Journal for Quality in Health Care*. In press.

Whelan, A., Wrigley, N., Warm, D., & Cannings, E. (2002). Life in a "food desert." *Urban Studies*, *39*(11), 2083–2100.

Wilson, J. R. (2014). Fundamentals of systems ergonomics/human factors. *Applied Ergonomics*, *45*(1), 5–13.

Wooldridge, A. R., Nguyen, T., Valdez, R. S., Milner, M. N., Dorneich, M. C., & Roscoe, R. (2018). Human factors and ergonomics in diversity, inclusion and social justice research. *Proceedings of the Human Factors and Ergonomics Society Annual Meeting*, *62*, 447–449.

Ye, N., & Holden, R. J. (2015). Exploring the context of chronic illness self-care using geospatial analyses. *Proceedings of the International Symposium on Human Factors and Ergonomics in Health Care*, *4*, 37–41.

Yin, K., Jung, J., Coiera, E., Laranjo, L., Blandford, A., Khoja, A., Tai, W.-T., Phillips, D. P., & Lau, A. Y. S. (2020). Patient work and their contexts: Scoping review. *Journal of Medical Internet Research*, *22*(6), e16656.

# Section II

## Patient Ergonomics Settings

# 2 A Human Factors and Ergonomics Approach to Understanding the Patient Experience in Emergency Medicine

*Enid Montague*
School of Computing
DePaul University

*Melinda Jamil*
Advocate Aurora Health

*Jie Xu*
Center for Psychological Sciences
Zhejiang University

*Mitesh Rao*
Emergency Medicine
Stanford University
OMNY Health

## CONTENTS

The Institute of Medicine noted that there are 90 million adults in the United States with limited health literacy who cannot fully benefit from what the health and health-care systems have to offer (National Academies, 2018). Effective communication between healthcare professionals and patients represents an important caveat in health care, both nationally and internationally (Blackburn et al., 2019). Past experience of accessing primary care recursively informed patient decisions about where to seek urgent care, and difficulties with access were implicit in patient accounts of emergency department (ED) use (MacKichan et al., 2017). In a sense, the inherent inequality between clinicians' and patients' knowledge and obscurity of the care process are direct contributors to not only their lack of engagement but their difficulty in adhering to provided care plans. Patient ergonomics can promote equity between patients and clinicians by simply making the work of being a patient visible and by prioritizing patient needs in the design process.

## 2.1   HUMAN FACTORS AND ERGONOMICS RESEARCH ABOUT PATIENTS IN THE ED

Very little human factors and ergonomics (HFE) research exists on patients in the ED. It is possible to find research simultaneously examining one or two of the following themes, but little if any combining all three: (1) HFE research methods and principles; (2) EDs; and (3) patient-centeredness.

One of the earliest articles in HFE literature examining hospital environments' effects on patients was Ronco (1972). Much like the patient experience literature cited here, the primary data collection method was a survey-based tool, in this case a semantic differential questionnaire gathering patient impressions of hospital rooms. This study did not examine ED environments, but did clearly propose that HFE specialists who research hospital design must not only consider the needs of doctors, nurses, and other hospital staff, but also the needs of patients.

A more recent article used HFE principles within the ED, but did not explicitly take a patient-centered approach (Wears & Perry, 2002). This study identified opportunities in an ED to improve patient safety and system efficiency. Although the authors examined a case study of a safety event in an ED and explored potential improvements, they did not employ primary research techniques to understand the patient experience.

The majority of HFE literature related to EDs tends to focus on healthcare clinicians (e.g. Guarrera et al., 2013; LaVergne et al., 2017). Although an exceedingly important component of the patient experience, these studies do not directly measure the impact on patients. One panel of HFE experts looked at research approaches for pre-hospital emergency medicine and performance of teams (Bitan et al., 2018). Experts discussed research methods including *in-situ* simulation of emergent events where data were collected via video recordings, in-person observations of real pre-hospital patient cases, radio transcripts, interviews, closed-circuit video recordings, GPS tracking, and event recording. Although these methods could be very useful in the ED as well, the logistics and requirements are much easier when provider participants have simulated scenarios rather than actual patients present (Patterson et al., 2008).

Given the relative dearth of patient-centered HFE studies in the ED, it might be most relevant to reference work studying patient needs in other healthcare environments. Previous research by Montague et al. (2010) involved interviews with patients, their families, and clinicians following childbirth about their perceptions of the obstetric environment, technology, and work tasks. Another study evaluated two experience-based co-design projects at a hospital in Sweden, put placed the patients at the center of the research as well as the design process for healthcare environments (Gustavsson et al., 2016). As part of this evaluation, they captured qualitative data about participants' (patients and clinicians) experiences, implemented improvements and follow-up measures. One lesson from research in these other contexts is the value of studying patients and clinicians separately to understand their varying perspectives of the work systems and the process of making patient work visible. It is often thought that patients are merely passive entities in hospital contexts, but these studies show that this is not the case.

## 2.2 PATIENT SATISFACTION IN THE ED

Outside of HFE, patient experience in the ED has primarily focused on patient satisfaction outcomes. Patient satisfaction is a common indicator of the quality of care in the ED. Although not necessarily the best measure of patient's needs or their relationships with clinicians or how well the ED functions, the patient's perception of the experience is the most commonly used indicator of patient reported quality. Patient experience with ED care is a rapidly expanding area of research and focus for healthcare leaders, and recent literature has demonstrated a strong correlation between high overall patient experience ratings and improved patient outcomes, profitability, and other healthcare system goals (Sonis et al., 2018). To access patient's understanding or perception of how the ED performs, methods beyond self-reported satisfaction measures are needed, yet satisfaction measures along with quality measures are the dominant driver of improvement-related efforts within the ED (Huang et al., 2004).

Studies have shown that patient satisfaction is context-dependent. Two common influential factors on patient satisfaction are ED crowding and waiting time. A poor ED service experience as measured by ED hallway use and prolonged boarding time after admission are adversely associated with ED satisfaction and predict lower satisfaction with the entire hospitalization. Therefore, efforts to decrease ED boarding and crowding might improve patient satisfaction (Pines et al., 2008). The initiation of a rapid entry and accelerated care process significantly decreased patient "leave before being seen" rates (Chan et al., 2005). Moreover, interventions to decrease perception of wait times and increase the perception of service being provided, when combined with management of patient expectations, can improve patient satisfaction

(Soremekun et al., 2011). Hence, finding unnecessary tasks in the ED workflow may decrease ED crowding and waiting times as well as enhance patient satisfaction with ED. In a study of patient satisfaction across care settings, the most impactful factors in the ED were personal concern, physician care, waiting, and nurse care (Ye et al., 2016). Moreover, patient characteristics such as age, race, socioeconomic status, and health status are correlated with patient satisfaction (Boudreuz et al., 2000). Perceived wait time, long ED stays, and late afternoon or night stays have further been found to be associated with reduced patient satifaction (Ye et al., 2016).

## 2.3   THE ROLE OF FAMILY MEMBERS IN THE ED

Family members' presence during ED visits may have an influence on the patient experience. Patients and family members perceived that communication, critical thinking, sensitivity, and caring are necessary for ED nurses (Cypress, 2012, 2014). Therefore, the lower the level of anxiety reported by accompanying persons when leaving the ED, the more satisfied they are likely to be with their ED visit. Ultimately, this translates to well-informed and confident accompanying persons as being beneficial for ensuring quality patient support (Ekwall et al., 2009). As demonstrated in resuscitative efforts in adults, adopting a more holistic perspective could support family presence (Baumhover & Hughes, 2009). However, the role of family members still remains understudied in the current literature.

## 2.4   TECHNOLOGIES THAT HAVE BEEN DESIGNED FOR ED PATIENTS

Current technologies play an important role in enhancing patient experiences or patient interactions with healthcare professionals in the ED. For instance, computerized whiteboard systems are viewed as a central and indispensable instrument for communication and information management in most EDs. Whiteboards keep track of patient information and provide an up-to-date view of the overall ED operation; they are used by patients and healthcare professionals (Aronsky et al., 2008). Moreover, electronic real-time patient feedback systems gather real-time, confidential feedback from patients at the point of care while utilizing customized assessment questions and reporting features. The system additionally provides daily, weekly, and monthly reports to help identify trends, root causes, safety, and quality gaps (The Beryl Institute, 2013). There are also technologies developed in non-healthcare domains that could be applied to enhancing patient/family member experience in the ED. For example, utilizing RFID (Radio Frequency Identification) Real-Time Location Systems can significantly improve the efficiency of ED workflow by tracking real-time patient location in the ED (Versel, 2011).

## 2.5   ED VISITS ARE CHALLENGING FOR OLDER ADULTS

Older adults have more complex ED visits as demonstrated by their longer ED stays (McClaran et al., 1996; Singal et al., 1992), higher number of tests ordered (Grief, 2003; Hwang & Morrison, 2007), and higher risks of hospitalization (Eagle et al.,

1993; Lucas & Sanford, 1998). ED visit estimates increased by 6.4% from 136.9 million in 2015 to 145.6 million in 2016. The 10-year volume change is 24.7%, and for the past 20 years, the increase has totaled 61.2% (the 1996 ED visit estimate was 90.3 million) (Augustine, 2019). Outcomes for older patients in the ED are often poor, as they are at increased risk of return ED visits, hospitalization, and even death (Aminzadeh & Dalziel, 2002; Meldon et al., 2003; Samaras et al., 2010).

According to the systematic review, the pattern of ED visits for older patients differs from those of younger patients (Aminzadeh & Dalziel, 2002). The main characteristics of older patients' interaction with the ED include: higher rate of ED visits (Eagle et al., 1993; Samaras et al., 2010; Shah et al., 2007); greater average level of urgency (Lim & Yap, 1999; Samaras et al., 2010); longer average stay time (Strange & Chen, 1998); higher chance of repeated visits (Lowenstein et al., 1986); and higher rate of adverse event experienced after discharge (Ballabio et al., 2008; Singal et al., 1992). With these characteristics in mind, it is clear why older patients are considered a vulnerable group among ED patients.

The treatment of older patients is also often perceived by the clinicians as an inherent challenge (Salvi et al., 2007). For example, prior research has noted that ED healthcare professionals reported high level of burden and stress when treating older patients (Schumacher et al., 2006). Clinicians have said that they not only have less confidence in managing older patients but also desire more training about how to manage these visits.

As the number of older adults in North America and Europe continues to increase, the challenges associated with ED older patient care will also increase (Cooke et al., 2011; Hwang & Morrison, 2007). The number of ED visits increased 14.8% from 2006 to 2014. Comparing the two years, the US population grew only 6.9% (Pines et al., 2013). This suggests that the increase in number of ED visits is explained not only by population growth, but also by changing age-related demographics. As the American population continues to age, it will be critical for the ED system to be able to accommodate the increase in demand.

Older patients' understanding of their care is important for overall satisfaction. For example, prior research indicated that the two major requests from ED patients include effective communication from clinicians (such as the use of plain language to explain the reasons for and the results of test) and shorter wait times (Cooke et al., 2006; Nerney et al., 2001). Another study found that there is a significant relationship between patient satisfaction in ED visits and the patient's understanding of the tests performed and the reason for admission (Downey & Zun, 2010). Older patients may have more difficulty remembering medical instructions. As a result, a different model of communication may need to be adopted for communication between clinicians and older patients to be effective (McCarthy et al., 2012).

## 2.6 CONCEPTUAL FRAMEWORK OF PATIENT ENGAGEMENT IN EMERGENCY MEDICINE

We explain *patient engagement* as the meaningful involvement of patients in their care provision, with the goal of better informed, engaged, and empowered patients. The meaning is purposively broad and comprehensive, as the term, *engagement*, has

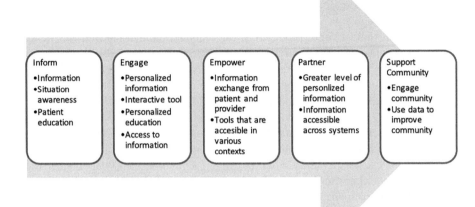

| Inform | Engage | Empower | Partner | Support Community |
|---|---|---|---|---|
| •Information<br>•Situation awareness<br>•Patient education | •Personalized information<br>•Interactive tool<br>•Personalized education<br>•Access to information | •Information exchange from patient and provider<br>•Tools that are accesible in various contexts | •Greater level of personlized information<br>•Information accessible across systems | •Engage community<br>•Use data to improve community |

**FIGURE 2.1**    Emergency department patient engagement framework.

been criticized for being a cursory, uninformative description of the diverse series of stages of involvement that lead to more empowered patients and communities. Patient engagement consists of multiple stages of involving patients in their care and is necessary for effective shared decision-making. This framework is based on the patient engagement framework from the National eHealth Collaboration (now a part of HIMSS) and is relevant to patient engagement in ED settings (National eHealth Collaborative, 2012) (Figure 2.1).

1. **Inform.** Stage one involves informing patients about the process they are about to go through, their surroundings, and the people on their care team. This can involve basic information such as where they are, but can also involve situation awareness, such as alerting patients to their location in the process and the broader system to the extent that they can determine what actions or interactions are likely to follow.
2. **Engage.** Stage two involves an additional layer of interactivity and personalization for information finding, wayfinding, and education and access to personal health information. This stage may also involve tracking functions where patients can view or document their personal progress. They may also be given information and receive education that is tailored to their specific symptoms or other characteristics (e.g. age).
3. **Empower.** Stage three provides patients with tools to directly engage and influence the type of care they receive. When patients are empowered, they can positively influence the type of care they receive. For example, patients in the ED may be proactively asked to participate in decisions about tests, physician consultations, or treatment plans. Patients are able to be active in

decisions made about the care they receive and provide feedback about that care. In this stage, patients are empowered to provide ratings about the care they receive, such as ratings of clinicians and the hospital.

4. **Partner.** Stage four involves using patient-generated information and knowledge to provide patient-specific information, wayfinding, and care plans. This stage includes providing patients with tailored tools that can accommodate their specific characteristics and illnesses.

5. **Support community.** Stage five involves using data to engage the community and support community health with a smart and connected health system focused on community goals. This stage could involve citizens sharing data about their symptoms in communities to provide support for additional resources. It can also involve the healthcare system sharing data with the community to better engage the community in the design of the response. For example, during the 2020 pandemic, public health systems encouraged citizens to share their COVID-19-related symptoms to help track the spread of the virus. Maps of COVID cases were generated and shared with communities who could then ask for additional resources or engage in community support for patients and healthcare workers. In the future, maps such as these could also illustrate potential disparities in access to resources and care outcomes as applicable to ED patients and general community health resources.

## 2.7   A CASE STUDY OF MODELING PATIENT EXPERIENCE IN THE ED

Our research is grounded in a mixed method study that utilized time-based observation, qualitative interview, and survey to understand patient experience. Whereas some studies have evaluated clinician workflow in the ED, this study focuses on patient work and activities. Depicting ED workflow enables us to achieve broader and deeper understanding of what happens in this department. Furthermore, comparing different ED workflows will result in finding the most efficient one leading to the improvement of crucial factors in ED such as waiting time and patient satisfaction. The analysis in this chapter is built upon an ED patient data set. We used RapidMiner to analyze the data and identify relationships between various factors. We used the findings to understand and describe work and information flow in ED. The goal of this work was to design a technology to support patients in the ED that was also inclusive of the needs of the older ED patients.

### 2.7.1   STUDY DESIGN

Patients and clinicians were included in the study to gain understanding of ED workflow and information flow. Three methods of data collection were used: observation, interview, and survey.

Sixty-one English-speaking adult patients and 12 clinicians were recruited for the study at an urban, academic medical hospital ED in Chicago, Illinois, in September

2013. Patients triaged as low acuity were recruited for observation and survey. Clinicians with varying work experience were recruited for survey and interview. All subjects consented prior to participation. Institutional review board approval was granted through Northwestern University. Patients clinically deteriorating and not capable of verbal communication were excluded from recruitment. Patients ranged from ages 22 to 83 with Mean = 54.9 and SD = 19.5. In total, 39.3% identified as White or Caucasian, 32.8% identified as Black or African-American, and 27.9% identified as "Other." The majority of patients had completed some college ($n = 13$) at the time of data collection.

### 2.7.2 Procedure

Patients triaged to the low-acuity floor of the ED and assigned a room were approached by a member of the research team about the study. Upon obtaining written consent, observers manually recorded events occurring throughout the duration of the patient's stay using a workflow task list developed by the investigators. This observation tool captured workflow tasks occurring in the ED, persons involved in the task, types of technology utilized, and observer commentary based on a sociotechnical system framework (Trist 1978). Observers recorded events using time stamps to indicate the beginning and end of tasks as well as annotated who completed the activity (clinician, patient, other). Some observers also took handwritten notes. Intermittently, 33 Likert-scale survey questions recalling encounters with ED staff and general patient experience were administered; the instrument used questions from a previous study questionnaire (Henry et al., 2013). Upon discharge, patient observation ceased.

Clinicians were recruited by e-mail to participate in survey and interview at a scheduled time by phone. Participants provided verbal consent; 11 structured interview questions were addressed: (1) provider–provider interaction during hand-off procedures; (2) patient–provider communication; and (3) provider perceptions of patient experience in the ED. Survey questions were added from a previously validated instrument (Fernando et al., 2013) that captured clinician perceptions of ED staff attentiveness, patient waiting time, and health information technology use. Clinicians were interviewed about the work system generally, not in regard to each patient.

## 2.8   OBSERVATIONAL DATA

Data from 34 patient visits were analyzed. Figure 2.2 shows an example of the data for one patient and a table of codes assigned for each activity. Patient data were manually collected and entered into spreadsheets by a research coder; each spreadsheet was then reviewed by a different coder for data validation. Data were reduced and cleaned before being entered into R 3.0.2 (R Core Team, 2013) and RapidMiner (Rapid-I, 2008) statistical software. The analysis primarily involved visualizing the time stamped codes of activity into a timeline of each patient experience. The durations, frequencies, and sequences of the activities that were involved in the visits could be derived from the data. The total length of the patient visits ranged from 64 to 952 minutes (Mean = 238.2, SD = 160.2). Members of the research team that

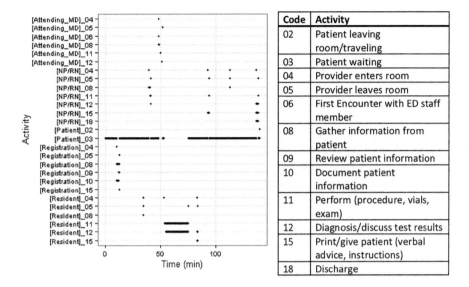

**FIGURE 2.2** A visualization of the process of one of the patient visits and corresponding activity codes. The moment the patient entered the room was considered time 0. The observation ended when the patient was discharged.

conducted observations met during a collaborative workshop to develop themes from the observations. Visualized patient visits, notes, and survey data were used as artifacts to generate themes.

### 2.8.1 THEMES

Themes were generated from an ethnographic analysis of all observational data with members of the research team who observed patients in the ED. Data for the thematic analysis included patient interviews, observation, coded observations, and survey responses.

Processes varied between patient visits. Some patients talked to the nurses first, while others talked to the attending MDs or other care clinicians first. No fixed sequence of patient interaction with healthcare professionals was found. In addition, no particular patterns were found for the distribution of waiting times. For some patients, waiting times were evenly distributed between their interactions with different clinicians. Other patients, however, interacted with multiple clinicians in a short period after a long wait. Figure 2.3 shows a visual comparison of three sample patient visits.

### 2.8.2 PATIENTS WAIT ALONE FOR LONG PERIODS OF TIME

Patient waiting time was calculated beginning the moment a patient was brought to an exam room (time the patient waited to be roomed was not calculated). The patient's total waiting time ranged from 17 to 275 minutes. The mean waiting time

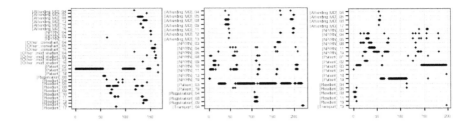

**FIGURE 2.3**   Different visual patterns in three patient visits.

was 131.4 minutes (SD = 65.5). In total, 30 out of 34 patients (88.2%) waited more than 1 hour in the exam room. The percentage of time patients were waiting out of their total visit time ranged 17.6% to 83.7%. On average, the patients spent 58.4% (SD = 16.5%) of their total visit time waiting. In total, 26 out of the 34 patients (76.5%) waited for care for more than 50% of their total visit time.

### 2.8.3   Patients Need to Interact with Multiple Healthcare Professionals

Healthcare professionals with different roles provided care in the visits. These roles included: attending physicians; resident physicians; consult physicians; physician assistants (PAs); nurses, patient care technicians; registration personnel; transportation personnel; social workers; and other healthcare professionals. The patients needed to interact with at least four different healthcare professionals in different roles. In some cases, the patients interacted with nine or more healthcare professionals during the visit.

### 2.8.4   Visualizing Patient Work Can Lead to
### New Patient-Centered Designs

For many patients, the process of being in the ED is a new and unfamiliar experience. Citizens aren't necessarily taught what to expect in an ED visit. This lack of familiarity can make it difficult for patients to know how to prepare or interact with healthcare professionals.

The variability in wait times can also make it difficult for the ED to effectively communicate situation awareness for any given patient. After reaching an exam room, patients in the study waited for care for an average of 2 hours. These long waiting periods negatively affected the patient experience because they (1) don't always have an accurate expectation of how long their visit might take and (2) these waiting periods are unused opportunities to provide support or resources. In many ways, long wait times may be an opportunity to enhance the patient experience.

These are opportunities for the system to support the patient with their work activities, by providing them with some knowledge of what to expect during the process, prepare them for questions that will be asked of them, collect additional details from the patient, or provide them with updates about their care that enhance their situation awareness.

Patient's interactions with multiple healthcare professionals can also add to the perception of visit complexity from the patient's perspective. Remembering names and roles of multiple professionals and cognitively managing the changes of healthcare professionals between shifts can be an overwhelming task if a patient is not prepared for it. Patients often do not view the multiple healthcare professionals providing their care as a team nor have a sense of who comprises that team. Consequently, they may not realize that these individuals are working closely together to provide their care and they may be reluctant to participate with healthcare professionals by asking questions or voicing concerns. Henry et al. (2016) found that patients in the ED were not only critical observers of how teams function in this setting but also made assumptions about whether or not communication between healthcare professionals occurred. Sometimes patients in the ED may need to act as a communication hub. For example, in Figure 2.1 (Patient Engagement Framework), a patient sees six different healthcare professionals during a visit. Many healthcare professionals ask similar questions about medications and symptoms; however, a patient may not know if there are new insights about the medications they are taking or if symptoms are communicated from one professional to another. This level of visualizing and tracking their care team is a complex task for many patients, particularly if they are unwell. Understanding how patients manage and interact with multiple healthcare professionals in a single visit can generate new opportunities to support patient work.

## 2.9 OPPORTUNITIES FOR HUMAN FACTORS AND ERGONOMICS RESEARCH ON PATIENTS IN THE ED

There are many opportunities for HFE researchers to contribute to understanding and improving patient work in the ED. The first task is to simply explore these systems from the patient's perspective. More studies are needed to understand patient work from the point at which patients decide to go to the ED through follow-up care after the ED visit. Understanding this process from home and community environments to hospital environments and back again is imperative to improving outcomes of satisfaction, readmission, and safety. However, new methodologies may be needed to better understand ED-related patient work that occurs across contexts: home, community, work, and clinical settings. Rigorous study of patient work is needed; it is simply not sufficient to have clinicians describe patient needs. A diversity of patients should be included in iterative design process, and these new designs should be rigorously evaluated for traditional HFE outcomes such as safety, efficiency, effectiveness in addition to broader patient experience outcomes such as feeling satisfied, informed, engaged, and empowered. Finally, as we look toward the future of HFE opportunities, we should be cognizant of the increasing need for automation and new technologies to assist a system with a reduced clinical workforce and increasing patient demands to do more with less effectively.

## REFERENCES

Aminzadeh, F., & Dalziel, W. B. (2002). Older adults in the emergency department: A systematic review of patterns of use, adverse outcomes, and effectiveness of interventions. *Annals of Emergency Medicine, 39*(3), 238–247.

Aronsky, D., Jones, I., Lanaghan, K., & Slovis, C. M. (2008). Supporting patient care in the emergency department with a computerized whiteboard system. *Journal of the American Medical Informatics Association, 15*(2), 184–194.

Augustine, J. J. (2019). The latest emergency department utilization numbers are in. *ACEPNow, 38*(10).

Ballabio, C., Bergamaschini, L., Mauri, S., Baroni, E., Ferretti, M., Bilotta, C., & Vergani, C. (2008). A comprehensive evaluation of elderly people discharged from an Emergency Department. *Internal and Emergency Medicine, 3*(3), 245–249.

Baumhover, N., & Hughes, L. (2009). Spirituality and support for family presence during invasive procedures and resuscitations in adults. *American Journal of Critical Care, 18*(4), 357–366; 367.

The Beryl Institute. (2013). Emergency department increases patient satisfaction with real-time patient feedback technology. Retrieved from http://www.theberylinstitute. org/?CASE012012.

Bitan, Y., Jaffe, E., Gisick, L. M., Hallihan, G., & Keebler, J. (2018). Creative research approaches for complex questions in pre-hospital emergency medicine. In *Proceedings of the International Symposium on Human Factors and Ergonomics in Health Care* (Vol. 7, No. 1, pp. 186–188). Sage CA: Los Angeles, CA: SAGE Publications.

Blackburn, J., Ousey, K., & Goodwin, E. (2019). Information and communication in the emergency department. *International Emergency Nursing, 42*, 30–35.

Chan, T. C., Killeen, J. P., Kelly, D., & Guss, D. A. (2005). Impact of rapid entry and accelerated care at triage on reducing emergency department patient wait times, lengths of stay, and rate of left without being seen. *Annals of Emergency Medicine, 46*(6), 491–497.

Cooke, M., Oliver, D., & Burns, A. (2011). *Quality care for older people with urgent and emergency care needs.* Retrieved from http://www.bgs.org.uk/campaigns/silverb/ silver_book_complete.pdf.

Cooke, T., Watt, D., Wertzler, W., & Quan, H. (2006). Patient expectations of emergency department care: Phase II--a cross-sectional survey. *Canadian Journal of Emergency Medicine, 8*(3), 148–157.

Cypress, B. S. (2012). Using the Synergy Model of patient care in understanding the lived emergency department experiences of patients, family members and their nurses during critical illness: A phenomenological study. *Dimensions of critical care nursing: DCCN, 32*(6), 310–321.

Cypress, B. S. (2014). The emergency department: Experiences of patients, families, and their nurses. *Advanced Emergency Nursing Journal, 36*(2), 164–176.

Downey, L. V., & Zun, L. S. (2010). The correlation between patient comprehension of their reason for hospital admission and overall patient satisfaction in the emergency department. *Journal of the National Medical Association, 102*(7), 637–643.

Eagle, D.J., Rideout, E., Price, P., McCann, C., & Wonnacott, E. (1993). Misuse of the emergency department by the elderly population: Myth or reality? *Journal of emergency nursing: Official Publication of the Emergency Department Nurses Association, 19*(3), 212–218.

Ekwall, A., Gerdtz, M., & Manias, E. (2009). Anxiety as a factor influencing satisfaction with emergency department care: perspectives of accompanying persons. *Journal of Clinical Nursing, 18*(24), 3489–3497.

Fernando, K., Adshead, N., Dev, S., & Fernando, A. (2013). Emergency department multiprofessional handover. *Clinical Teacher, 10*(4), 219–223.

Grief, C. L. (2003). Patterns of ED use and perceptions of the elderly regarding their emergency care: a synthesis of recent research. *Journal of Emergency Nursing, 29*(2), 122–126.

Guarrera, T., McGeorge, N., Stephens, R., Hettinger, A. Z., Clark, L., Hernandez, A.,... & Wears, R. (2013). Better pairing of providers and tools: Development of an emergency department information system using cognitive engineering approaches. In *Proceedings of the International Symposium on Human Factors and Ergonomics in Health Care* (Vol. 2, No. 1, pp. 63–63). Sage CA: Los Angeles, CA: SAGE Publications.

Gustavsson, S., Gremyr, I., & Kenne Sarenmalm, E. (2016). Designing quality of care– Contributions from parents: Parents' experiences of care processes in paediatric care and their contribution to improvements of the care process in collaboration with healthcare professionals. *Journal of Clinical Nursing*, 25(5–6), 742–751.

Henry, B., McCarthy, D. M., Nannicelli, A. P., Seivert, N. P., & Vozenilek, J. A. (2016). Patients' views of teamwork in the emergency department offer insights about team performance. *Health Expectations, 19*(3), 702–715.

Henry, B., Rooney, D., Eller, S., McCarthy, D., Seivert, N., Nannicelli, A., & Vozenilek, J. (2013). What patients observe about teamwork in the emergency department: Development of the PIVOT questionnaire. *Journal of Participatory Medicine, 5*, e4.

Huang, J. A., Lai, C. S., Tsai, W. C., Weng, R. H., Hu, W. H., & Yang, D. Y. (2004). Determining factors of patient satisfaction for frequent users of emergency services in a medical center. *Journal of the Chinese Medical Association, 67*(8), 403–410. Retrieved from https://www.ncbi.nlm.nih.gov/pubmed/15553800.

Hwang, U., & Morrison, R. S. (2007). The geriatric emergency department. *Journal of the American Geriatrics Society, 55*(11), 1873–1876.

LaVergne, D., Casucci, S., McGeorge, N., Guarrera-Schick, T., Clark, L., Hettinger, Z.,... & Bisantz, A. (2017). Development and description of a synthetic, high-fidelity, emergency department patient dataset for the evaluation of healthcare IT products. In *Proceedings of the International Symposium on Human Factors and Ergonomics in Health Care* (Vol. 6, No. 1, pp. 75–78). Sage CA: Los Angeles, CA: SAGE Publications.

Lim, K., & Yap, K. (1999). The presentation of elderly people at an emergency department in Singapore. *Singapore Medical Journal, 40*(12), 742–744.

Lowenstein, S. R., Crescenzi, C. A., Kern, D. C., & Steel, K. (1986). Care of the elderly in the emergency department. *Annals of Emergency Medicine, 15*(5), 528–535.

Lucas, R. H., & Sanford, S. M. (1998). An analysis of frequent users of emergency care at an urban university hospital. *Annals of Emergency Medicine, 32*(5), 563–568.

MacKichan, F., Brangan, E., Wye, L., Checkland, K., Lasserson, D., Huntley, A., . . . Purdy, S. (2017). Why do patients seek primary medical care in emergency departments? An ethnographic exploration of access to general practice. *The BMJ Open, 7*(4), e013816.

McCarthy, D. M., Waite, K. R., Curtis, L. M., Engel, K. G., Baker, D. W., & Wolf, M. S. (2012). What did the doctor say? Health literacy and recall of medical instructions. *Medical Care, 50*(4), 277–282.

McClaran, J., Berglas, R. T., & Franco, E. D. (1996). Long hospital stays and need for alternate level of care at discharge. Does family make a difference for elderly patients? *Canadian Family Physician, 42*, 449.

Meldon, S. W., Mion, L. C., Palmer, R. M., Drew, B. L., Connor, J. T., Lewicki, L. J., . . . Emerman, C. L. (2003). A brief risk-stratification tool to predict repeat emergency department visits and hospitalizations in older patients discharged from the emergency department. *Academic Emergency Medicine, 10*(3), 224–232.

Montague, E. N., Winchester III, W. W., & Kleiner, B. M. (2010). Trust in medical technology by patients and healthcare providers in obstetric work systems. *Behaviour & Information Technology, 29*(5), 541–554.

National Academies of Sciences, Engineering, and Medicine (2018). *Community-Based Health Literacy Interventions: Proceedings of a Workshop.* Washington, DC: National Academies Press.

National eHealth Collaborative. (2012). The patient engagement framework. Retrieved from http://www.nationalehealth.org/patient-engagement-framework.

Nerney, M. P., Chin, M. H., Jin, L., Karrison, T. G., Walter, J., Mulliken, R., . . . Friedmann, P. D. (2001). Factors associated with older patients' satisfaction with care in an inner-city emergency department. *Annals of Emergency Medicine, 38*(2), 140–145.

Patterson, M. D., Blike, G. T., & Nadkarni, V. M. (2008). In situ simulation: Challenges and results. *In Advances in Patient Safety: New Directions and Alternative Approaches* (Vol. 3: Performance and Tools). Agency for Healthcare Research and Quality (US).

Pines, J. M., Iyer, S., Disbot, M., Hollander, J. E., Shofer, F. S., & Datner, E. M. (2008). The effect of emergency department crowding on patient satisfaction for admitted patients. *Academic Emergency Medicine, 15*(9), 825–831.

Pines, J. M., Mullins, P. M., Cooper, J. K., Feng, L. B., & Roth, K. E. (2013). National trends in emergency department use, care patterns, and quality of care of older adults in the United States. *Journal of the American Geriatrics Society, 61*(1), 12–17.

R Core Team. (2013). R: A language and environment for statistical computing. Vienna, Austria: R Foundation for Statistical Computing. Retrieved from http://www.R-project.org.

Rapid-I. (2008). RapidMiner. Retrieved from http://www.rapidminer.com.

Ronco, P. G. (1972). Human factors applied to hospital patient care. *Human Factors, 14*(5), 461–470.

Salvi, F., Morichi, V., Grilli, A., Giorgi, R., De Tommaso, G., & Dessi-Fulgheri, P. (2007). The elderly in the emergency department: A critical review of problems and solutions. *Internal and Emergency Medicine, 2*(4), 292–301.

Samaras, N., Chevalley, T., Samaras, D., & Gold, G. (2010). Older patients in the emergency department: A review. *Annals of Emergency Medicine, 56*(3), 261–269.

Schumacher, J. G., Deimling, G. T., Meldon, S., & Woolard, B. (2006). Older adults in the Emergency Department: Predicting physicians' burden levels. *Journal of Emergency Medicine, 30*(4), 455–460.

Shah, M. N., Bazarian, J. J., Lerner, E. B., Fairbanks, R. J., Barker, W. H., Auinger, P., & Friedman, B. (2007). The epidemiology of emergency medical services use by older adults: An analysis of the National Hospital Ambulatory Medical Care Survey. *Academic Emergency Medicine, 14*(5), 441–447.

Singal, B. M., Hedges, J. R., Rousseau, E. W., Sanders, A. B., Berstein, E., McNamara, R. M., & Hogan, T. M. (1992). Geriatric patient emergency visits part I: Comparison of visits by geriatric and younger patients. *Annals of Emergency Medicine, 21*(7), 802–807.

Sonis, J. D., Aaronson, E. L., Lee, R. Y., Philpotts, L. L., & White, B. A. (2018). Emergency department patient experience: A systematic review of the literature. *Journal of Patience Experience, 5*(2), 101–106.

Soremekun, O. A., Takayesu, J. K., & Bohan, S. J. (2011). Framework for analyzing wait times and other factors that impact patient satisfaction in the emergency department. *Journal of Emergency Medicine, 41*(6), 686–692.

Strange, G. R., & Chen, E. H. (1998). Use of emergency departments by elder patients: A five-year follow-up study. *Academic Emergency Medicine, 5*(12), 1157–1163.

Trist, E. L. (1978). "On socio-technical systems". In W. A. Pasmore and J. J. Sherwood (eds.). *Socio-Technical Systems*. La Jolla, CA, University Associates.

Versel, N. (2011). Emergency room patients tracked with RFID tags. Retrieved from http://www.informationweek.com/healthcare/electronic-health-records/emergency-room-patients-tracked-with-rfid-tags/d/d-id/1100842.

Wears, R. L., & Perry, S. J. (2002). Human factors and ergonomics in the emergency department. *Annals of Emergency Medicine, 40*(2), 206–212.

Ye, G., Rosen, P., Collins, B., & Lawless, S. (2016). One size does not fit all: Pediatric patient satisfaction within an integrated health network. *American Journal of Medical Quality, 31*(6), 559–567.

# 3 The Patient Ergonomics Approach to Care Transitions

## Care Transitions as a Patient Journey

*Nicole E. Werner and Rachel A. Rutkowski*
Department of Industrial and Systems Engineering
University of Wisconsin-Madison

*Alicia I. Arbaje*
Department of Medicine,
Division of Geriatric Medicine and Gerontology
The Johns Hopkins University School of Medicine

## CONTENTS

Care transitions are a persistent challenge for healthcare quality and patient safety. Although the Affordable Care Act of 2010 targeted care transitions specifically as part of health policy reform (Naylor et al., 2011), a decade of research focused on care transition improvement and intervention development has not resulted in desired outcomes. There continue to be high readmission rates to hospitals and emergency departments (EDs) with one-fifth of older adults rehospitalized within 30 days of hospital discharge (Jencks et al., 2009). Furthermore, one of five patient discharges from the hospital to home included an adverse event within 3 weeks after discharge, 60% of which were found to be avoidable (Feltner et al., 2014). In addition, patients and their families often report dissatisfaction with healthcare quality related to care transitions (Arbaje et al., 2008).

Although care transitions remain a challenge, there has been some progress in developing interventions to improve transitional care. The Affordable Care Act of 2010 made care transition improvement a priority by integrating both incentives and penalties related to transitional care (Burton, 2012). Further, health services researchers have made progress in developing interventions to improve care transitions (Coleman et al., 2004; Feltner et al., 2014; Naylor et al., 2004). For example, several models have been successful in reducing rehospitalizations within 30 or more days after hospital discharge. These models include the Care Transition Intervention (www.caretransitions.org), Re-Engineered Discharge (Project RED, Boston University), Transitional Care Model (U Pennsylvania), and Better Outcomes by Optimizing Safe Transitions (BOOST, www.hospitalmedicine.org/BOOST) (Coleman et al., 2004; Naylor et al., 2004). However, current interventions have some limitations. Many are disease-specific (Phillips et al., 2004), require substantial financial and provider resources (Coleman et al., 2004; Naylor et al., 2004), or focus primarily on hospital discharge, which, although important, represents only a single type of care transition a patient may experience over the course of their patient journey (McMartin, 2013; Phillips et al., 2004). Finally, many of these interventions have multiple components, and it is unknown which components are affecting patient outcomes (Arbaje et al., 2014; Li & Williams, 2015).

Care transitions represent complex sociotechnical processes that occur dynamically across time and space and involve a series of interacting and interdependent components (Werner, et al., 2017). Although numerous definitions of care transition exist in the literature, there are key features that are shared across definitions (Table 3.1). We conceptualize these features in a framework based on the Systems Engineering Initiative for Patient Safety (SEIPS) 2.0 model (Holden et al., 2013): work system (the context in which care transitions happen), engagement (who is doing the work of care transitions), and process (the processes that comprise care transitions).

Much of the current structure of the healthcare system does not facilitate care transitions. For example, the fragmented nature of the healthcare system, where healthcare organizations and healthcare providers often function in ways that are independent from one another, makes communication and coordination a challenge and often leads to ambiguity as to who is responsible for care transition success (Schoenborn et al., 2013). Further, incentives and reimbursement structures are such that provider time spent coordinating care is not financially beneficial for

**TABLE 3.1**

**Work System Categorization of the Care Transition Definition**

| Care Transition Component | Component Description |
|---|---|
| **Work System: Context in Which Care Transitions Happen** | |
| Physical movement | The physical location of where patients receive care changes |
| Organization change | The organizational structure within which patients receive care changes |
| **Engagement: Who Does the Work of Care Transitions** | |
| Engagement | The actors performing the care transition processes, i.e., who is actually bearing the burden of care |
| **Process: What Processes Comprise a Care Transition** | |
| Continuity of care | The care received by the patient continues and remains appropriate at each change to location and organization |
| Information management | The management and communication of information across healthcare settings, levels of care, and healthcare actors including providers, patients, and families |

organizations. The healthcare system technological structure also does not support care transitions in that electronic health record systems are often not interoperable across settings and processes of information transfer differ between organizations. For example, even if a healthcare provider makes an effort to share pertinent patient information with a subsequent healthcare provider, studies have found that only a fraction of the sender's intended message and information is received by the receiving entity (Anderson & Helms, 1995). Without either a universal platform for sharing patient information or provider willingness or ability to follow patients across healthcare settings, the burden of facilitating care transitions continually falls on patients and caregivers (Scott et al., 2017).

For patients and caregivers, assuming the burden of care transitions means managing multiple aspects of their movement from one setting or institution to another. This responsibility includes managing information, coordination, and communication, engaging necessary actors, ensuring the continuity of care, and arranging and enacting the logistic aspects of the care transition such as physically transferring patients from one setting to another. Unfortunately, patients and caregivers often do not have the necessary information, resources, training, or confidence to successfully manage care transitions. Further, the responsibility of managing one's own care transitions and this continual state of being underequipped to manage care transitions are especially detrimental to patients with complex acute or chronic conditions as they have heightened vulnerability during this period (Coleman, 2003).

As a response to the persistent suboptimal outcomes currently associated with care transitions, the field of patient ergonomics has begun to study care transitions from the perspective of patients and caregivers (Werner et al., 2016, 2017, 2018). This work has identified: challenges specific to the patient work associated with care transitions; methodological and conceptual challenges and opportunities for analyzing and improving care transitions from a patient ergonomics perspective; and recommendations for the design of the next generation of care transitions interventions. The following sections present and discuss these findings. The focus on this chapter is on inter-healthcare setting care transitions (e.g., from the hospital or ED to the home or from the hospital to a skilled nursing facility).

## 3.1 THE PATIENT ERGONOMICS PERSPECTIVE ON CARE TRANSITIONS

### 3.1.1 THE PROCESS-LEVEL VIEW OF CARE TRANSITION: CAPTURING THE HOLISTIC PATIENT JOURNEY

As patients transition in and out of healthcare settings with increasing frequency, patient ergonomics approaches have shifted from conceptualizing healthcare processes as episodic and occurring in a single work system to considering them as a part of a continuous process or holistic *patient journey*.

The physical movement from the hospital to home is the first step in patients' care transitions. Usually patients are discharged with some sort of care plan. These care plans could involve patients attending follow-up appointments with their primary care physician or a specialist, filling prescriptions for new or existing medications, and/or receiving home health care. For many patients and caregivers, especially older adults, implementing the care plan as part of the care transition process is time and labor intensive. In a study of older adults diagnosed with heart failure recently discharged from the hospital, Werner and colleagues (2018) found that the care transition process takes place in four phases and can extend to 12 or more weeks, with the physical discharge from the hospital representing only a small portion of that time.

To fully understand care transitions, patient ergonomists have adopted a process-level perspective. Within this context, a process has been defined as "a series of tasks performed by individuals using various tools and technologies in a specific environment" (Carayon, 2006, p. 17). This not to say that tasks should not be included in patient ergonomic analyses of care transitions. It is important to consider multiple levels of analysis to understand the complex sociotechnical system (Kleiner, 2006), and there are instances where a focus on tasks and human–task interaction is integral to research and design.

One advantage of the process-level approach is that examining care transitions longitudinally allows for emergent properties of the systems to be identified (Werner et al., 2017). By definition, "an emergent property … cannot be deduced solely by examining the components of the system in isolation" (Dekker et al., 2013, p. 360). In other words, if an analysis is bound by individual system constraints and does not capture the process as it occurs across systems, certain emergent properties may not be revealed. For example, Werner and colleagues (2017) studied one aspect of care transitions—medication management—as patients transitioned from the hospital to home with home healthcare services. A process-level analysis identified the emergent properties related to the care transition. They found that as a result of the medication management process during the care transition taking place over time, space, and organization, the following system properties emerged: (1) role and task ambiguity/confusion related to medication management were ubiquitous at all process stages and for all actors; (2) the process involved individuals performing work across systems in loosely coupled teams; and (3) *cross-boundary spanners*—who served as communication and coordination hubs for the work that occurred across system boundaries—played a key role in the medication management process.

Other studies have also identified role and task ambiguity resulting from the longitudinal multi-work system nature of care transitions. A study by Mitchell and colleagues (2018) on patients' and caregivers' perspectives on care transitions found that patients and caregivers described feeling abandoned by their providers after leaving the hospital. They described frustration with being unable to get in touch with their inpatient providers to ask questions about or request changes to their discharge care plans. In one case, role and task ambiguity led to a hospital readmission. In this case, after multiple failed attempts to get in touch with their inpatient providers for clarification of a prescription, the patient experienced an adverse health event resulting in rehospitalization (Mitchell et al., 2018).

Another advantage of a process-level approach is that conceptualizing care transitions as a process can support patient ergonomists in distinguishing the *work as it is imagined versus work as it is done* during care transitions. Research that explored the performance-shaping system factors influencing the hospital-to-home care transitions of older adults with heart failure (Werner et al., 2018) found that during the care transition, the burden of care shifted from professional healthcare providers to patients and caregivers. However, these researchers also found that patients and caregivers often do not have the skills or capacity to facilitate successful care transitions (Wolff et al., 2008). This research further highlighted the gaps between the hospital-to-home care transition process as it is performed by the older adult versus how it is "imagined" as reflected in current discharge processes and instructions. For example, they found that rather than the traditional view of care transitions as a single episode of physically moving from the hospital to the home, hospital-to-home care transitions were experienced by patients and caregivers as a complex multiphase process that unfolded over several months. In addition, (Mitchell et al., 2018) found that patients and caregivers were leaving the hospital feeling *underresourced and undertrained* to carry out the provider's discharge care plans; that discharge care plans failed to reflect the specific needs, preferences, and abilities of patients and caregivers; and that patients and caregivers felt excluded and disregarded throughout the course of the discharge planning process, leading to a sense of doubt and distrust toward providers. Similarly, Werner and colleagues (2018) found that the discharge care plan instructions and expectations provided by physicians did not align with patients' and caregivers' informational needs nor their physical, financial, and social abilities to enact the care plan.

A third advantage of a process-level approach to the study of care transitions is it allows for the identification of variance propagation throughout the process, including process barriers and related work system consequences and errors (Carayon et al., 2015, 2020; Werner et al., 2017). The identification of variance propagation can further lead to the improved identification of the connections between system barriers, variances, and errors as they occur across a complex longitudinal process (Carayon et al., 2015). Connecting barriers through a complex longitudinal process is critical to identifying the antecedents of barriers that occur across work system boundaries. Once a barrier propagates through a complex longitudinal process, it may change or propagate to the creation of new barriers. When this happens, the ability to identify the antecedents of such a barrier, if it is identified downstream in the complex longitudinal process, is substantially decreased (Waterson, 2009). For example, Werner and colleagues (2017) describe the medication management process during an older adult's care transition from the hospital to home with skilled home health care. The older adult missed medication doses, which had been an issue indicated in the three hospital admissions the patient had experienced in a 30-day period. During their analysis, Werner and colleagues discovered missing information in the discharge instructions, which propagated through the medication management process to lead to another missed medication dose. However, there was no feedback mechanism for the home healthcare nurse to let the hospital know that the discharge instruction error was contributing to the missed medication. Therefore, if the older adult is again admitted to the hospital, it is unlikely that hospital providers would be able to identify the antecedent to the hospital admission.

Although there are many advantages to a process-level approach, it is important to recognize a potential disadvantage: studying care transitions as they occur longitudinally over time, space, and setting could produce an overwhelming complexity of numerous interactions, actors, and tasks (Carayon, 2006). However, the process itself could be used to restrict the number of variables. Focusing on a specific process bounds the analysis of the system to include only those system components pertinent to the process. This may be best explained in terms of configuration (Holden et al., 2013). As Holden and colleagues (2013) posited in their update to SEIPS 2.0—configuration is proposed as the phenomenon in which,

> […] only a subset of all possible interactions is actually relevant in a given work process or situation. What is 'relevant' is based on the strength of influence of the interactions on work process performance. Thus, for a particular process or situation, one can distinguish a configuration of a finite number of relevant elements that interact to strongly shape the performance of that process. There will also be an infinite set of networked elements that are present but not relevant because they weakly shape performance (p. 6).

Thus, the potential disadvantage converts to an advantage to studying care transitions as complex longitudinal processes in that the concept of configuration allows for work systems to be both analyzed and aligned based on the specific care transition process. For example, in Werner and colleagues' (2017) study of the medication management process during older adults' hospital-to-home healthcare transitions, they were able to focus their analysis only on those components of the system that affected that process. This served to bound and focus the extent of the analysis.

### 3.1.2 CARE TRANSITIONS AS WORK SYSTEM BOUNDARY SPANNING

Patients and their caregivers rarely perform the patient work of care transitions in one setting. Instead, patients typically experience frequent care transitions across a myriad of healthcare settings, the home being only one of those settings (Xie et al., 2016). Each healthcare setting that patients experience during a care transition can be conceptualized as a unique work system—that is, each has its own physical environment, employees or participants, tools and technology, and tasks interacting within a given structure (Holden et al., 2013). These individual work system settings that occur along the healthcare continuum are often viewed as independent systems. However, when attempting to mitigate the consequences of suboptimal care transitions, focusing on an individual work system is not sufficient to fully capture the experiences of patients and caregivers. Instead, to fully understand care transitions and anticipate adverse patient outcomes, we must include all the relevant work systems involved in a care transition in our analyses and interventions.

Although a multisystem approach is required, its implementation is complex. The fragmented nature of health care throughout the longitudinal management of care poses challenges for the safety and efficiency of healthcare delivery across the patient journey. It also presents the researcher with the challenge of conducting an analysis that includes multiple system boundaries, increasing the complexity of the interactions that might occur across these boundaries (Carayon, 2006; Olson & Olson, 2000). In addition, the work of the patient journey typically includes both professionals and nonprofessionals. Nonprofessional work, such as those activities performed by patients and caregivers, occurs under vastly different sociotechnical conditions than does professional work (Valdez et al., 2016). Consider the patient and caregiver dyad (i.e. team). Unlike professional teams, patients and caregivers do not have imposed operational guidelines, and their roles may change at any time (Valdez et al., 2016). For example, patients and caregivers may switch roles, with the caregiver becoming the patient (i.e. the caregiver becomes acutely ill). Moreover, the patient and caregiver dyad includes emotional, motivational, and other psychosocial characteristics of a patient and caregiver dyad that are likely to differ from professional healthcare providers (Valdez & Brennan, 2015; Valdez et al., 2016). Thus, a step forward to studying care transitions as they cross system boundaries across the patient journey would be to define the associated work system boundaries and study the interactions that occur across those boundaries.

However, work system boundaries have been notoriously difficult to define (Rivera-Rodriguez et al., 2013; Werner et al., 2016; Xie et al., 2016). Work system boundaries can be delineated from the micro level (e.g. human–computer interaction) to the macro level (e.g. human–organization interaction). At the macro level, boundaries can be temporal, geographical, organizational, and cultural. Deciding how to define system boundaries for a system analysis is a challenge that could either facilitate or impede analysis and design of care transitions as boundary-spanning work (Rivera-Rodriguez et al., 2013).

Werner and colleagues' (2017) study of medication management during older adults' hospital-to-home healthcare transitions found that specific medication management sub-processes and tasks occurred within work system boundaries; however, the process as a whole occurred across multiple work system boundaries. System boundaries included the organizational boundaries of the hospital, home healthcare agency, and the home/community; temporal boundaries of differing conceptualizations regarding process length across actors; and engagement boundaries of professionals' and nonprofessionals' (e.g. patients, caregivers) health-related work (Figure 3.1).

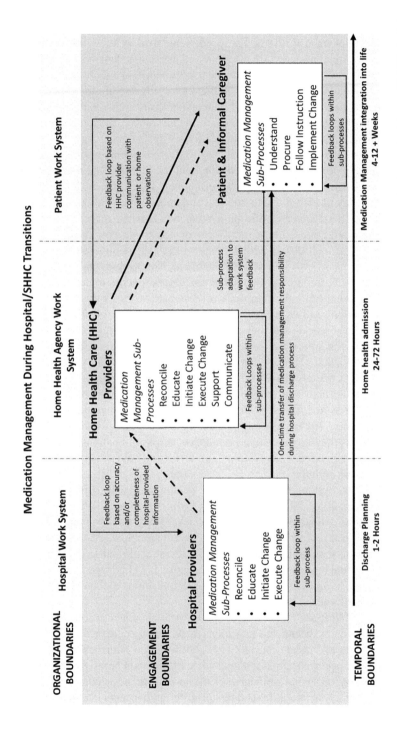

**FIGURE 3.1** The medication management process across older adults' care transitions from the hospital to skilled home healthcare (SHHC) depicting how the process occurs across organizational, temporal, and engagement boundaries.

Initial approaches to studying cross-system boundaries, such as those used in the rail industry, have focused on work system interactions (Carayon, 2006; Santos-Reyes & Beard, 2006). Carayon (2006) highlights how the study of interactions across "organizational, geographical, cultural and temporal boundaries increas[es] the number and type of interactions between systems, and therefore amplif[ies] the complexity of work systems" (p. 526). In other words, the study of interactions as a way to align systems becomes more challenging as work crosses sociotechnical boundaries.

Despite the challenges, understanding the work system interactions that occur among people, technologies, and organizations is critical to understanding how components within a system shape processes (Carayon et al., 2006). Thus, as described in the preceding section, a useful approach may be to focus on the care transition as a process that crosses work system boundaries. Such an approach allows for the feasibility of analysis while simultaneously acknowledging the inherent complexity of the interactions underlying the process.

Understanding how work system barriers and facilitators interact and lead to suboptimal care transitions informs the development of improved interventions for this complex and risk-prone process (Werner et al., 2016). For example, an enhanced understanding of the barriers and facilitators that patients and caregivers experience in their home and community in combination with the barriers and facilitators that they encounter when in the hospital has the potential to identify specific transition-related challenges. Investigating these cross-system interactions could lead to targeted support for patients' transitions and provide the indicators that would result in better aligning these systems for future patients (Ozkaynak et al., 2018).

However, system alignment across organizational, engagement, and temporal boundaries crossed by care transitions is not always an easy task, as system attributes are different for these various work systems. For example, the work settings are distinctive; the motivations and incentives of actors performing the work are disparate; and the levels of knowledge and training, tools available, and organizational structures are not the same. Understanding the differences between what constitutes positive outcomes for patients compared to how professionals perceive positive outcomes could help shape what a balanced system should look like to address the disparate needs of these two groups.

### 3.1.3 METHODOLOGICAL CONSIDERATIONS

To date, patient ergonomic methods for studying care transitions have used mostly qualitative methods, often conducting in-depth (ethnographic) field studies using observations, interviews, and contextual inquiry. For example, researchers studying hospital-to-home healthcare transitions used observational methods to capture the behavior of patients and clinicians before, during, and after the transition (Arbaje et al., 2019; Werner et al., 2017). They followed up these observations with interviews of the actors involved in the transition. These methods yield rich qualitative data and a depth of understanding of care transitions as they are experienced by patients and caregivers.

However, in-depth observational and interview methods have limitations. Field research data collection is resource-intensive in terms of time, cost, and personnel.

Further, field work can be intrusive for patients and caregivers, often requiring participants to allow researchers into their hospital rooms and homes. These limitations are especially limiting in light of the longitudinal nature of care transitions, whose study requires extensive resources and managing participant retention (see the case study in Section 3.2). Despite these limitations, there is potential for integrating qualitative methods with quantitative approaches in future studies. For example, the proliferation of electronic health record data, activity monitoring devices, smart texting, connected medical devices, and other consumer-facing health information technology can be instrumental in capturing real-time experiences of the transition—experiences that are not easy to capture using traditional field methods (see also Volume I of this handbook).

## 3.2   CASE STUDY OF A PATIENT ERGONOMIC APPROACH TO CARE TRANSITIONS: EXPLORING OLDER ADULTS' CARE TRANSITIONS FROM THE EMERGENCY DEPARTMENT TO HOME

One care transition that is becoming increasingly ubiquitous among older adults is to and from the ED to the home (Ringer et al., 2018). The ED represents a high-risk healthcare domain for the one in five older adults that are treated there annually in the United States (National Center for Health Statistics, 2017) (see Chapter 2 in this volume). Following a visit to the ED, older adults are susceptible to a myriad of suboptimal outcomes such as increased risk of readmission to the ED, increased risk of admission to the hospital or nursing home, and a decrease in quality of life (McCusker et al., 2009; Suffoletto et al., 2016).

Notably, each of the aforementioned patient safety challenges related to older adults' ED care is incurred *after* the older adult has returned home following discharge from the ED. Thus, efforts to improve ED care transitions for older adults must use a patient ergonomics approach that combines investigation of the ED and its formal healthcare professionals as well as older adults, their caregivers, and the homes and communities to which they are discharged after receiving care in the ED. This approach has the potential to provide insights about and support the execution of the care processes occurring across multiple contexts (Holden et al., 2015).

We used a patient ergonomics approach to: (1) map the process of older adults' care transitions from the ED to home; and (2) identify process variances based on the currently accepted ED care paradigm (Doutcheva et al., 2017). To capture older adults' experiences during the care transition from the ED to home, we conducted initial interviews in the ED with ($n = 15$) community-dwelling older adults ($\geq 65$ years; 53% female; average age $= 74$ years, range $= 65$–94 years), who were subsequently discharged home. The initial interview was followed by a second interview 2 weeks post ED discharge ($n = 11$) and a third interview 4 weeks post ED discharge ($n = 4$). The initial ED interview lasted up to 30 minutes. The second and third interviews were conducted in the older adults' homes and each lasted up to 1 hour.

SEIPS 2.0 guided a content analysis of interview data exploring older adults' experiences of receiving treatment in the ED and returning home. We coded transcripts of the interviews (transcribed verbatim from audio recordings of the interviews) using SEIPS 2.0 system components to identify when participants described care transition experiences related to person(s), tools and technology, tasks, organization, physical environment, and external environment. We reviewed each coded section to determine whether the system components were barriers or facilitators to care transition processes. We then mapped the described care transition process for each participant and identified any variances from the expected process (i.e. the currently accepted ED care paradigm). Finally, we overlaid the process maps with any associated system component barriers and facilitators.

Our results revealed three critical features related to the process of older adults' ED care transitions. First, we found *patients' experiences of the ED care transition process did not match the current expected ED care transition paradigm.* Variances to the process, or deviation from the expected process, were identified at different stages. Some patients experienced multiple variances across process stages. For example, many patients were unable to receive timely follow-up care with a primary care provider, so they used the ED to resolve their remaining concerns. Episodes of care were often cyclical rather than linear, with older adults frequently returning to the ED.

Second, we found *patients experienced process variances to the expected ED care transition paradigm that led either to a complete process breakdown or to successful execution of the process.* In the case of process breakdown, variances to the process led to an unsuccessful care transition and negative consequences for patient care.

Third, we found *breakdown or successful execution of the ED care transition depended upon how the work system responded to process variances.* We found that when variances could have led to process breakdown, there were some instances where systems were resilient and created counter variances in response to the original variance in support of process success. These were only possible because of certain work system factors. These included: individual factors such as the ability of patients to be their own self-advocate; sociocultural factors such as a patient's socioeconomic status; organizational factors such as family and community support; and environmental factors such as having stairs in the home that made ambulation difficult. However, some patients were not supported by resilient work systems. That is, the work system was not able to respond adequately to counter process breakdown and support a successful care transition.

In light of these three critical features of the process of older adults' care transitions from the ED, our results suggest that for older adults, care transitions do not typically follow the "ideal" ED care paradigm. We identified process variances and illustrated how patient care outcomes differed across participants, depending on the extent to which components within their work systems were able to counter these variations. Based on these findings, it will be important for providers to take steps to better understand the work systems to which older adults are being discharged and to reconsider both the ED discharge process and paperwork to account for the actual care transition process (i.e. the process variances) experienced by older adults. Future work should support the development of tools to empower clinicians to identify potential post-discharge work system barriers to successful care transitions and provide actionable intervention for identified barriers.

## 3.3 CASE STUDY OF A PATIENT ERGONOMICS APPROACH TO CARE TRANSITIONS: INFORMATION MANAGEMENT DURING HOSPITAL TO SKILLED HOME HEALTHCARE TRANSITIONS

In the United States, those who require skilled home healthcare ("home health") services (e.g. nursing, rehabilitation therapy) following hospital discharge are among those at highest risk of experiencing suboptimal outcomes, including rehospitalization (Wolff et al., 2008). Seventeen percent of US hospitalized older adults experience hospital-to-home healthcare transitions (Medicare Payment Advisory Commission, 2015), and rehospitalization rates among home health patients remain high (Madigan et al., 2012), suggesting that patient safety threats persist.

Information management (IM) refers to the ability to collect, organize, and communicate patients' needs, status, and care plans to care providers during hospital-to-home healthcare transitions. Care providers include hospital-based healthcare professionals, patients and caregivers, home health providers, primary care providers, specialists, and pharmacists. Many patient safety issues occur *after* hospital discharge and are highly related to IM activities, including those related to home health (Moore et al., 2003).

We investigated IM during hospital-to-home healthcare transitions. There is little understanding about *IM-related process failures* during hospital-to-home healthcare transitions. IM-related process failures occur when IM fails to achieve its intended outcome. The objectives of this study were to: (1) describe the current IM process in the context of the hospital-to-home healthcare transition from home health providers' perspectives; and (2) identify IM-related process failures. This qualitative study elicited contextual factors influencing the quality of care during the hospital-to-home healthcare transition. We conceptualized the care transition as beginning with the home health preadmission process (from hospital referral to home visit scheduling) and ending with the initial home visit (~48 hours after hospital discharge). We chose this period to narrow the study focus and perform in-depth analysis of the initial care transition period when information is quickly being assembled and acted upon. The study was conducted at five home health sites associated with three home health agencies. It encompassed both rural and urban sites across the United States. We recruited adults aged ≥45 years and their family caregivers.

We used the information chaos conceptual framework to guide our data collection and analyses. This framework (Beasley et al., 2011) describes five IM-related process failures, comprising information chaos (i.e. confusion and disorganization of information): information overload; underload; scatter; conflict; and erroneous information. We analyzed data from over 180 hours of observation and 80 hours of interviews. To characterize IM goals, we performed a content analysis of observation notes and interviews based on our framework, created process-flow diagrams, and reviewed the findings with home health subject matter experts.

The average age of the patients ($n = 60$) was 73.8 years (range, 48–98) and the caregivers ($n = 40$) was 62.9 years (range, 21–87). Our study population was slightly younger than the US home health population. We found *information conflict* was a frequent challenge during the initial home visit after hospital discharge. There were often mismatched expectations (>80% of the time) on the part of the patients and caregivers regarding what services the home health agency would provide and what role(s) caregivers needed to take on. Most often, the patients and caregivers expected the home health provider to provide more services than were possible under the scope of their insurance benefits. However, in some instances, home health services exceeded patients' and caregivers' expectations (e.g. a caregiver at one site was surprised to learn they could receive occupational therapy in the home). Clarifying conversations between home health providers, patients, and caregivers were the most useful means of resolving mismatched expectations.

Patients and caregivers often felt *information overload* during the initial home visit, overwhelmed by educational materials and tasks to complete as part of the care plan. Although contingency planning was intended to reduce anxiety, it sometimes increased anxiety in the short term, as patients and caregivers were asked to consider "worst-case scenarios" and plan for events they had not anticipated.

We described the IM process and identified IM-related process failures during patients' hospital-to-home healthcare transitions. First, we found that IM was complex and involved coordinating information from multiple sources across settings and over time. IM required a high reliance on many information sources, managers, and targets to reduce risk throughout the care transition. Despite this high reliance, the home health agency had little control over the accessibility, accuracy, and usefulness of information from sources outside of the agency (e.g. physicians, patients). Hence, suboptimal IM carried a significant risk of propagating IM-related process failures, unless there were systems to recognize and mitigate these failures.

Second, physicians were notably absent from the hospital-to-home healthcare transition. Neither hospital-based nor ambulatory care-based physicians (including primary care physicians) were easily accessible to assist home health providers, patients, or caregivers with contingency planning. Efforts to improve care transitions need to address the underlying reasons for physicians' absence during the critical care transition period, such as lack of awareness, accountability, or reimbursement.

Third, it is critical to recognize the importance and potential negative impact of information overload on the safety of hospital-to-home healthcare transitions. Patients and caregivers were especially susceptible to feeling overwhelmed when presented with information or asked to engage in contingency planning. Cognitive impairment, fatigue, sleep deprivation, psychological distress, and the effort of the sheer number of tasks they needed to complete after discharge compounded the overload. Providing more information and education may not be the most effective solution to empowering patients and caregivers during care transitions. Information needs to be parsimonious and tailored to the ability of the recipients to receive and process the information. A review of regulatory requirements contributing to information overload should be undertaken.

IM during hospital-to-home healthcare transitions is complex, characterized by information scatter, information overload (especially for patients and caregivers), absent physicians, and a high reliance on potentially inaccurate information sources. These findings highlight the importance of developing multifaceted approaches to address *both* information overload and underload, while also addressing information scatter and information conflict. Future studies could examine barriers leading to IM-related process failures relating to the initial hospitalization or the type of home health service provided. Studies could also expand the study period to beyond the first 48 hours, examine contextual factors in the work system, such as patterns of barrier propagation, outcomes resulting from suboptimal IM, and ideas for design implications to support collaborative IM during care transitions.

## 3.4 RECOMMENDATIONS AND IMPLICATIONS

### 3.4.1 IMPLICATIONS FOR SYSTEM DESIGN

As noted previously, because care transitions have not historically been studied from a patient ergonomics perspective, they have been viewed as episodic, not as a set of longitudinal processes occurring in a structural context as they are experienced by patients and caregivers (Arbaje et al., 2019; Werner et al., 2017, 2018). This misconception is due in part to earlier research not fully elucidating *the first-person experiences of patients and their caregivers* during the care transition. Understanding the perspective and experience of patients and their caregivers is critical to the patient ergonomics approach.

To reach a clearer understanding of patient perspectives and experiences of care transitions, future patient ergonomics research must broaden its current scope to encompass a wide range of patient populations (e.g. pediatric patients, rural patients, and other underserved populations; see Chapters 7–11 in this volume) as well as care transition domains (e.g. skilled nursing facility to home, home to long-term care, ambulatory care center to home). In addition, future research should include all of the work systems included in the care transition. For example, analyses could include the community pharmacy (see Chapter 5 in this volume) and primary care professionals who support patients when they are in the home or community (see Chapter 4 in this volume).

To effectively use research findings for designing and implementing interventions, it will be important to identify the work system barrier and facilitator interactions as they occur across system boundaries that lead to positive and negative consequences for the care transition process. Further research could identify the interactions among multiple barriers and facilitators across boundaries and determine how the crossing of work system boundaries affects those interactions. This type of analysis would provide insights into the components and interactions influencing the care transition process that would otherwise not be observable by only addressing interactions within traditionally defined system boundaries. In-depth information about system interactions and their consequences for patients could lead to the alignment of work systems to improve care delivery across the patient journey. Finding the right balance across all systems will be difficult, but efforts should focus on creating the most positive outcomes for the greatest number of actors.

Further, it will be critical to consider feedback and adaptive mechanisms as they operate across work systems. For example, there are limited, if any, feedback mechanisms provided to patients, home health agencies, and other systems of care post hospital discharge when process failures occur (Arbaje et al., 2019; Werner et al., 2017). Given that feedback mechanisms are an important component of the practice of high-reliability organizations, developing protocols for eliciting feedback on care transition quality would enhance improvement efforts. For example, feedback could take the form of dashboards identifying high-risk care transitions in real time (Arbaje et al., 2019). Organizations could charge quality officers and hospital case managers with monitoring these dashboards on a daily basis and enacting organizational protocols to respond to care transition issues (Arbaje et al., 2019).

### 3.4.2 Advancing Patient Ergonomics Methods to Study and Design Care Transitions

The study of care transitions as complex longitudinal and work system boundary-spanning processes has only recently begun. Consequently, it is not yet clear how the current methods and conceptual models available to patient ergonomists will be able to holistically capture and guide redesign of the care transition. For example, the research described in this chapter almost exclusively leverages a qualitative approach to studying care transitions, but there remain many opportunities for real-time capture of patients' and caregivers' experience of care transitions through smart texting, sensors, and connected medical devices, to name a few.

Moreover, the conceptual frameworks available for systems design were not necessarily designed to capture work that occurs across multiple work systems. Therefore, models and frameworks need to be tested and validated and adapted as needed to this context. It is possible that new models may be necessary to fully explicate the boundary-spanning work on care transitions. The SEIPS 2.0 model has shown some promise in this regard, in particular the concept of configuration has been useful in analyzing the work system elements and interactions among those elements that affect the care transition process, regardless of the specific work system boundary (Werner et al., 2017). At some point in system redesign, it will be important for the patient ergonomist to be able to identify the boundaries being crossed during the care transition process.

### 3.4.3 A Patient Ergonomics Approach for the Next Generation of Care Transition Interventions

A patient ergonomics approach will be essential for designing the next generation of care transition interventions to improve patient outcomes. For example, the finding that there is a significant mismatch in the perception of discharge procedures between the patient's reality and the clinician's "ideal" should be instructive to those developing or implementing discharge procedures. This finding suggests that the discharge process should be expanded to include both the hours or days leading up to discharge and the weeks following discharge. Discharge planning should also address the concerns of older adults about returning home as well as potential barriers to self-care when returning home. Discharge planning should include conversations with caregivers, as they are often the key actors in the hospital-to-home transition work. In addition, discharge planning should include other professionals such as social workers and case workers who could address nonmedical concerns and barriers such as transportation needs, lack of family caregiver support, or food insecurity in the context of the patient's care transition process.

A patient ergonomics approach to understanding the hospital-to-home transition process also has found that a successful care transition necessitates improved connections among hospital professionals, professionals in the community, and community organizations. One study has found that using patient navigators is an effective intervention with regard to enhancing connections across providers. These navigators work with multiple inpatient, outpatient, and community organizations during the care transition (Manderson et al., 2012) and can reduce some of the burden placed on patients and their caregivers during the care transition.

Another issue identified in patient ergonomics research is that the care transition often requires individuals to perform tasks that are beyond their capacity (Mitchell et al., 2018; Werner et al., 2018). To better understand the types of interventions that might address this concern, future research should focus on capacity issues, particularly how patients and caregivers might be better equipped to handle care responsibilities. Yet other interventions could include patient- or clinician-facing tools to assess and manage care transition workload based on individual patient needs.

Future research might also identify and elucidate the social and community support networks that could have a critical role in alleviating care transition-related burden for patients and caregivers. These might include meal delivery services, affordable caregiving services, or financial support through community-based and governmental (e.g. area agency on aging) organizations. This information could then be incorporated into effective care transition interventions.

The information in this chapter not only describes the patient ergonomics approach to studying the care transition process, but also offers information on how research results can inform the future generation of care transitions interventions. Interventions that are not informed by a clear and comprehensive understanding of the care transition as a longitudinal multiphase process are not likely to succeed. It is important to understand that the patient ergonomics approach is integral to ensuring that interventions designed to improve patient outcomes will actually achieve that result.

## REFERENCES

Anderson, M. A., & Helms, L. B. (1995). Communication between continuing care organizations. *Research in Nursing & Health, 18*(1), 49–57.

Arbaje, A. I., Hughes, A., Werner, N., Carl, K., Hohl, D., Jones, K., Bowles, K. H., Chan, K., Leff, B., & Gurses, A. P. (2019). Information management goals and process failures during home visits for middle-aged and older adults receiving skilled home healthcare services after hospital discharge: A multisite, qualitative study. *The BMJ Quality & Safety, 28*(2), 111–120.

Arbaje, A. I., Kansagara, D. L., Salanitro, A. H., Englander, H. L., Kripalani, S., Jencks, S. F., & Lindquist, L. A. (2014). Regardless of age: Incorporating principles from geriatric medicine to improve care transitions for patients with complex needs. *Journal of General Internal Medicine, 29*(6), 932–939.

Arbaje, A. I., Wolff, J. L., Yu, Q., Powe, N. R., Anderson, G. F., & Boult, C. (2008). Postdischarge environmental and socioeconomic factors and the likelihood of early hospital readmission among community-dwelling Medicare beneficiaries. *The Gerontologist, 48*(4), 495–504.

Beasley, J. W., Wetterneck, T. B., Temte, J., Lapin, J. A., Smith, P., Rivera-Rodriguez, A. J., & Karsh, B. T. (2011). Information chaos in primary care: Implications for physician performance and patient safety. *Journal of the American Board of Family Medicine, 24*(6), 745–751.

Burton, R. (2012). Improving care transitions. *Robert Wood Johnson Health Policy Brief,* September 2012, 1–6.

Carayon, P. (2006). Human factors of complex sociotechnical systems. *Applied Ergonomics, 37*(4), 525–535.

Carayon, P., Hundt, A. S., Karsh, B., Gurses, A., Alvarado, C., Smith, M., & Brennan, P. F. (2006). Work system design for patient safety: The SEIPS model. *Quality and Safety in Health Care, 15*(suppl 1), i50–i58.

Carayon, P., Ju, F., Cartmill, R., Hoonakker, P., Wetterneck, T. B., & Li, J. (2015). Medication error propagation in intensive care units. *Proceedings of the Human Factors and Ergonomics Society Annual Meeting, 59*(1), 518–521.

Carayon, P., Wooldridge, A., Hoonakker, P., Hundt, A. S., & Kelly, M. M. (2020). SEIPS 3.0: Human-centered design of the patient journey for patient safety. *Applied Ergonomics, 84*, 103033.

Coleman, E. A. (2003). Falling through the cracks: Challenges and opportunities for improving transitional care for persons with continuous complex care needs. *Journal of the American Geriatrics Society, 51*(4), 549–555.

Coleman, E. A., Smith, J. D., Frank, J. C., Min, S.-J., Parry, C., & Kramer, A. M. (2004). Preparing patients and caregivers to participate in care delivered across settings: The care transitions intervention. *Journal of the American Geriatrics Society, 52*(11), 1817–1825.

Dekker, S. W., Hancock, P. A., & Wilkin, P. (2013). Ergonomics and sustainability: Towards an embrace of complexity and emergence. *Ergonomics, 56*(3), 357–364.

Doutcheva, N., Shah, M. N., Borkenhagen, A., Finta, M. K., Duckles, J., Sellers, C. R., Seshadri, S., Lampo, D., & Werner, N. E. (2017). Process variances in older adults' care transitions from emergency department to home: Process breakdown versus process resiliency. *Proceedings of the Human Factors and Ergonomics Society Annual Meeting, 61*(1), 565–566.

Feltner, C., Jones, C. D., Cené, C. W., Zheng, Z.-J., Sueta, C. A., Coker-Schwimmer, E. J., Arvanitis, M., Lohr, K.N., Middleton, J.C., & Jonas, D. E. (2014). Transitional care interventions to prevent readmissions for persons with heart failure: A systematic review and meta-analysis. *Annals of Internal Medicine, 160*(11), 774–784.

Holden, R. J., Carayon, P., Gurses, A. P., Hoonakker, P., Hundt, A. S., Ozok, A. A., & Rivera-Rodriguez, A. J. (2013). SEIPS 2.0: A human factors framework for studying and improving the work of healthcare professionals and patients. *Ergonomics, 56*(11), 1669–1686.

Holden, R. J., Schubert, C. C., Eiland, E. C., Storrow, A. B., Miller, K. F., & Collins, S. P. (2015). Self-care barriers reported by emergency department patients with acute heart failure: A sociotechnical systems-based approach. *Annals of Emergency Medicine, 66*(1), 1–12, e12.

Jencks, S. F., Williams, M. V., & Coleman, E. A. (2009). Rehospitalizations among patients in the Medicare fee-for-service program. *New England Journal of Medicine, 360*(14), 1418–1428.

Kleiner, B. M. (2006). Macroergonomics: Analysis and design of work systems. *Applied Ergonomics, 37*(1), 81–89.

Li, J., & Williams, M. V. (2015). Care transitions: It's the how, not just the what. *Journal of General Internal Medicine, 30*(5), 539–540.

Madigan, E. A., Gordon, N. H., Fortinsky, R. H., Koroukian, S. M., Pina, I., & Riggs, J. S. (2012). Rehospitalization in a national population of home health care patients with heart failure. *Health Services Research, 47*(6), 2316–2338.

Manderson, B., Mcmurray, J., Piraino, E., & Stolee, P. (2012). Navigation roles support chronically ill older adults through healthcare transitions: A systematic review of the literature. *Health & Social Care in the Community, 20*(2), 113–127.

McCusker, J., Roberge, D., Vadeboncoeur, A., & Verdon, J. (2009). Safety of discharge of seniors from the emergency department to the community. *Healthcare Quarterly,* 12 Spec No Patient, 24–32. 10.12927/hcq.2009.20963.

McMartin, K. (2013). Discharge planning in chronic conditions: An evidence-based analysis. *Ontario Health Technology Assessment, 13*(4), 1–72.

Medicare Payment Advisory Commission. (2015). Report to the congress: Medicare payment policy. Retrieved from http://www.medpac.gov/docs/default-source/reports/chapter-7-medicare-s-post-acute-care-trends-and-ways-to-rationalize-payments-march-2015-report-.pdf.

Mitchell, S. E., Laurens, V., Weigel, G. M., Hirschman, K. B., Scott, A. M., Nguyen, H. Q., Howard, J.M., Laird, L., Levine, C., Davis, T. C., Gass, B., Shaid, E., Li, J., Williams, M.V., & Jack, B.W. (2018). Care transitions from patient and caregiver perspectives. *The Annals of Family Medicine, 16*(3), 225–231.

Moore, C., Wisnivesky, J., Williams, S., & McGinn, T. (2003). Medical errors related to discontinuity of care from an inpatient to an outpatient setting. *Journal of General Internal Medicine, 18*(8), 646–651.

National Center for Health Statistics. (2017). Health, United States, 2016: With chartbook on long-term trends in health. Retrieved from https://www.cdc.gov/nchs/data/hus/hus16.pdf#074.

Naylor, M. D., Aiken, L. H., Kurtzman, E. T., Olds, D. M., & Hirschman, K. B. (2011). The importance of transitional care in achieving health reform. *Health Affairs, 30*(4), 746–754.

Naylor, M. D., Brooten, D. A., Campbell, R. L., Maislin, G., McCauley, K. M., & Schwartz, J. S. (2004). Transitional care of older adults hospitalized with heart failure: A randomized, controlled trial. *Journal of the American Geriatrics Society, 52*(5), 675–684.

Olson, G. M., & Olson, J. S. (2000). Distance matters. *Human-Computer Interaction, 15*(2), 139–178.

Ozkaynak, M., Valdez, R., Holden, R. J., & Weiss, J. (2018). Infinicare framework for integrated understanding of health-related activities in clinical and daily-living contexts. *Health Systems, 7*(1), 66–78.

Phillips, C. O., Wright, S. M., Kern, D. E., Singa, R. M., Shepperd, S., & Rubin, H. R. (2004). Comprehensive discharge planning with postdischarge support for older patients with congestive heart failure: A meta-analysis. *Journal of the American Medical Association, 291*(11), 1358–1367.

Ringer, T., Dougherty, M., McQuown, C., Melady, D., Ouchi, K., Southerland, L. T., & Hogan, T. M. (2018). White paper-geriatric emergency medicine education: Current state, challenges, and recommendations to enhance the emergency care of older adults. *Academic Emergency Medicine Education and Training, 2*(Suppl 1), S5–s16.

Rivera-Rodriguez, A. J., McGuire, K., Carayon, P., Kleiner, B., Wears, R., Robertson, M., Holden, R., & Waterson, P. (2013). Multi-level ergonomics: Determining how to bound your system. *Proceedings of the Human Factors and Ergonomics Society Annual Meeting, 57*(1), 1104–1108.

Santos-Reyes, J., & Beard, A. N. (2006). A systemic analysis of the Paddington railway accident. *Proceedings of the Institution of Mechanical Engineers, Part F: Journal of rail and rapid transit, 220*(2), 121–151.

Schoenborn, N. L., Arbaje, A. I., Eubank, K. J., Maynor, K., & Carrese, J. A. (2013). Clinician roles and responsibilities during care transitions of older adults. *Journal of the American Geriatrics Society, 61*(2), 231–236.

Scott, A. M., Li, J., Oyewole-Eletu, S., Nguyen, H. Q., Gass, B., Hirschman, K. B., Mitchell, S., Hudson, S.M., Williams, M.V., & Project ACHIEVE Team. (2017). Understanding facilitators and barriers to care transitions: Insights from Project ACHIEVE site visits. *The Joint Commission Journal on Quality and Patient Safety, 43*(9), 433–447.

Suffoletto, B., Miller, T., Shah, R., Callaway, C., & Yealy, D. M. (2016). Predicting older adults who return to the hospital or die within 30 days of emergency department care using the ISAR tool: Subjective versus objective risk factors. *Emergency Medicine Journal, 33*(1), 4–9.

Valdez, R. S., & Brennan, P. F. (2015). Exploring patients' health information communication practices with social network members as a foundation for consumer health IT design. *International Journal of Medical Informatics, 84*(5), 363–374.

Valdez, R. S., Holden, R. J., Caine, K., Madathil, K., Mickelson, R., Novak, L. L., & Werner, N. (2016). Patient work as a maturing approach within HF/E moving beyond traditional self-management applications. *Proceedings of the Human Factors and Ergonomics Society Annual Meeting, 60*(1), 657–661.

Waterson, P. (2009). A critical review of the systems approach within patient safety research. *Ergonomics, 52*(10), 1185–1195.

Werner, N. E., Gurses, A., Leff, B., & Arbaje, A. I. (2016). Improving care transitions across healthcare settings through a human factors approach. *Journal for Healthcare Quality, 38*(6), 328–343.

Werner, N. E., Malkana, S., Gurses, A. P., Leff, B., & Arbaje, A. I. (2017). Toward a process-level view of distributed healthcare tasks: Medication management as a case study. *Applied Ergonomics, 65*, 255–268.

Werner, N. E., Tong, M., Borkenhagen, A., & Holden, R. J. (2018). Performance-shaping factors affecting older adults' hospital-to-home transition success: A systems approach. *The Gerontologist, 59*(2), 303–314.

Wolff, J. L., Meadow, A., Weiss, C. O., Boyd, C. M., & Leff, B. (2008). Medicare home health patients' transitions through acute and post-acute care settings. *Medical Care, 46*(11), 1188–1193.

Xie, A., Gurses, A. P., Hundt, A. S., Steege, L., Valdez, R. S., & Werner, N. E. (2016). Conceptualizing sociotechnical system boundaries in healthcare settings within and across teams, organizations, processes, and networks. *Proceedings of the Human Factors and Ergonomics Society Annual Meeting, 60*(1), 866–870.

# 4 Patient Ergonomics in the Wild

## Tailoring Patient Ergonomics Models and Methods to Home and Community Settings

Jenna Marquard
Department of Mechanical and Industrial Engineering
University of Massachusetts Amherst

## CONTENTS

There is no doubt that health-related activities occurring outside of formal healthcare settings have a substantial impact on human health, and there are a growing number of technologies, interventions, and policies aimed at supporting health-related activities occurring outside of formal care settings (Braveman & Gottlieb, 2014; Institute of Medicine, 2014; National Research Council, 2011; Zayas-Cabán & Valdez, 2011).

Although this focus is notable and important, these technologies, interventions, and policies must account for the unpaid, health-related work that patients perform and the work systems within which they perform it (Holden et al., 2013; Valdez et al., 2015). If human factors and ergonomics (HFE) researchers and practitioners are to improve patients' health and well-being via new or redesigned technologies, interventions, and policies, they would benefit by taking a patient-centered approach, considering how the entire patient work system impacts varied health-related processes and outcomes. One key patient work system component that should be considered is the context in which the majority of patient work occurs, that is, primarily the home and community settings. Although home and community settings cannot easily be changed by HFE researchers and practitioners, these contexts have a significant impact on other aspects (e.g. tasks and tools) of patient work systems and therefore should be included in any efforts to understand or improve patient work.

The definitions of home and community are diverse, depending on the research and practice fields in which they are used. In the context of this chapter, specific to patient ergonomics, we define home as the *physical location where one lives, often as a member of a family or household*. Home could include locations such as houses, apartments, prisons, or the streets. We define the community as *physical or virtual spaces where inhabitants have shared characteristics*. These shared community characteristics could be based on factors such as geography (e.g. "my neighborhood"), role (e.g. "my fellow elementary school teachers"), interest (e.g. "my fitness tracking app competitors"), or some combination of these. These settings are often integral to health-related activities such as medication (Mickelson et al., 2016) and health information management (HIM) (Zayas-Cabán, 2012). Whereas healthcare professionals often enter home and community settings (e.g. home healthcare nurses providing services) and many individuals' homes are located in formal healthcare settings (e.g. individuals living in a nursing home), this chapter does not address the unique complexities of these intersectional settings.

We consider the end goal of patient ergonomics research and practice to be redesigning patients' work systems to improve patient work to ultimately improve their health and well-being. We use the term redesigning, rather than designing, to acknowledge that all patients have an existing work system. This chapter will provide an overview of existing research in the following areas as related to home and community settings:

This chapter will then describe practical considerations for conducting patient ergonomics research in home and community settings. Finally, we will present two case studies that describe example approaches for conducting patient ergonomics research. The first case study describes the development and evaluation of a system meant to support individuals with diabetes and hypertension (Marquard et al., 2013; Martinez et al., 2017). The second case study describes the iterative design of a system to support medication management taken by individuals with or at risk for developing HIV (Marquard et al., 2018; Stekler et al., 2018).

## 4.1  MODELS AND FRAMEWORKS TO GUIDE PATIENT ERGONOMICS IN HOME AND COMMUNITY SETTINGS

Although formalized patient ergonomics research in home and community settings is relatively new, there are longstanding, related bodies of work in diverse fields—including public health (Ulin et al., 2012; Satcher, 2005), nursing (Anderson & McFarlane, 2019; Andrews & Boyle 2002), anthropology (Kiefer, 2006; Lambert & McKevitt, 2002), psychology (Sarafino & Smith, 2014; Smith, 1996), and consumer product design (Halskov & Hansen, 2015; Ritter et al., 2014). Approaches from these fields, in addition to approaches developed within the ergonomics community, may be used to inform inquiry into and redesign of patient work systems in home and community settings.

Figure 4.1 shows example years in the life of individuals based on the work system models described in the following section. Figure 4.1a shows an example year in the life of a patient interacting with multiple healthcare institutions. For this individual, there is patient–professional work occurring during interactions with the health system and patient work occurring during what is termed "the care-between-the-care"—typically performed in home and community settings (Brennan & Casper, 2015). The nature of patient work during the "the care-between-the-care" is diverse, ranging from recovery from acute episodes to long-term management of chronic conditions. Although less common, some individuals operate entirely outside of any formal healthcare systems, as shown in Figure 4.1b. These individuals may be well and not perceive they need formal care. These individuals alternatively may be ill and choose not to interact with healthcare systems for reasons ranging from perceived self-sufficiency to mistrust in the healthcare system or lack of access to

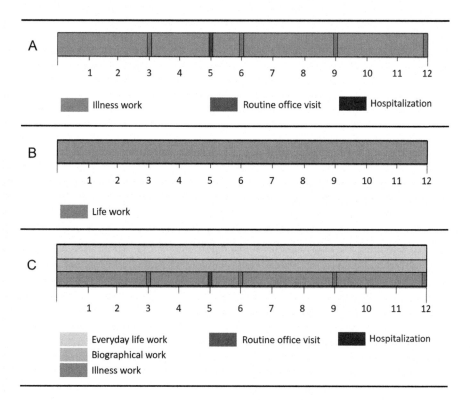

**FIGURE 4.1** Example years in the life of individuals.

healthcare services. Holden et al. (2013) describe institutions, home, and community settings as the key environments where healthcare professional and patient works are conducted, so for individuals not interacting with in any formal healthcare systems, the home and community settings are the sole environments in their work systems. Although the individuals illustrated in Figures 4.1a and b both conduct health-related work in home and community settings, the nature of the work between these types of individuals is distinctly different. The individual illustrated in Figure 4.1b has no (or very little) "care-between-the-care," so the term "patient" may not be an appropriate term to describe this type of individual. The health informatics community has purposefully chosen the term "consumer" when they refer to health informatics interventions focused on laypeople, many of whom are not currently interacting with the formal healthcare system. The important body of research related to "patient work" described in this chapter could certainly be expanded to include all "consumer health work." Figure 4.1c represents patient work as comprised of three streams of parallel efforts, which includes but are not limited to illness work.

### 4.1.1 WORK SYSTEM MODELS

A committee commissioned by the National Research Council (NRC, 2011) published a report detailing the people, tasks, technologies, and environmental factors (i.e. the work system factors) involved in health care that occurs in the home. The NRC report (2011) largely focuses on the type of individual illustrated in Figure 4.1a, specifying three broad categories of *people* (each with subcategories), namely care recipients, informal caregivers, and formal caregivers. They define categories of *tasks* related to

> (1) health maintenance—promoting general health and well-being, preventing disease or disability; (2) episodic care—optimizing outcomes of health events that pertain to pregnancy, childbirth, and mild or acute illness or injury; (3) chronic care—managing ongoing treatment of chronic disease or impairment; and (4) end-of-life care—addressing physical and psychological dimensions of dying.

For the individual illustrated in Figure 4.1b conducting only heath maintenance tasks, there is no appropriate "people" category within this framework. The NRC report consider *technologies* to be either medical devices or health information technologies, falling into 12 categories ranging from medication administration equipment to assistive technologies. They describe home *environments* as having physical, social, community, and policy components. Their detailed delineation of these factors, particularly the environmental factors, can be used as a framework of what must be accounted for when HFE researchers make inquiries into or engage in patient work system redesign efforts in home and community settings.

The SEIPS 2.0 Model delineates the interactions between structural work system elements, work processes, and varied outcomes (Holden et al., 2013). SEIPS 2.0 (Holden et al., 2013) is an extension of the Systems Engineering Initiative for Patient Safety (SEIPS) work system model (Carayon et al., 2006). The need for SEIPS 2.0 arose because of the emergence of "patient work" as a key concept for capturing the important, unpaid health-related work that individuals do (Valdez et al., 2015 , 2016, 2017). Whereas Carayon et al.'s 2006 SEIPS framework largely addressed paid professional work, SEIPS 2.0 also includes patient work and collaborative professional–patient work (Holden et al., 2013). Within the SEIPS 2.0 framework (Holden et al., 2013), a patient work system includes interactions between six system components: person(s), tasks, tools and technologies, internal environments, organizations, and an external environment. Based on our definition of home being the "physical location where one lives, often as a member of a family or household" and community being the "physical or virtual spaces where inhabitants have shared characteristics," the home and community contexts align with the SEIPS 2.0 Internal Environment and Organization components. The *Internal Environment* refers to physical characteristics of spaces within the home and community such as "lighting, noise, vibration, temperature, physical layout and available space, and air quality" (Holden et al., 2013). The *Organization* component with respect to patient work in the home and community settings includes "communication infrastructure, living arrangements, family roles and responsibilities, work and life schedules, interpersonal relationships, culture, social norms and rules, and financial and health-related resources" (Holden et al., 2013). Similar to the NRC framework, SEIPS 2.0 can be used to inform inquiries into or patient work system redesign efforts in home and community settings.

Corbin and Strauss (1985) describe a model of individuals' work that overlaps with aspects of the models described earlier and is highly relevant to healthcare-related human factors research conducted in home and community settings. The model focuses on three types of work related to chronic illness management, though the model could be adapted to other types of patient work such as recovery from acute episodes of care. "Illness work," perhaps the most commonly examined in patient ergonomics research, involves "tasks necessary to manage or treat a chronic illness and its sequelae, including symptoms, disability or loss of function, including but not limited to: regimen work, crisis prevention and handling, symptom management, and diagnostics" (Corbin & Strauss, 1985). "Biographical work" involves "defining and maintaining an identity over the life course" and involves aspects such as "(a) Contextualizing (making the illness part of ongoing life); (b) Coming to terms with the illness, its consequences and one's own mortality; (c) Restructuring one's self-concept, and finally; (d) Recasting one's biography into the future" (Corbin & Strauss, 1985). Finally, "Everyday life work" is defined as "the daily round of tasks that helps keep a household going," including "externally-focused tasks such as bill-paying, shopping, driving, cooking, and cleaning, as well as internal tasks, such as managing stress, anxiety, and emotion" (Corbin & Strauss, 1985). Figure 4.1c shows an example year in the life of one individual, from the perspective of Corbin and Strauss's model. Strauss et al. (1985) also include the concept of articulation, the work of coordinating within and between these three lines of work. As noted by Valdez et al. (2015), these types of work are so interwoven that any descriptive, design, or evaluation, that is, patient ergonomics research, in home or community settings must attend to all three lines of work.

More recently, Holden and colleagues have developed patient work system frameworks, where patient (and informal caregiver) work performance is shaped by four interacting components: Person(s); Tasks; Tools (or Technologies); and Context

(Holden, Schubert, et al., 2015; Holden et al. 2017). In the earlier publication, Holden, Schubert, et al. (2015) developed a model based on interviews, surveys, and observations of patients with heart failure ($n = 30$) and their informal caregivers ($n = 14$). In this framework, the context component is the most closely related to the home and community settings, and includes physical–spatial, social–cultural, and organizational elements. Holden et al. (2017) further synthesized the macroergonomic factors present in patient work within three distinct studies, each focusing on one chronic illness (asthma, heart failure and/or chronic obstructive pulmonary disease, and heart failure). Each of the three studies collected data based on different sociotechnical systems models. They used their analysis to create a consolidated macroergonomic patient work system framework that includes three interacting levels (person(s), tasks, and tools) within three domains (physical context, social context, and organizational context). In their framework, the physical, social, and organizational domains align closely with the home and community contexts. Again, these patient work frameworks can provide insight into the factors that must be accounted for when inquiring into or redesigning patient work systems in the home or community.

One recent study, focused on defining the work of caregivers for persons with dementia, included both a patient work system framework and the Corbin and Strauss (1985) model in their analyses. When Ponnala et al. (2020) conducted a content analysis of transcripts from interviews with 20 caregivers, they developed their coding framework based on the work of Corbin and Strauss and mapped their results to HFE patient work literature (Holden, Schubert, et al., 2015). Their analysis highlights the idea that these frameworks and models can help emphasize different aspects of the patient work system.

### 4.1.2 SOCIAL DETERMINANTS OF HEALTH AND THEIR LINK TO WORK SYSTEM MODELS

The work system models described earlier are based on the idea that patient work systems have diverse characteristics and that this diversity is important to capture and account for in-patient work system redesign. There is a large body of evidence showing the powerful role of "Social Determinants of Health" (SDOH) in shaping health outcomes (Braveman & Gottlieb, 2014). Evidence supporting the impact of SDOH in shaping health outcomes is so compelling that they are a key component of the federal government's Healthy People 2020 initiative (U.S. Department of Health and Human Services, n.d.), which provides "science-based, 10-year national objectives for improving the health of all Americans." Although SDOH components are often implicit in varied aspects of the patient work system models described in the previous section, patient work system understanding and redesign efforts could benefit from explicit linkages to SDOH models and frameworks, particularly because SDOH tend to persist over time. Due to the persistence and intractability of SDOH, patient work system redesign efforts by HFE researchers and practitioners need to account for these enduring factors in addition to trying to change them. For example, there are aspects of several SEIPS 2.0 patient work system components, particularly the person, internal environment, organization, and external environment components that include largely nonmalleable SDOH concepts.

There are several frameworks outlining SDOH factors and their relationships with one another, all of which include some aspects of home and community. Understanding these persistent factors can help determine what aspects of the patient work system are more easily changeable by HFE researchers and practitioners. For example, Dahlgren and Whitehead's (1991) model—although not explicitly termed SDOH—includes social and community networks and a wide range of living and working conditions that influence health. Kaplan et al. (2000) include social relationships, living conditions, neighborhoods and communities, and institutions (e.g. school, work) in their framework. Ansari et al. (2003) describe a public health model of SDOH that includes community and societal characteristics such as social networks and support structures, social and community participation, and residences (urban, rural, remote). The MacArthur Research Network on Socioeconomic Status and Health includes environmental resources and constraints (e.g. neighborhood factors, social capital, work situation, family environment, social support, discrimination) as important elements in their model (John D. and Catherine T. MacArthur Foundation, 2019).

SDOH models and frameworks, and the applications for them, can therefore provide guidance to HFE researchers and practitioners on what elements should be documented during field research in home or community settings and what should be accounted for in redesign. Understanding SDOH can also help HFE researchers and practitioners identify the disciplines (e.g. sociology, public policy) necessary to more comprehensively understand and redesign patient work systems. Of note, Hall's cultural iceberg model (1989) can help HFE researchers further understand the complex organizational components of the work system and SDOH models. Hall distinguishes between external, surface elements of culture that can more easily be seen (e.g. food, holidays, language) and internal, deep elements of culture that take more effort to capture (e.g. attitudes toward authority, approaches to decision-making, concepts of time).

## 4.2  INQUIRY INTO PATIENT WORK SYSTEMS IN HOME AND COMMUNITY SETTINGS

HFE studies aimed at understanding patient work in home and community settings have, not surprisingly, typically focused on single chronic conditions such as heart failure (Mickelson et al., 2016), diabetes (Crowley et al., 2014), hypertension (Marquard et al., 2013), breast cancer (Gorman et al., 2018), chronic pain (Nio Ong et al., 2011), children with medical complexities (Valdez et al., 2020), and those with and at risk for HIV (Marquard et al., 2018).

For example, Zayas-Cabán (2012) used home interviews and observations to identify myriad HIM tasks, public and private locations where these tasks occurred, and traditional and nontraditional health information storage artifacts. These variations showed the significant need for consumer health information technology designers to balance foundational intervention design elements that support all users, with tailored aspects of the intervention that support individual variations.

Mickelson et al. (2015) analyzed photographs, observation notes, interviews, video recordings, medical record data, and surveys to determine what cognitive artifacts older adults used to manage their medications, typically in their home environment. These artifacts, ranging from scales and blood pressure cuffs to electronic health record (EHR) medication lists, were largely viewed as necessary and helpful for medication management work. However, there was often conflicting or missing information across and within the cognitive artifacts older adults used to manage their medications. In addition, some artifacts were not appropriately designed to accommodate the needs of older users and the range in users' access to appropriate technologies. The authors concluded that, to be most useful, paper- and technology-based artifacts must account for contexts of use in addition to users' needs, limitations, abilities, tasks, and routines.

Mickelson et al. (2016) used observations and interviews framed by the SEIPS 2.0 framework, along with five well-known macrocognitive processes (sensemaking, planning, monitoring, decision-making, and coordinating), to describe the medication management work conducted by older adults with heart failure (Crandall et al., 2006; Patterson & Hoffman, 2012). Their descriptive research identified recommendations for technologies that would support these individuals' macrocognitive patient work.

Look and Stone (2018) analyzed the complex work of medication management outside of formal healthcare settings from the perspective of older adults' informal caregivers. Through focus groups with these caregivers, they identified two broad categories of medication management support: direct activities requiring physical handling of medications (e.g. sorting) and indirect cognitive activities (e.g. decision-making). Their analysis identified the crucial role of informal caregivers in medication management for older adults and the types of tools and strategies they use in their homes and communities to do their work.

As a result of collecting and analyzing data related to patient work in the home and community settings being time-intensive, it is important that HFE researchers consider how to make their data and analyses available to others. For example, using the previously described models and frameworks to guide data collection and analysis can aid in synthesizing quantitative and qualitative data across multiple studies. These data could ideally be used by myriad types of individuals—hardware and software designers, clinicians, and lay people—without burdening participants.

## 4.3 REDESIGNING AND EVALUATING PATIENT WORK SYSTEMS IN HOME AND COMMUNITY SETTINGS

The patient work panels made clear that much of the HFE work to date has been focused on describing patient work in home and community settings, rather than on patient work system design and/or evaluation. This is not surprising, as research in emerging fields often focuses (rightly) on understanding current work systems before attempting to alter them.

Redesign and evaluation of patient work systems in home and community settings are fraught with challenges. Formative design and evaluation (e.g. needs assessments, iterative usability testing)—aimed at improving the design of the intervention—are more common in home and community settings than summative evaluations, which assess the intervention outcomes such as those detailed in the SEIPS 2.0 structure–process–outcomes framework (Holden et al., 2013). Such a summative evaluation based on the SEIPS 2.0 framework would at a minimum consider how structural work system elements impact patient, professional, and collaborative patient/professional processes, which then impact a range of outcomes. For formative design and summative evaluation, it is nearly impossible to include an appropriate representation of individuals, organizations, and internal environments in the evaluation, thereby reducing the external validity or generalizability of the findings. In the formative design and evaluation, this means a potentially narrow sample of participants are providing (still invaluable) guidance on intervention design choices. In the summative evaluation, the effectiveness for all will likely be judged based on the effectiveness for some. Although some studies may do well at recruiting a diverse range of participants based on their individual characteristics (e.g. age, ethnicity) (Valdez et al., 2012), it is rare that they recruit from a diverse range of organizations (e.g. family roles and responsibilities) or internal environments (e.g. noise levels). It is even rarer that researchers attend to the impact of the intersectionality of these elements. If we believe these patient work system factors related to home and community settings have an impact on work processes and outcomes, as detailed in the SEIPS 2.0 and NRC frameworks, they likely should be included in the identification of participants to include in the design and evaluation. However, because of the resource burdens associated with conducting field research in home and community settings, it is infeasible for researchers to include participants varying across all these intersecting characteristics. Rather, researchers must identify which characteristics they presume will *most influence* design choices and diversify their sample of participants based on those characteristics.

There is also significant tension in the choices of outcomes measured in evaluations of patient work system interventions and how those outcomes are measured. In general, HFE researchers and practitioners often focus on outcomes from a safety–performance–satisfaction triad, with different domains weighing these three types of outcomes differently (Lee et al., 2017). Interventions targeted at high-risk domains may prioritize safety, interventions targeted at lower-risk workplaces may prioritize performance, and consumer product developers may prioritize satisfaction (Lee et al., 2017). For patient work system interventions in home and community settings, it is not always clear how these factors should be prioritized.

Satisfaction is often measured by HFE researchers via measures of perceived usability, usefulness, or adoption and is typically viewed as a prerequisite required for the individual to initiate and continue engaging with the intervention (e.g. an mHealth device) (Ware et al., 2019). Researchers have found that aspects of home and community settings impact satisfaction. For example, Fischer et al. (2014) reviewed studies addressing elderly individuals' use and acceptance of information technology for health. They identified that challenges with technologies were not only technical but based on the nature of the patient's broader work system.

Safety is often viewed as an (unmeasured) requirement of the intervention, not as an ultimate outcome measure. More recently, two panels have focused on the role of patients in patient safety (Papautsky et al., 2018, 2019). Two of the 2018 panelists described contexts in home and community where patients play a role in improving patient safety, one involving improving medication safety practices and the other addressing how mobile apps and wearables may prevent visits to clinical settings (a location where significant safety issues occur). Studies measuring the impact of patient work interventions in home and community settings on safety will likely increase over time.

Measuring any of these outcomes for patient work interventions in home and community settings is significantly challenged by shifting *organizational* and *internal environment* factors over various time frames (hour-to-hour, month-to-month, year-to-year). For example, an mHealth device may be used throughout diverse locations (e.g. home, work, school) within a single day, and housing situations (e.g. moving from an apartment in a city to a home in a rural setting) along with family dynamics (e.g. birth or death of a family member) may shift over time. For the same individual, changes in one's *organizational* and *internal environment* may improve or diminish patient work system redesign outcomes. The individual may also be changing other health-related behaviors (e.g. dietary or exercise routines, sleep habits, meditation) in parallel with the HFE redesigns. In addition, usual care (the control group) is also often changing over time. These challenges make teasing out the true impact of patient work system redesigns in home and community settings particularly challenging. Not surprisingly, many studies have found less than ideal outcomes for patient work system redesigns deployed in home and community settings (Beatty & Lambert, 2013; Yu et al., 2012), though this is not uncommon for interventions deployed in naturalistic settings.

In 1962, Rogers initially proposed the "Diffusion of Innovations theory" to explain how, why, and at what rate new ideas and technology spread (Rogers, 1962, 2004). Rogers divided individuals into five categories: innovators; early adopters; early majority; late majority; and laggards. There are now thousands of articles across many disciplines based on the Diffusion of Innovations theory. *Researcher-driven* technology-based patient work interventions in home and community settings are often deployed only after they are shown to be effective through lengthy evaluations, meaning technologies may be outdated by the time of broad dissemination. The technology platforms on which they are developed may therefore only be desirable to late adopters or laggards. If these technologies are deployed in home and community settings to individuals who were early adopters of those technologies, but have moved on to new technologies, the intervention may be deemed neither useful nor usable (e.g. web-based interventions without well-designed mobile viewing capacity). *Commercially driven* technology-based patient work interventions in home and community settings may be more suitable to early adopters, but may also have limited outcomes evaluation. This trade-off signals the need for HFE researchers and practitioners to determine where on the safety–performance–satisfaction outcomes triad a particular patient work intervention is located (Lee et al., 2017).

## 4.4   PRACTICAL CONSIDERATIONS

Conducting patient work research in home and community settings raises practical, in addition to methodological, challenges (Furniss et al., 2014; Holden, McDougald Scott, et al., 2015; Holden, Valdez, et al., 2015). Valdez and Holden (2016) provide an overview of the vastly differing priorities of community members, the study team, and the project when conducting human factors research in the home and community. They also provide practical advice on how those differing priorities can be addressed through strategies before, during, and after visits with participants. In the following two sections, we elaborate on two issues of significant concern: identifying a population of interest and identifying when and where to meet them.

### 4.4.1 Defining a Population of Interest

Much of the human factors research within home and community settings remains clinically motivated. Studies are often focused on individuals having a specific condition or diagnosis, such as hypertension, asthma, or diabetes. The population of interest is typically then narrowed by factors such as geography, gender, race, or ethnicity. For example, a descriptive study may ask, "What work system changes would make *African American women* with *diabetes* healthier?" or "What work system changes would make *pregnant women* with *diabetes* in *rural communities* healthier?" A study with a specific design change in mind might ask, "Does using a smartwatch and mobile app help *African American women* better control their *diabetes*?"

Determining how widely or narrowly to scope a population of interest is difficult. There exists much variability within groups having the same condition or diagnosis, so narrowing the population of interest can be helpful in designing useful and useable patient work system interventions. In addition, conducting home and community-based research is logistically challenging and often qualitative, making data rich and cumbersome to analyze. Choosing a more focused population may reduce the sample size of participants needed to adequately understand the population of interest. Yet, narrowing the population of interest has drawbacks, as significant insights may be lost about excluded populations and their contexts of use, so the generalizability of findings will be narrower. Researchers also need to determine whether home and community factors (e.g. health insurance access) should be used as factors for narrowing the population.

Making decisions about the population of interest also requires explicit decision-making about design equity. Many patient work interventions are not inherently accessible to all individuals because of factors such as socioeconomic status, language, disabilities, or geography. If an effective intervention is accessible to majority groups and not others, it may increase existing, or create new, gaps in health outcomes— termed intervention-generated inequalities (Veinot et al., 2018). If an intervention is customized or tailored to individuals, evaluating the impact of the nonuniform intervention becomes especially challenging. Instead, the evaluation could focus on how robust the customizable intervention is to diverse patient work systems.

One approach to evaluation is to conduct maximum variance sampling, which purposefully involves selecting a wide range of extremes in the study population (Benda et al., 2020). Because patient work systems are so diverse, maximum variance sampling could be useful even when a population of interest appears relatively narrow. For example, with respect to the home and community settings, a research team could include a variety of housing types in their sample.

### 4.4.2 MEETING INDIVIDUALS WHERE THEY ARE

Home and community-based studies often base recruitment in formal healthcare settings, with healthcare workers making first contact with potential participants. This "meet the researcher where they are" approach, even if the research is focused on what happens in home and community, is starting from a clinically focused perspective. By linking home and community-based research to individuals with specific conditions or diagnoses, and by recruiting from formal healthcare settings, studies will be biased toward participants recently interacting with the healthcare system.

Researchers should consider where in the healthcare continuum the participants are or should be, including: not currently interacting with any formal healthcare system, recently discharged from an acute care setting, post outpatient surgery, self-managing between frequent office visits, or self-managing between infrequent office visits. This consideration will help determine whether recruitment efforts should be conducted at formal healthcare settings or in informal settings, such as community centers. If researchers recruit participants from diverse locations, they must also consider that participant characteristics may be fundamentally different across recruitment locations.

From a researcher perspective, collecting data within the patient work system setting allows the research team to make assessments of the patient work system internal environment that would be difficult to glean via participant self-report. Although this approach significantly increases time burden on the research team, going to the participant's home provides invaluable information about the context in which the patient work is done. This consideration can particularly be important for studies aimed at *understanding* home and community work systems. However, participants may prefer for the researcher to not enter their home environment. For this reason, participants should have the flexibility in where they meet the research team. If assessments of the patient work system internal environment are important, the research team should develop alternative methods such as photographs, videos, or structured data capture tools. For example, Yin et al. (2018) proposed an approach for capturing rich longitudinal patient work in a less obtrusive way than repeated observations. Their method of body-worn cameras and self-report diaries will be tested with 40 participants with type 2 diabetes and at least one chronic comorbidity over a 24-hour period, coupled with pre- and post-study quantitative questionnaire and qualitative interview data. They will use these data to assess the durations, times, contexts, and patterns of patient work. The vizHOME project provides another example approach to patient work system data collected in home and community settings (Brennan et al., 2015; Werner et al., 2018). The team used LiDAR, a laser emitting scanner, to capture 3D home interiors. These homes could then be visualized in a virtual reality CAVE. The goal of capturing and visualizing these data was to understand how the home environment affects how, where, and how well people use healthcare tools and technologies. Although an initial set of participants allowed researchers into their home, future studies can use these 3D models in lieu of entering patient homes.

For studies aimed at *redesigning* patient work systems, choices in how much support to provide to participants are important and challenging. Early formative design interactions should lean toward more engagement with participants via home visits, telephone calls, and meetings to identify design challenges that should be remedied. Final designs should reflect the levels of engagement that would occur if the design were going to be deployed after the research is conducted, such as troubleshooting guides based on the formative design interactions, or else there will not be clarity around whether the design will be scalable beyond the research study.

## 4.5 CASE STUDIES

### 4.5.1 Managing Hypertension in Patients with Diabetes

The CONtrolling Disease Using Inexpensive Information Technology—Hypertension in Diabetes (CONDUIT-HID) project aimed to develop and implement a novel, technology-supported model of care to manage hypertension in patients with diabetes (Marquard et al., 2013; Martinez et al., 2017). CONDUIT-HID focused on improving the "care-between-the-care" for individuals already engaged with the formal healthcare system. From the perspective of patient work system redesign, the research team took a patient-centered approach to design the technology-supported model of care. Patients were engaged in formative design work and summative outcome evaluation. Patient work models were not used to guide these design activities but were used instead to guide the qualitative analysis of participant interviews. The descriptions below are some of the key macroergonomic patient work system factors related to the study.

- **Patient.** Individuals with hypertension.
- **Tools.** Low cost, commercial, off-the-shelf clinically validated blood pressure (BP) monitor and software.
- **Tasks.** Participants took their BP readings several times a week using an electronic blood pressure cuff. The patient-generated BP data obtained in home and community setting were integrated with clinical data in the patients' EHR. These data allowed chronic care nurses to monitor patients' BP readings without the patient coming into the formal care setting, to provide information-rich phone call consultations with patients regarding medication adjustments and lifestyle changes.
- **Physical context.** Participants almost all took their BP readings at home. Their homes varied widely in size, type (e.g. single family home), and nature (e.g. amount of clutter).
- **Social context.** Participants were often supported (though sometimes not) by family in managing their hypertension and using the technologies.
- **Organizational context.** Participants were already receiving care within a Central Massachusetts health system. Most had existing routines related to managing their hypertension. They lived in varied geographies and different distances from their health system access points. They lived in a state offering public health insurance but varied widely in their financial situations.

The project included multiple formative design components. Research team members acted as patient and nurse proxies, recording all challenges they encountered while using the system for 10 days and creating mediation strategies (Marquard & Zayas-Cabán, 2011; Zayas-Cabán et al., 2009). Most of these strategies (e.g. training protocols, simplified take-home instructions) were implemented. The team then conducted a pilot study with 26 participants, each using the system for 9 months (Marquard et al., 2013). The key measure of success was whether the patients could use the intervention from their homes or workplaces without the research team intervening to help them. Data collection methods included in-home observations with one or two study nurses and one to three human factors researchers at each visit as well as phone calls with patients. The team recorded challenges the participants encountered while using the system in their home; after each visit, the human factors researchers revised the materials provided to the patient or elements of the technologies when possible—though this was challenging to do with commercial off-the-shelf technologies. Participants also called the research team if they encountered challenges outside of home visits; these challenges were resolved when possible.

The CONDUIT-HID intervention was evaluated via a randomized controlled trial (RCT) of 196 patient participants, 99 of whom received the intervention and 97 of whom received standard care. Data collected during the RCT included home and office BP readings and health system utilization data. The quantitative study data showed no differences in pre/post BP readings, or utilization data, between the intervention and control groups. But, pre/post BP readings for both groups dropped, perhaps because "standard care" protocols also changed over the study period and appeared to show equal improvements in BP.

To better understand participants' interactions with the intervention, the team conducted interviews with 21 intervention participants (Martinez et al., 2017). Study nurses purposively sampled a diverse set of participants for the interviews. Participants were asked high-level questions about their overall experience with the intervention, followed by questions focusing on their successes, problems, and general reactions. The interview data were coded using the SEIPS 2.0 framework. Participants generally felt the CONDUIT-HID intervention was easily integrated into their daily routines and the system was user-friendly and reliable. However, minimizing usability issues and supporting participant workflow were important—but not enough—for intervention success. Those who benefited most appeared to have improved their mental models related to their hypertension (e.g. identifying cause–effect patterns in their behaviors and BP readings), with these changed models resulting in improved self-management skills.

Although using the SEIPS 2.0 framework to analyze participant interviews proved insightful, the project would have benefited from having an initial assessment of the participant population based on a patient work system model and using that understanding to drive design choices. Because the research team was committed to using off-the-shelf technologies to improve access and scalability, this understanding would have primarily guided the choice of technologies and interaction points with the healthcare system. Although the design choices largely worked for the participant population, conducting a framework-based assessment of participants' patient work systems would have provided more grounding for these choices.

## 4.5.2 Improving Medication Adherence in Patients with and At-Risk for HIV

The Unobtrusive Sensing of Medication Intake (USE-MI) project aims to develop and implement a proof-of-concept, low-cost, and innovative system designed to improve medication-taking measurement and adherence. The descriptions below are some of the key macroergonomic patient work system factors related to the study.

- **Patient.** Individuals with and at-risk for HIV
- **Tools.** Wrist-worn device, smartphone app, and a tagged medication container.
- **Tasks.** Participants receive custom pill-taking reminders, and the system detects and logs pill-taking behaviors via a combination of NFC tags, wrist movement data, and user feedback. Participants can view adherence data via the smartphone app.
- **Physical context.** Participants interacting with the USE-MI system do so in many locations in their homes and communities and at many different times. Thus, the number of intersecting home and community-related factors was exponentially higher than in CONDUIT-HID.
- **Social context.** Participants largely did not want others to know about their condition and did not want the purpose of the system to be obvious to others.
- **Organizational context.** Participants were already receiving care in a Seattle clinic serving patients with HIV/AIDS. Most had existing routines related to medication taking. They lived in mostly urban settings, many were experiencing financial hardship, and had a range of access to health insurance.

The project has included multiple formative design components to date. As a result of USE-MI's requirement for several custom-developed, complex components that must be linked together (i.e. back-end server, phone, watch, NFC-tagged pill bottle), the formative design process is much more involved than in CONDUIT-HID. The team initially conducted a survey ($n = 225$) of individuals taking antiretroviral therapy and HIV pre-exposure prophylaxis (Stekler et al., 2018). Participants were asked about several elements within the patient work system frameworks, including information about themselves, tools they currently use for medication taking, and work processes related to taking their medications. By looking at the links between patient work system factors and their self-reported adherence, this survey helped identify a subset of individuals for whom the system could be most valuable.

The team then conducted interviews with and observations of, and administered questionnaires to, individuals with and at-risk for HIV ($n = 17$) (Marquard et al., 2018). In semi-structured face-to-face interviews, participants responded to questions about their patient work systems and processes, including how they stored, took, and remembered to take their medications. They completed a questionnaire assessing their perceived adherence levels, medication-taking practices, preferences for gaining feedback about their medication-taking patterns, and general demographic measures. The team video-recorded participants wearing a wrist device while taking placebo pills from a bottle, and participants also gave feedback about two candidate devices.

As soon as a relatively stable version of the system was developed, eight different research team members used the system "in the wild" throughout its iterative development (some for several months), either with their own medications or with placebo medications. The research team members systematically discussed and resolved usability and technical challenges that would create frustration for patients. Although the research team's work systems likely did not match participants', this approach allowed the research team to identify and resolve myriad issues. The team is now pilot testing the system for an extended time with ten patient participants to glean their feedback before revising the system design and deploying it in an evaluative trial.

In this study, the research team used patient work system factors to guide their early formative work. The team targeted the work system factors that they viewed as more likely to affect system outcomes. Assessing only a subset of work system factors reduced the burden on participants and the research team, but by doing so may have failed to identify key factors affecting system use.

## 4.6  CONCLUSION

The home and community settings are widely acknowledged as important contexts in which patient work is done, yet capturing these contexts and their diversity is labor-intensive. Although many aspects of patients' home and community settings are difficult for HFE researchers or practitioners to change, knowledge of the home and community settings can be design guiding, informing design choices for those aspects of patients' work systems that are malleable.

Several models and frameworks exist to guide the assessment and redesign of patient work systems, including general work system frameworks, social determinants of health models, and more recent patient-work-specific frameworks. The HFE community would benefit if individual studies used these well-specified frameworks to guide patient work system inquiry, design, and evaluation in home and community settings. Using these common frameworks would allow HFE researchers and practitioners to share data across studies and conduct cross-study data analyses.

The chapter also outlines practical considerations for patient-work-focused activities in the home and community. HFE researchers and practitioners must make explicit choices about their study population of interest. Studies focused on narrowly defined populations may allow for depth of data collection within a subgroup at the expense of generalizability, whereas broadly defined populations may allow for more generalization at the expense of deeply understanding subgroups within the population. It is only via very large studies (or syntheses of studies using common data collection frameworks) that this necessary depth and breadth of understanding can be achieved.

As a result of the rich and diverse nature of individuals' homes and community settings, HFE researchers and practitioners are well served by entering these contexts. If this is not feasible, alternative methods such as photographs, videos, or structured data capture tools can help provide insight beyond traditional questionnaires or interviews.

To fully understand how patient work is currently conducted or would be affected by system design changes (e.g. new technologies, policies), the home and community settings must be captured, documented, and systematically analyzed. This process requires careful consideration of population scoping and data collection approaches.

Robust, generalizable knowledge of patient work conducted in home and community settings will necessitate coordinated data syntheses and analyses across HFE research and practice communities.

## ACKNOWLEDGMENTS

Preparation of this chapter was supported by the National Institute of Nursing Research (NINR) through the UManage Center: UMass Center for Building the Science of Symptom Self-Management grant P20NR016599 and National Institute of Allergy and Infectious Diseases (NIAID) through the Unobtrusive Sensing of Medication Intake (USE-MI) grant 5R01MH109319-04. Any opinions, findings, and conclusions or recommendations expressed in this publication are those of the authors and do not necessarily reflect the views of the funding agencies.

## REFERENCES

Anderson, E. T., & McFarlane, J. M. (2019). *Community as Partner. Theory and Practice in Nursing*. Philadelphia: Wolters Kluwer.

Andrews, M. M., & Boyle, J. S. (2002). Transcultural concepts in nursing care. *Journal of Transcultural Nursing*, 13(3), 178–180.

Ansari, Z., Carson, N. J., Ackland, M. J., Vaughan, L., & Serraglio, A. (2003). A public health model of the social determinants of health. *Social and Preventive Medicine*, 48(4), 242–251.

Beatty, L., & Lambert, S. (2013). A systematic review of internet-based self-help therapeutic interventions to improve distress and disease-control among adults with chronic health conditions. *Clinical Psychology Review*, 33(4), 609–622.

Benda, N. C., Montague, E., & Valdez, R. S. (2020). Design for inclusivity. In: Arathi Sethumadhavan and Farzan Sasangohar (eds.). *Design for Health* (pp. 305–322). Academic Press, Cambridge, MA.

Braveman, P., & Gottlieb, L. (2014). The social determinants of health: It's time to consider the causes of the causes. *Public Health Reports*, 129(1_suppl2), 19–31.

Brennan, P. F., & Casper, G. (2015). Observing health in everyday living: ODLs and the care-between-the-care. *Personal and Ubiquitous Computing*, 19(1), 3–8.

Brennan, P. F., Ponto, K., Casper, G., Tredinnick, R., & Broecker, M. (2015). Virtualizing living and working spaces: Proof of concept for a biomedical space-replication methodology. *Journal of Biomedical Informatics*, 57, 53–61.

Carayon, P., Hundt, A. S., Karsh, B. T., Gurses, A. P., Alvarado, C. J., Smith, M., & Brennan, P. F. (2006). Work system design for patient safety: The SEIPS model. *The BMJ Quality & Safety*, 15(suppl 1), i50–i58.

Corbin, J., & Strauss, A. (1985). Managing chronic illness at home: Three lines of work. *Qualitative Sociology*, 8(3), 224–247.

Crandall, B., Klein, G., Klein, G. A., & Hoffman, R. R. (2006). *Working Minds: A Practitioner's Guide to Cognitive Task Analysis*. Cambridge: MIT Press.

Crowley, M. J., Holleman, R., Klamerus, M. L., Bosworth, H. B., Edelman, D., & Heisler, M. (2014). Factors associated with persistent poorly controlled diabetes mellitus: Clues to improving management in patients with resistant poor control. *Chronic illness*, 10(4), 291–302.

Dahlgren, G., & Whitehead, M. (1991). *Policies and Strategies to Promote Social Equity in Health*. Stockholm: Institute for Future Studies, 1–69.

Fischer, S. H., David, D., Crotty, B. H., Dierks, M., & Safran, C. (2014). Acceptance and use of health information technology by community-dwelling elders. *International journal of medical informatics*, 83(9), 624–635.

Furniss, D., Randell, R., O'Kane, A. A., Taneva, S., Mentis, H., & Blandford, A. (2014). Fieldwork for healthcare: Guidance for investigating human factors in computing systems. *Synthesis Lectures on Assistive, Rehabilitative, and Health-Preserving Technologies*, 3(2), 1–146.

Gorman, R. K., Wellbeloved-Stone, C. A., & Valdez, R. S. (2018). Uncovering the invisible patient work system through a case study of breast cancer self-management. *Ergonomics*, 61(12), 1575–1590.

Hall, E. T. (1989). *Beyond Culture*. New York: Anchor.

Halskov, K., & Hansen, N. B. (2015). The diversity of participatory design research practice at PDC 2002–2012. *International Journal of Human-Computer Studies*, 74, 81–92.

Holden, R. J., Carayon, P., Gurses, A. P., Hoonakker, P., Hundt, A. S., Ozok, A. A., & Rivera-Rodriguez, A. J. (2013). SEIPS 2.0: A human factors framework for studying and improving the work of healthcare professionals and patients. *Ergonomics*, 56(11), 1669–1686.

Holden, R. J., Schubert, C. C., & Mickelson, R. S. (2015). The patient work system: An analysis of self-care performance barriers among elderly heart failure patients and their informal caregivers. *Applied Ergonomics*, *47*, 133–150.

Holden, R. J., McDougald Scott, A. M., Hoonakker, P. L., Hundt, A. S., & Carayon, P. (2015). Data collection challenges in community settings: Insights from two field studies of patients with chronic disease. *Quality of Life Research*, 24(5), 1043–1055.

Holden, R. J., Valdez, R. S., Hundt, A. S., Marquard, J., Montague, E., Nathan-Roberts, D.,... & Zayas-Cabán, T. (2015). Field-based human factors in home and community settings: challenges and strategies. In *Proceedings of the Human Factors and Ergonomics Society Annual Meeting* (Vol. 59, No. 1, pp. 562–566). Sage CA: Los Angeles, CA: SAGE Publications.

Holden, R. J., Valdez, R. S., Schubert, C. C., Thompson, M. J., & Hundt, A. S. (2017). Macroergonomic factors in the patient work system: Examining the context of patients with chronic illness. *Ergonomics*, 60(1), 26–43.

Institute of Medicine. (2014). *Capturing Social and Behavioral Domains in Electronic Health Records: Phase 1*. Washington, DC: The National Academies Press.

John D. and Catherine T. MacArthur Foundation. (2019). *Research network on socioeconomic status & health*. Retrieved from: https://www.macfound.org/networks/research-network-on-socioeconomic-status-health/.

Kaplan, G. A., S. A. Everson, and J. K. Lynch. (2000). The contribution of social and behavioral research to an understanding of the distribution of disease: A multilevel approach. Paper commissioned by the Committee on Capitalizing on Social Science and Behavioral Research to Improve the Public's Health. In *Promoting Health Strategies from Social and Behavioral Research (see Appendix A)*. Washington, DC: National Academy Press.

Kiefer, C. W. (2006). *Doing Health Anthropology: Research Methods for Community Assessment and Change*. New York: Springer Publishing Company.

Lambert, H., & McKevitt, C. (2002). Anthropology in health research: From qualitative methods to multidisciplinarity. *The BMJ*, 325(7357), 210–213.

Lee, J. D., Wickens, C. D., Liu, Y., & Boyle, L. N. (2017). *Designing for People: An Introduction to Human Factors Engineering*. New York: CreateSpace.

Look, K. A., & Stone, J. A. (2018). Medication management activities performed by informal caregivers of older adults. *Research in Social and Administrative Pharmacy*, 14(5), 418–426.

Marquard, J. L., & Zayas-Cabán, T. (2011). Commercial off-the-shelf consumer health informatics interventions: Recommendations for their design, evaluation and redesign. *Journal of the American Medical Informatics Association*, 19(1), 137–142.

Marquard, J. L., Garber, L., Saver, B., Amster, B., Kelleher, M., & Preusse, P. (2013). Overcoming challenges integrating patient-generated data into the clinical EHR: Lessons from the CONtrolling Disease Using Inexpensive IT–Hypertension in Diabetes (CONDUIT-HID) Project. *International Journal of Medical Informatics*, 82(10), 903–910.

Marquard, J. L., Saver, B., Kandaswamy, S., Martinez, V. I., Simoni, J. M., Stekler, J. D., Ganesan, D., Scanlan, J. (2018). Designing a wrist-worn sensor to improve medication adherence: Accommodating diverse user behaviors and technology preferences. *Journal of the American Medical Informatics Association Open*, 1(2), 1 October, 153–158.

Martinez, V. I., Marquard, J. L., Saver, B., Garber, L., & Preusse, P. (2017). Consumer health informatics interventions must support user workflows, be easy-to-use, and improve cognition: Applying the SEIPS 2.0 model to evaluate patients' and clinicians' experiences with the CONDUIT-HID intervention. *International Journal of Human–Computer Interaction*, 33(4), 333–343.

Mickelson, R. S., Willis, M., & Holden, R. J. (2015). Medication-related cognitive artifacts used by older adults with heart failure. *Health Policy and Technology*, 4(4), 387–398.

Mickelson, R. S., Unertl, K. M., & Holden, R. J. (2016). Medication management: The macrocognitive workflow of older adults with heart failure. *Journal of Medical Internet Research Human Factors*, 3(2), e27.

National Research Council. (2011). *Health Care Comes Home: The Human Factors*. Washington, DC: National Academies Press.

Nio Ong, B., Jinks, C., & Morden, A. (2011). The hard work of self-management: Living with chronic knee pain. *International Journal of Qualitative Studies on Health and Well-being*, 6(3), 7035.

Papautsky, E. L., Holden, R. J., Valdez, R. S., Belden, J., Karavite, D., Marquard, J.,.... & Muthu, N. (2018). The patient in patient Safety: Starting the conversation. In *Proceedings of the International Symposium on Human Factors and Ergonomics in Health Care* (Vol. 7, No. 1, pp. 173–177). Sage India: New Delhi, India: SAGE Publications.

Papautsky, E. L., Holden, R. J., Valdez, R. S., Gruss, V., Panzer, J., & Perry, S. J. (2019, September). The patient in patient safety: Clinicians' experiences engaging patients as partners in safety. In *Proceedings of the International Symposium on Human Factors and Ergonomics in Health Care* (Vol. 8, No. 1, pp. 265–269). Sage CA: Los Angeles, CA: SAGE Publications.

Patterson, E. S., & Hoffman, R. R. (2012). Visualization framework of macrocognition functions. *Cognition, Technology & Work*, 14(3), 221–227.

Ponnala, S., Block, L., Lingg, A. J., Kind, A. J., & Werner, N. E. (2020). Conceptualizing caregiving activities for persons with dementia (PwD) through a patient work lens. *Applied Ergonomics*, 85, 103070.

Ritter, F. E., Baxter, G. D., & Churchill, E. F. (2014). User-centered systems design: A brief history. *Foundations for Designing User-Centered Systems* (pp. 33–54). London: Springer.

Rogers, E. M. (1962). *Diffusion of Innovations*. New York: Free Press.

Rogers, E. M. (2004). A prospective and retrospective look at the diffusion model. *Journal of Health Communication*, 9(S1), 13–19.

Sarafino, E. P., & Smith, T. W. (2014). *Health Psychology: Biopsychosocial Interactions*. Hoboken: John Wiley & Sons.

Satcher, D. (2005). *Methods in Community-Based Participatory Research for Health*. San Francisco: John Wiley & Sons.

Smith, J. A. (1996). Beyond the divide between cognition and discourse: Using interpretative phenomenological analysis in health psychology. *Psychology and Health*, 11(2), 261–271.

Stekler, J.D., Scanlan, J.M., Simoni, J.M., Crane, H.M., Fredericksen, R., Marquard, J., Saver, B.G. (2018). Medication-taking practices and preferences to inform development of a wrist-worn device to monitor HIV ART and PrEP adherence. *AIDS Education and Prevention*, 30(5): 357–68.

Strauss, A. L., Fagerhaugh, S., Suczeck, C., & Wiener, C. (1985). *Social Organization of Medical Work*. Chicago: Université de Chicago Press. *La Trame de la Négociation: Sociologie Qualitative et Interactionnisme*.

U.S. Department of Health and Human Services, Office of Disease Prevention and Health Promotion. *Healthy people 2020 social determinants of health*. Retrieved from:

https://www.healthypeople.gov/2020/topics-objectives/topic/social-determinants-of-health.

Ulin, P. R., Robinson, E. T., & Tolley, E. E. (2012). *Qualitative Methods in Public Health: A Field Guide for Applied Research*. San Francisco: John Wiley & Sons.

Valdez, R. S., & Holden, R. J. (2016). Health care human factors/ergonomics fieldwork in home and community settings. *Ergonomics in Design*, 24(4), 4–9.

Valdez, R. S., Gibbons, M. C., Siegel, E. R., Kukafka, R., & Brennan, P. F. (2012). Designing consumer health IT to enhance usability among different racial and ethnic groups within the United States. *Health and Technology*, 2(4), 225–233.

Valdez, R. S., Holden, R. J., Novak, L. L., & Veinot, T. C. (2015). Transforming consumer health informatics through a patient work framework: Connecting patients to context. *Journal of the American Medical Informatics Association*, 22, 2–10.

Valdez, R. S., Holden, R. J., Caine, K., Madathil, K., Mickelson, R., Lovett Novak, L., & Werner, N. (2016). Patient work as a maturing approach within HFE: Moving beyond traditional self-management applications. In *Proceedings of the Human Factors and Ergonomics Society Annual Meeting* (Vol. 60, No. 1, pp. 657–661). SAGE Publications.

Valdez, R. S., Holden, R. J., Khunlerkit, N., Marquard, J., McGuire, K., Nathan-Roberts, D.,... & Ramly, E. (2017). Patient work methods: Current methods of engaging patients in systems design in clinical, community and extraterrestrial settings. In *Proceedings of the Human Factors and Ergonomics Society Annual Meeting* (Vol. 61, No. 1, pp. 625–629). SAGE Publications.

Valdez, R. S., Lunsford, C., Bae, J., Letzkus, L. C., & Keim-Malpass, J. (2020). Self-management characterization for families of children with medical complexity and their social networks: Protocol for a qualitative assessment. *Journal of Medical Internet Research Protocols*, 9(1), e14810.

Veinot, T. C., Mitchell, H., & Ancker, J. S. (2018). Good intentions are not enough: How informatics interventions can worsen inequality. *Journal of the American Medical Informatics Association*, 25(8), 1080–1088.

Ware, P., Dorai, M., Ross, H. J., Cafazzo, J. A., Laporte, A., Boodoo, C., & Seto, E. (2019). Patient adherence to a mobile phone–based heart failure telemonitoring program: A longitudinal mixed-methods study. *Journal of Medical Internet Research mHealth and uHealth*, 7(2), e13259.

Werner, N. E., Jolliff, A. F., Casper, G., Martell, T., & Ponto, K. (2018). Home is where the head is: A distributed cognition account of personal health information management in the home among those with chronic illness. *Ergonomics*, 61(8), 1065–1078.

Yin, K., Harms, T., Ho, K., Rapport, F., Vagholkar, S., Laranjo, L., Coiera, E., Gershuny, J., & Lau, A. Y. (2018). Patient work from a context and time use perspective: A mixed-methods study protocol. *The BMJ Open*, 8(12), e022163.

Yu, C. H., Bahniwal, R., Laupacis, A., Leung, E., Orr, M. S., & Straus, S. E. (2012). Systematic review and evaluation of web-accessible tools for management of diabetes and related cardiovascular risk factors by patients and healthcare providers. *Journal of the American Medical Informatics Association*, 19(4), 514–522.

Zayas-Cabán, T. (2012). Health information management in the home: A human factors assessment. *Work*, 41(3), 315–328.

Zayas-Cabán, T., & Valdez, R. S. (2011). Human factors in home care. In P. Carayon (Ed.), *Handbook of Human Factors and Ergonomics in Health Care and Patient Safety* (pp. 743–762). Mahwah, NJ: Lawrence Erlbaum.

Zayas-Cabán, T., Marquard, J. L., Radhakrishnan, K., Duffey, N., & Evernden, D. L. (2009). Scenario-based user testing to guide consumer health informatics design. In *AMIA Annual Symposium Proceedings* (Vol. 2009, p. 719). American Medical Informatics Association.

# 5 Community Retail Pharmacies

## The Incipiency of Patient Ergonomics Research in the Retail Pharmacy Setting

Michelle A. Chui, Ashley Morris, and David Mott
School of Pharmacy, Social and
Administrative Sciences Division
University of Wisconsin

## CONTENTS

There are approximately 67,000 retail/community pharmacies dispensing 4.4 billion prescriptions each year (IQVIA Institute, 2017). Many patients interact with community pharmacists every month when refilling their prescriptions, significantly more often than patients see their physicians or other primary healthcare providers. Consequently, the pharmacy is a critical point of care for patients. In addition to verifying the accuracy of written and dispensed prescriptions and assuring patients' understanding of how to take their medication, community pharmacists serve an invaluable role to patients as the triage point when seeking over-the-counter (OTC) products. While in the pharmacy, patients expect to receive their new and refilled prescriptions in a timely manner, to be educated about potential changes to their medication regimen, and to receive recommendations about OTC medications. These encounters are referred to as patient counseling, in which the pharmacist informs the patient about their medication, indication, directions, and potential side effects, as well as verifies that the patient does not have any additional questions about their medication(s).

These patient encounters have been developed by pharmacists and have been standardized for decades (standardized by the Indian Health Service until OBRA '90 which is the federal legislation that set the pharmacist–patient counseling standards followed today) (Perri et al., 1995; Scott & Wessels, 1997). It is common for systems-focused pharmacy researchers interested in retail pharmacies to concentrate on what the pharmacist or pharmacy technicians must do in their work environment, wherein the patient is only a small part of the tasks and interactions pharmacists perform (Patwardhan et al., 2014). Traditionally therefore, patients have typically been considered the recipients of information, rather than active and equal team players. Shifting the focus to the patient not only requires understanding and addressing pharmacist–patient interactions from the patient's perspective, but also requires attending to how patients interact with medications once they leave the pharmacy.

Although all patients benefit from patient–pharmacist interactions and well-designed medication labels among other system elements, these needs are more pronounced in certain populations, such as older adults. In the United States, older adults are the largest users of prescription medication and OTC medications accounting for up to 40% of all nonprescription medication use (Glaser & Rolita, 2009). There is an expectation that community-dwelling patients, and older adults in particular, should be able to manage their prescriptions and OTC medications effectively and safely at home. However, this is not always the case. Approximately 30% of hospital admissions of older adults are drug-related, with more than 11% attributed to medication nonadherence and 10–17% related to adverse drug reactions (Winterstein et al., 2002; Salvi et al., 2012). Older adults discharged from the hospital on more than five drugs are more likely to visit the emergency department (ED) and be rehospitalized during the first 6 months after discharge (Alarcon et al., 1999). Given that older adults are more likely to experience adverse reactions, it is particularly critical for pharmacists in community settings to address necessary risks. Researchers have attempted to improve these outcomes with limited success, possibly because the focus of interventions has predominantly been on improving pharmacist work system components (such as technology and pharmacist education) without a strong focus on the patient, the patient work system, and patient-centered outcomes.

Human factors and ergonomics research focused on community pharmacies is currently being extended in two important ways. First, research has moved into the domain of patient ergonomics where the focus is on the patient and the tasks they need to perform in the context of their home and community environments, including that of the retail pharmacy. Moreover, current efforts build upon historical efforts to improve medication labeling by explicitly involving the patients in a direct manner to consider their perspectives as end users. This chapter will share improvements in product labeling design for prescription and OTC medications and advancements in patient counseling to support pharmacists and patients as they interact in the pharmacy. This chapter also includes a case study that describes the development of a pharmacy intervention to improve OTC medication safety in older adults.

## 5.1 PRODUCT LABELING: AN OVERVIEW

Product labeling includes all the printed information on the outside of the medication bottle. The information included on the bottle varies for prescription and OTC medications, but typically includes the list of ingredients and basic instructions for how to take that medication. Patient misunderstanding of instructions on drug (prescription or OTC) labels is common and is a likely cause of medication error and less effective treatment (Wahlberg, 2017). In one study in which patients were asked to read and demonstrate understanding of dosage instructions for five common prescription medications, up to one-third of patients misunderstood at least one. The themes associated with the common causes of misunderstanding were label language, complexity of instructions, implicit versus explicit dosage intervals, presence of distractors, label familiarity, and attentiveness to label instructions. This study concluded that prescription drug label instructions are awkwardly phrased, vague, and unnecessarily difficult (Wolf et al., 2007). This study shows patients that take prescription medications demonstrate variable levels of cognitive function. When designing medication instructions for people to follow, it is critical to account for this variability in patient understanding.

Research has shown that patient-centered instructions are better recalled and understood more quickly than standard instructions (Morrow et al., 2005). Research published in the 1990s and early 2000s found that older and younger adults possess similar schema for taking medications and designing instructions that are compatible with this schema improves the memory for medication information (Morrow et al., 1991, 1993, 1996), which consequently improves medication adherence (Morrow et al., 1988). People prefer larger print and line spacing, additional white space, list instructions, and extended surface areas (pull-out labels) on medication containers (Wogalter, 1999; Wogalter et al., 1996; Vigilante Jr. & Wogalter, 1999; Morrow et al., 1995). Labels with such designs lead to an improvement in response time and knowledge acquisition performance (younger adults are faster than older adults) (Wogalter & Vigilante, 2003; Shaver & Wogalter, 2003; Mendat et al., 2005). Pictorials and icons were found to be useful to those with low health literacy or inadequate reading skills (Sojourner & Wogalter, 1997; Morrow et al., 1998). A recent review of literature continues to support the idea that consumer outcomes are influenced by information design (Tong et al., 2014).

A multitude of factors contribute to difficulty in understanding instructions on drug labels (prescription or OTC) available in a community pharmacy, perhaps the most relevant of which is health literacy. The National Academy of Medicine defines health literacy as "the degree to which individuals have the capacity to obtain, process, and understand basic health information and services needed to make appropriate health decisions" (National Network of Libraries of Medicine, 2020). Studies have shown that patients with low health literacy demonstrate heightened difficulty with instructions found on container labels of common prescription medications and are thus at increased risk for medication errors. Following the prompt "take two tablets by mouth twice daily", three in five participants with low health literacy and one in five participants with adequate health literacy made mistakes (Davis et al., 2006; Sparks et al., 2018). Patients who misunderstand medication use instructions are at high risk of adverse drug events (ADEs) (Wolf et al., 2016). Therefore, patients with low health literacy that come to the pharmacy for prescription or OTC medications are an example of a population that requires additional care from pharmacists. Unfortunately, pharmacists do not often recognize low health literacy in patients, and this key characteristic is not being made known to pharmacists during usual patient encounters. There is a need to consider redesigning aspects of the healthcare system to raise pharmacists' awareness of a patient's health literacy to make each encounter more valuable for the patient. This will be discussed later in Section 5.2.

### 5.1.1 IMPROVING OVER-THE-COUNTER LABELING

In a study by Tong et al. (2015), researchers examined consumer's reported hypothetical behaviors regarding dosage and storage as a measure of an OTC medication label's usability and consumer's functional health literacy. Out of 50 participants, about half were female and half indicated regular use of written information as part of their occupation. Most were at least high school graduates and spoke English at home. Participants were asked to find and understand key points of information of an OTC label and were evaluated using a 13-item questionnaire. Results showed that research participants were able to successfully locate relevant information pertaining to dosage and storage, but one-third of the participants reported a deviation from the label's dosage instructions. One-third of the participants also reported an inappropriate storage condition or location that deviated from the storage instructions. These deviations could potentially adversely impact medication use (Tong et al., 2017). Medication safety concerns because of poor usability of the medication label were shared by the local regulatory body for therapeutic goods.

The Australian Therapeutic Goods Administration (TGA) proposed implementing standardized OTC medication label designs in 2012 and again in 2014. Tong et al. (2018) then set out to develop and test alternative OTC medication label formats for standardization and explore consumer perspectives of the labels. Informed by the results of a qualitative needs analysis (including semistructured interviews and focus groups with participants) and in collaboration with a UK information design expert, the research team developed four new labels for one OTC pain reliever (in Australia), diclofenac: one based on the design outlined by the Australian TGA; one based on the design of the US Drug Facts label; and two based on findings from the needs analysis alone. The newly developed labels and the baseline label were presented as part of a complete OTC package and individually evaluated by participants. Participants were given one of the four newly developed labels and were asked to complete a user testing questionnaire developed specifically for this study.

Questionnaire items included information acquisition (e.g. "What is the active ingredient in [insert diclofenac brand]?") and information comprehension (e.g. "Pretend your father has just bought some [insert diclofenac brand] from the pharmacy. He tells you that he forgot to tell the pharmacist that he has a stomach ulcer at the moment. What would you tell your father about taking [*insert diclofenac brand*]?"). After completing the questionnaire, the participants were asked to provide feedback on the four newly developed labels plus the existing label. Although the methods for conducting the qualitative needs analysis were preference-based (e.g. self-reported user opinions) rather than performance-based (e.g. behavior measures), results demonstrated that the newly designed labels all performed better than the existing label with respect to perceived usability, color, design, content, and/or content ordering (Tong et al., 2018).

Bix et al. (2009) have also studied the design of medication labels, focusing specifically on warning labels such as child resistant and product tampering warnings on OTC pain relievers (Bix et al., 2009). These particular warnings are intended to be viewed at the point of purchase and are important to reduce the unintentional poisoning of children. As such, they are required to be conspicuous and prominent, to inform a consumer's purchase decision. Eye tracking was used to quantify three measures related to the relative prominence and conspicuousness of the warnings: time spent examining the warnings compared to other areas of the label; ability to recall information from the OTCs viewed; and legibility of the warnings relative to the other label elements. Results showed that less than 20% registered any time in the product tampering warning zone, and less than 50% in the child-resistant warning zone. Participants were least frequently able to recall both the child-resistant and product tampering warnings of all categories they were asked to recall. These warnings were also the least legible (participants had the most difficulty deciphering the message). Therefore, despite legal requirements to highlight these warnings, the current design of OTC pain reliever packaging failed to effectively convey these important messages.

Bix et al. (2018) leveraged this initial study to embark on a new study to optimize OTC labels for older adults. They hypothesized that placing a warning label (which contains critical information for avoiding adverse drug effects) on the front panel of the packaging will increase attention to these warnings and support better decision-making. Another factor that was studied in this research was the impact of color highlighting on attention and decision-making. This study used eye tracking, change detection, and visual search tasks to investigate how well different OTC label designs attract attention to critical information, promote decision-making, and facilitate rapid cross-product comparisons. They hoped to produce a label that successfully communicates critical drug information to at-risk older consumers, thereby empowering them to make better medication selection decisions and ultimately reduce adverse drug effects. The results of this research show improved patient attention to interactive and horizontal warning placements as opposed to auxiliary labels placed vertically on prescription vials (Bix et al., 2018).

### 5.1.2 IMPROVING PRESCRIPTION LABELING

In 2013, the United States Pharmacopeia (USP) introduced new Patient-Centered Prescription Label Standards. The standards provided, for the first time, a universal approach to the format, appearance, content, and language of instructions for prescription medication labels placed on containers dispensed by pharmacists and offered directions on how prescription labels should be organized in a "patient-centered" manner (United States Pharmacopeia, 2012). Guidance included an emphasis on explicit instructions and improved readability (Ianzito, 2018). Multiple studies have since shown that patient-centered labels can be effective at improving medication adherence, functional health literacy, and improved comprehension (Tai et al., 2016; Trettin, 2015; Wolf et al., 2016). These redesigns included increasing font size and dedicating 50% of the label space to information intended for the patient.

A project conducted by the staff at Wisconsin Health Literacy recognized that a state-wide implementation of new medication labels would require stakeholder input. The project was designed to utilize iterative phases of patient stakeholder input in order to effectively operationalize the USP Standards. First, a research team recruited an 11-member Patient Advisory Council. The council consisted of individuals identifying with a wide range of age, race, geographic location, health status, and general literacy levels. The council was asked to review the materials to ensure they were clear and understandable by patients of all literacy levels.

Wisconsin Health Literacy staff then conducted two individual semistructured interviews and two focus groups of adult patients. The purpose was to discover what the patients like and do not like about labels. In a group exercise, staff cut apart the different elements on a typical medication label and asked the participants to design their own labels. Results provided guidance to create redesigned labels (see Table 5.1) (Sparks et al., 2018; Gerhard, 2019).

Lastly, Wisconsin Health Literacy developed a "Vote for your Favorite Label" Internet survey to gain insight into patient label preferences. Via social media, the public was invited to select which of two labels they preferred and what they liked or did not like about each. They also answered a few questions about the two labels and were invited to write about a medication label experience.

The feedback was consistent from the advisory panel, focus group, individual interviews, and survey results and led to a redesign of the medication label (see Figure 5.1). The new labels have been implemented in 64 pharmacies. Over 500 patient surveys were completed at multiple sites. In total, 83% of patients like the new labels better or the same (only 13% said they liked the old labels better). Patients felt that the letters were larger, the labels were easy to understand, and important information was easy to find. Patients emphasized that the label should be designed for them and not pharmacists.

**TABLE 5.1**

**Results of Semi-structured Interviews and Focus Groups**

| Patients Like | Patients Do Not Like |
|---|---|
| Color, bolding, large font | Information only used by the pharmacist |
| White space | Many confusing dates |
| Indication for drug use | Addresses |
| Most important information at top | Unclear directions (e.g. twice daily) |
| Name of medication | All capital letters |
| Prescriber name | Pharmacy information at the top |

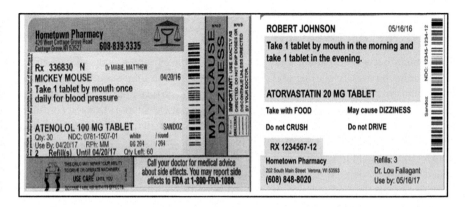

**FIGURE 5.1**   Before and after labels at a participating pharmacy.

The effect of the label change on medication refill adherence was examined. Lower levels of medication refill adherence are associated with higher healthcare costs and increased utilization of healthcare services (Schwartzberg et al., 2018). A pre-post research design was used to examine whether medication refill adherence changed after the label was modified. Medication refill data for patients who were subscribers to a health plan for low-income patients were obtained from the health plan. Patients who had medications refilled at one of six pharmacies that changed their label were included in the analysis. Analysis showed that refill adherence, measured as the proportion of days covered (PDC), significantly improved in the 13 months after the label was changed relative to the 13 months before the label was changed for patients taking medication in three therapeutic categories (asthma controllers, antihypertensives, and oral contraceptives). The analysis also showed that a significant proportion of patients taking asthma controllers and oral contraceptives who initially had low levels (PDC <=0.50) or medium levels (PDC = >0.50–0.80) of refill adherence in the preperiod moved to a higher level of medication adherence after the label change was in effect. Another analysis conducted by the study team showed that label changes were associated with increases in medication refill adherence among older adults enrolled in Medicare Part D prescription medication insurance programs. Both analyses showed that changing the label to be more patient-centric was significantly associated with improvements in mediciation refill adherence.

Results of this study showed that small changes on a prescription label, informed by patient stakeholders and consistent with USP standards for patient-centric labels, may significantly improve patients' effective use of medications. The next phase of this project will be to evaluate the patient-centered outcomes of the labeling redesign to strengthen what we already know about patient preferences. Pilot results from data collected from patients in one pharmacy who are members of a state Medicaid plan suggest that the average medication possession ratio (MPR), a measure of medication adherence, significantly improved after the label change for asthma medications, antihypertensives, and oral contraceptives. There is also some initial evidence that MPRs improved the most for patients with the lowest medication adherence.

## 5.2  COLLABORATIVE PHARMACIST–PATIENT WORK: AN OVERVIEW

Encounters between a patient and their pharmacist are crucial facets of care in the community pharmacy setting, and patient counseling is a long-standing component of the pharmacist responsibilities (Milosavljevic et al., 2018). Pharmacists should tailor conversations with their patients and prioritize patient support tasks accordingly as they grasp an understanding of their patient population demographics (Shoemaker et al., 2011; Ngoh, 2009). Unfortunately, we know pharmacists carry biases that may impact their patient interactions, and the encounters between a patient and their pharmacist may vary depending on the physical space of the encounter (e.g. drive-through window versus the traditional walk-in window).

### 5.2.1  The Presence of Biases in Pharmacist–Patient Interactions

As discussed earlier in this chapter, health literacy is an important component to successful patient–pharmacist encounters. In a perfect scenario, pharmacists would have an established understanding of their patient's health literacy and would be able to adjust communication accordingly to effectively share information. However, pharmacists fall victim to the false-consensus effect, wherein they unintentionally assume that patients understand the directions for use in the same way that the pharmacist would. However, we know that others, especially patients with differing experiences (e.g. education, lifestyle), do not always think the same way that pharmacists do.

The false-consensus effect is important to consider in the pharmacy setting because of its impact on another bias, the overconfidence effect (belief that everyone knows one's own knowledge). This can be dangerous for patient–pharmacist encounters as pharmacists are critical agents for teaching health information and providing resources, and the overconfidence effect may lead to pharmacists providing fewer resources to patients.

> I was going over all of her medications after she was released from the hospital. I asked her to show me how she used her Spiriva. The directions said, 'Inhale the contents of one capsule once a day.' She put the capsule in the inhaler. Then she inhaled but she never pierced the capsule. She was just getting plain air. Even though I thought the directions were clear, she was not taking the medicine properly.
>
> *(Community Pharmacist) (Sparks et al., 2018)*

### 5.2.2  Prescription Pickup Interactions in Different Physical Pharmacy Spaces

Drive-through services were widely established in community pharmacies in the United States in the 1990s in response to a demand for convenience. This service allows patients to pick up and receive patient counseling at two locations: the drive-through window where patients drive up, stay in their cars, and communicate through a microphone while exchanging prescriptions, patient and insurance information, and money through a sliding drawer, and the traditional walk-in window where patients walk through the pharmacy to speak face to face with pharmacy staff. Patients can choose where they receive their prescriptions, which may be a reflection on preferences beyond convenience (Chui et al., 2009). Moreover, the two physical locations may have different advantages and disadvantages related to medication safety and adherence, as well as other outcomes of interest to patients.

We conducted a study in which patient encounters at the drive-through and walk-in windows of one community pharmacy were simultaneously observed, characterized, and recorded for analytic purposes. Pharmacists acknowledged patients more frequently and spent longer times with them at the walk-in window. In addition, patients accepted counseling more often at the walk-in window. Patients more likely to require additional assistance, such as individuals with limited English proficiency, further showed a preference for this location. In contrast, drive-through encounters were more likely to involve at least one "more confidential" prescription (such as a medication to treat mental illness). It is possible there are other reasons a patient may use the drive-through window, such as the perception that the drive-through window is more efficient, a perception that counseling is not needed (e.g. refilling medications), or that they are picking up prescriptions for someone else. There is potential to investigate these preferences further so as to define and understand differences between the way pharmacy services should be offered in either drive-through or walk-in window use groups.

### 5.2.3 ENABLING PHARMACISTS TO BETTER SUPPORT PATIENT WORK

From the patient ergonomics perspective, training can help pharmacists understand the patient perspective and what patients can be expected to know, which may alleviate the prevalence of the false-consensus and overconfidence effect during pharmacy encounters. Training has shown to be effective at reducing unconscious bias between healthcare professionals and patients. Training modules may include education about bias, the false-consensus effect, the overconfidence effect, and cultural competency. Training-based workshops for pharmacists may include the development of skills such as looking for common identities and counter-stereotypical information as well as practicing patient–pharmacist encounters as a "patient" to learn the perspective of certain groups (e.g. high school level education, no clinical training) (Stone & Moskowitz, 2011).

Unfortunately, the existing tools that support tailoring patient conversations require patients to perform additional work (e.g. filling out a survey for pharmacists to review before the encounter). Much of the research that has been done in the community pharmacy setting has aimed to improve patient interaction with their environment and with their pharmacist to reduce adverse outcomes. Recent evidence indicates that pharmacists are moving to employ innovative work that improves the frequency and quality of these encounters (Melton & Lai, 2017; Murray et al., 2019; Santina et al., 2018; Al Juffali et al., 2019). Pharmacists (and patients) can be better supported for quality encounters by improving pharmacist access to the electronic health record, where pertinent patient information is available.

## 5.3   A CASE STUDY: CONSIDERING PATIENT ERGONOMICS IN THE DEVELOPMENT OF A PHARMACY INTERVENTION TO IMPROVE OVER-THE-COUNTER MEDICATION SAFETY IN OLDER ADULTS

ADEs associated with OTC medications cause 178,000 hospitalizations each year (United Health Foundation, 2005), representing a major patient safety concern. Older adults (aged 65+) are particularly vulnerable to ADEs. Of the 2.2 million older adults considered at risk of a major ADE, more than 50% were because of concurrent use of an OTC and prescription medication (Qato et al., 2008). This case study describes a multiphase effort to develop, implement, and evaluate a system redesign intervention to decrease high-risk OTC medication misuse in the community pharmacy setting.

### 5.3.1   Patient Barriers to Safe Selection of OTCs

In order to understand barriers to safe OTC selection from an older adult's perspective, walking interviews were conducted with 20 older adults while they selected an OTC product in a Shopko Store (Stone et al., 2017). Older adults were recruited and, upon arrival to the store to participate in the study, were provided with scenarios and asked to navigate through the pharmacy and select an OTC medication.

Four significant barriers to safe OTC medication selection were identified (see Figure 5.2). These include assumptions of OTC safety, difficulty navigating the OTC aisles to select a medication, difficulty using the labeling information to select a medication, and a reluctance to use the pharmacist as an information resource or to confirm medication choice. In this work system analysis, the focus was placed on the older adults specifically to understand their needs. In our analysis, the pharmacist was referred to by patients as an information source consistent with a tool.

Many older adults incorrectly reported that OTCs are safe because of their availability without prescription or that they were safe with other medications as long as the label did not specifically warn against it. Most reported reading the labels, but noted that even when they read the label and saw "what's in it," that the active ingredients did not have inherent meaning to them. Older adults had significant difficulty making comparisons between medications due to the overwhelming number of similarly marketed choices in the OTC aisles. Even in cases in which participants made direct comparisons between two medications, labels were still misinterpreted, (e.g. a participant stated she could not take extra acetaminophen because of her prescriptions, but then selected a combination product containing acetaminophen). In another case, a participant noted a previous negative reaction to ibuprofen and then stated she could only take Advil (brand name for ibuprofen). Although older adults reported that their pharmacist was a valuable resource for prescription information, they were often reluctant to ask questions about OTC medications, in part due to their perceptions that all OTC medications are safe.

These results suggest that there are significant barriers to the design of the OTC area in retail settings. The underlying assumption that self-managing older adults can navigate the pharmacy work system to safely select and use OTC medications may be incorrect.

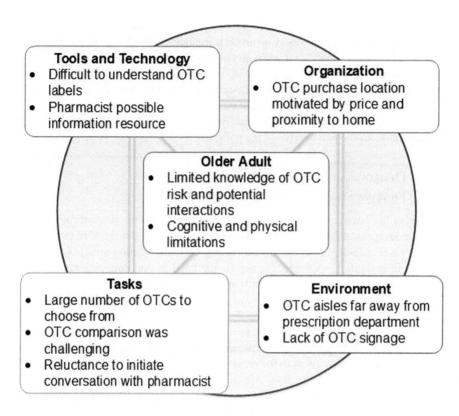

**Tools and Technology**
- Difficult to understand OTC labels
- Pharmacist possible information resource

**Organization**
- OTC purchase location motivated by price and proximity to home

**Older Adult**
- Limited knowledge of OTC risk and potential interactions
- Cognitive and physical limitations

**Tasks**
- Large number of OTCs to choose from
- OTC comparison was challenging
- Reluctance to initiate conversation with pharmacist

**Environment**
- OTC aisles far away from prescription department
- Lack of OTC signage

**FIGURE 5.2**   Older adult work system barriers.

### 5.3.2   Patient Tasks Associated with Selecting an OTC Medication

Very little research has been conducted to understand patient decision-making in terms of OTC medication selection in a community pharmacy. Utilizing the observation data collected in the walking interviews, a deductive analysis was conducted to capture the breadth of tasks associated with "patient work." This analysis led to a list of tasks that were articulated by older adults as they selected an OTC medication. In a second study, as part of a larger participatory design project, a separate patient stakeholder group was recruited to review the list of tasks and add any missing tasks to the list. A total of 25 tasks were identified. Participants were presented with notecards, each with a task involved in the process of selecting an OTC. Examples of tasks included: reaching a medication that was very high or very low on the shelf, comparing the strengths of different medications, and determining if the warning labels applied to you.

Participants were then asked to sort the task notecards based on the level of difficulty (not at all difficult to extremely difficult) and frequency (never to all of the time). Determining the unit cost of medications and determining if an OTC was safe to take with their prescription medications were the most difficult tasks performed. Reading the warnings on medication labels and determining the relevance of medication warnings were the most frequently performed tasks. Results showed that the process of an older adult selecting an OTC medication has many steps, not necessarily in a particular order, and with varying difficulty, suggesting that the "work" that older adults perform to select an OTC medication is physically and cognitively challenging (Reddy et al., 2018). The insights provided by the participants helped to further identify the problem from the patient's perspective, prioritizing the most difficult and frequent barriers to OTC safety that would need to be addressed by the intervention from the perspective of the patient.

### 5.3.3 Development of a System Redesign to Support Pharmacist and Patient Collaborative Work

To address the barriers identified in our preliminary studies, we conceptualized a system redesign intervention, grounded in the SEIPS 2.0 model (Holden et al., 2013) that addresses older adult barriers to decreasing OTC medication misuse (see Figure 5.2). The intervention, a system redesign, is intended to maintain patient autonomy and self-care engagement, while improving the selection behaviors of older adults. The physical layout of the OTC aisle was redesigned to facilitate pharmacist–older adult communication (see Figure 5.3). The high-risk OTC medications (e.g. pain, sleep, cough/cold) currently displayed in one aisle that is not within the line of sight of and relatively far away from the prescription department were duplicated in a new "Senior Section" that is closest to the prescription department and within line of sight of the pharmacists and technicians. Although the medications were still available in the regular pharmacy aisle, this new section provides safe medication choices for older adults without exposing them to medication that may not be safe for them to

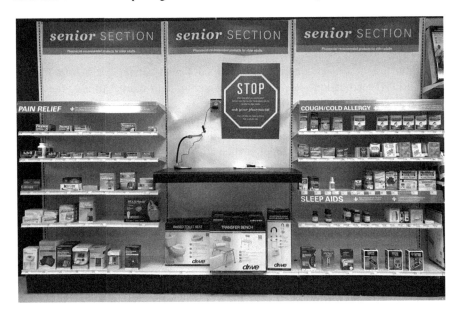

**FIGURE 5.3**   The pharmacy aisle redesign for older adults: The Senior Section.

select and use. This new section was also stocked with other items commonly purchased by older adults, so they would be able to find all pharmacy-related products in one section.

Human factors principles associated with vision, contrast, symbols, and color to denote warning were incorporated to architect safe decision-making. Given that much of OTC medication selection occurs based on prior experience, the contents of the signs (especially the stop sign content) were developed to trigger older adults to question their selection of an OTC with regard to a safe and effective choice (see Figure 5.3). This content was intended to help older adults recognize they may lack the knowledge necessary to make an appropriate decision. The overall goal of the redesign was to inform patients of the safety concerns with OTC medications and spark the desire to discuss their selection with a pharmacist before making a decision (Reddy et al., 2018).

## 5.4 RECOMMENDATIONS AND IMPLICATIONS

We know a great deal about the impact of poor medication use. Many studies have determined the morbidity and mortality associated with poor medication adherence and medication errors (Kaur, 2019; Bassett et al., 2019). Pharmacy-focused researchers have attempted to improve these outcomes with limited success, possibly because the focus of interventions has solely been on improving work system components inside the retail pharmacy setting (such as technology and pharmacist education) without strong focus on the patient and patient-centered outcomes. There is a large body of research that investigates user-driven information design of drug product labeling, an inherently patient-centric component of the work system, which shows promising results for improving medication outcomes (Abedtash & Duke, 2015; Davol, 2015; Herron & Vu, 2013; Morrow et al., 2005; Vredenburgh, 2009). Information design research has not yet expanded beyond drug product labeling into other components of the retail pharmacy work system, however. There remains a critical gap in understanding the underlying reasons for these poor patient medication outcomes and how the retail pharmacy may address such issues.

Research using patient ergonomics in the community retail pharmacy is in its infancy, but has great potential for improving the patient experience, which could help patients more effectively and safely use prescription and OTC medications. One area in which patient ergonomics could play a key role in is conceptualizing and testing ways to help patients be an active and equal team players with their physician and pharmacist. Patients are generally the recipients of information (and drugs). However, in order to create a true patient-centered experience, patients need the knowledge, confidence, and tools to engage in two-sided dialogue with their healthcare professionals.

Further, patients' role as active team players must not end after patients leave the pharmacy. Patients receive a tremendous amount of information when they are counseled by their pharmacist in the community pharmacy. Patients must organize the information and plan their medication use and side effect monitoring in ways that fit with their lifestyle and their existing work system at home. The cognitive burden of remembering and managing complex medication regimens is extremely challenging, and research using patient ergonomics could elucidate ways to support patient work surrounding their medication use.

## ACKNOWLEDGMENTS

The authors would like to acknowledge Jamie Stone for her assistance with the literature search and formatting.

## REFERENCES

Abedtash, H., & Duke, J. D. (2015). An interactive user interface for drug labeling to improve readability and decision-Making. *Journal of American Informatics Association Annual Symposium* (pp. 278–286). San Francisco, CA: American Medical Informatics Association.

Al Juffali, L., Al-Aqeel, S., Knapp, P., Mearns, K., Family, H., & Watson, M. (2019). Using the human factors framework to understand the origins of medication safety problems in community pharmacy: A qualitative study. *Research in Social and Administrative Pharmacy*, 15(5), 558–567.

Alarcon, T., Barcena, A., Gonzalez-Montalvo, J. I., Penalosa, C., & Salgado, A. (1999). Factors predictive of outcome on admission to an acute geriatric ward. *Age Ageing*, 28(5), 429–432.

Bassett, S. M., Schuette, S. A., O'Dwyer, L. C., & Moskowitz, J. T. (2019). Positive affect and medication adherence in chronic conditions: A systematic review. *Health Psychology*, 38(11), 960.

Bix, L., Becker, M. W., Breslow, R., Liu, L., Harben, A., & Esfahanian, S. (2018). Optimizing OTC labeling for use by older adults. *Innovation in Aging*, 2(suppl_1), 82.

Bix, L., Bello, N. M., Auras, R., Ranger, J., & Lapinski, M. K. (2009). Examining the conspicuousness and prominence of two required warnings on OTC pain relievers. *Proceedings of the National Academy of Sciences United States of America*, 106(16), 6550–6555.

Chui, M. A., Halton, K., & Peng, J. M. (2009). Exploring patient-pharmacist interaction differences between the drive-through and walk-in windows. *Journal of the American Pharmacists Association*, 49(3), 427–431.

Davis, T. C., Wolf, M. S., Bass, P. F., 3rd, Thompson, J. A., Tilson, H. H., Neuberger, M., & Parker, R. M. (2006). Literacy and misunderstanding prescription drug labels. *Annals of Internal Medicine*, 145(12), 887–894.

Davol, P. A. (2015). Evaluating the labeling-user interface and device design-user interface in usability validation studies for combination products: Resolving the catch-22. *International Symposium on Human Factors and Ergonomics in Health*, 4(1), 134–137). SAGE Publications.

Gerhards, K. (2019). *A sticking point for medication adherence.* Retrieved from University of Wisconsin-Madison School of Pharmacy: https://pharmacy.wisc.edu/redesigning-prescription-labels/.

Glaser, J., & Rolita, L. (2009). *Educating the older adult in over-the-counter medication use.* Retrieved 2020, from Medscape: https://www.medscape.com/viewarticle/705665#:~:text=Studies%20in%20the%20U.S.%20have, being%20used%20by%20older%20adults.

Herron, M., & Vu, K. P. (2013). The value of including a picture of the medicine on pharmaceutical labels. *Human Factors and Ergonomics Society*, 57(1), 688–692. SAGE Publications.

Holden, R. J., Carayon, P., Gurses, A. P., Hoonakker, P., Hundt, A. S., Ozok, A. A., & Rivera-Rodriguez, A. J. (2013). SEIPS 2.0: A human factors framework for studying and improving the work of healthcare professionals and patients. *Ergonomics*, 56(11), 1669–1686.

Ianzito, C. (2018). *Building a better prescription bottle*. Retrieved from AARP Healthy Living: https://www.aarp.org/health/healthy-living/info-2018/prescription-pill-bottle-drug-safety.html.

IQVIA Institute. (2017). *Medicines use and spending in the U.S.: A review of 2016 and outlook to 2021*. IQVIA Institute for Human Data Science.

Kaur, R. J. (2019). Elderly and medication non-adherence. *Journal of the Indian Academy of Geriatrics*, 15(1), 1–4.

Melton, B. L., & Lai, Z. (2017). Review of community pharmacy services: What is being performed, and where are the opportunities for improvement? *Integrated Pharmacy Research and Practice*, 6: 79-89.

Mendat, C. C., Watson, A. M., Mayhorn, C. B., & Wogalter, M. S. (2005). Age of differences in search time for two over-the-counter (OTC) drug label formats. *Proceedings of the Human Factors and Ergonomics Society Annual Meeting*, 49(2), 200–203). Los Angeles, CA: SAGE Publications.

Milosavljevic, A., Aspden, T., & Harrison, J. (2018). Community pharmacist-led interventions and their impact on patients' medication adherence and other health outcomes: A systematic review. *International Journal of Pharmacy Practice*, 26(5): 387–397.

Morrow, D. G., Hier, C. M., Menard, W. E., & Leirer, V. O. (1998). Icons improve older and younger adults' comprehension of medication information. *The Journals of Gerontology Series B: Psychological Sciences and Social Sciences*, 53(4), 240–254.

Morrow, D. G., Leirer, V. O., Andrassy, J. M., Tanke, E. D., & Stine-Morrow, E. A. (1996). Medication instruction design: Younger and older adult schemas for taking medication. *Human Factors*, 38(4), 556–573.

Morrow, D. G., Weiner, M., Young, J., Steinley, D., Deer, M., & Murray, M. D. (2005). Improving medication knowledge among older adults with heart failure: A patient-centered approach to instruction design. *The Gerontologist*, 45(4), 545–552.

Morrow, D., Leirer, V. O., & Andrassy, J. M. (1993). Designing medication instructions for older adults. *Proceedings of the Human Factors and Ergonomics Society Annual Meeting*, pp. 37(2), 197–201). Los Angeles: SAGE Publications.

Morrow, D., Leirer, V., & Altieri, P. (1995). List formats improve medication instructions for older adults. *Educational Gerontology: An International Quarterly*, 21(2), 151–166.

Morrow, D., Leirer, V., & Sheikh, J. (1988). Adherence and medication instructions review and recommendations. *Journal of the American Geriatrics Society*, 36(12), 1147–1160.

Morrow, D., Leirer, V., Altieri, P., & Tanke, E. (1991). Elders' schema for taking medication: implications for instruction design. *Journal of Gerontology*, 46(6), 378–385.

Murray, M. E., Barner, J. C., Pope, N. D., & Comfort, M. D. (2019). Impact and feasibility of implementing a systematic approach for medication therapy management in the community pharmacy setting: A pilot study. *Journal of Pharmacy Practice*, 32(6), 664–670.

National Network of Libraries of Medicine. (2020). *Health literacy*. Retrieved from National Network of Libraries of Medicine: https://nnlm.gov/initiatives/topics/health-literacy.

Ngoh, L. (2009). Health Literacy: A barrier to pharmacist-patient communication and medication adherence. *Journal of the American Pharmacists Association*, 49(5), e132–e146.

Patwardhan, P. D., Amin, M. E., & Chewning, B. A. (2014). Intervention research to enhance community pharmacists' cognitive services: A systematic review. *Research in Social and Administrative Pharmacy*, 10(3):475–93.

Perri, M., Kotzan, J., Prtichard, L., Ozburn, W., & Francisco, G. (1995). OBRA '90 impact on pharmacists and patients. *Journal of the American Pharmacists Association*, NS35(2):24–28.

Qato, D. M., Alexander, G. C., Conti, R. M., Johnson, M., Schumm, P., & Lindau, S. T. (2008). Use of prescription and over-the-counter medications and dietary supplements among older adults in the United States. *Journal of the American Medical Association*, 300(24), 2867–2878.

Reddy, A., Lester, C. A., Stone, J. A., Holden, R. J., Phelan, C. H., & Chui, M. A. (2018). Applying participatory design to a pharmacy system intervention. *Research in Social and Administrative Pharmacy, 15*(11), 1358–1367.

Salvi, F., Marchetti, A., D'Angelo, F., Boemi, M., Lattanzio, F., & Cherubini, A. (2012). Adverse drug events as a cause of hospitalizations in older adults. *Drug Safety*, 35, 29–45.

Santina, T., Lauzier, S., Gagnon, H., Villeneuve, D., Moisan, J., Gregoire, J. P., & Guillaumie, L. (2018). The development of a community pharmacy-based intervention to optimize patients' use of and experience with antidepressants: A step-by-step demonstration of the Intervention Mapping Process. *Pharmacy*, 6(2), 39.

Schwartzberg, J., Sparks, S., & Mott, D. (2018). Improving prescription medication labels to help patient understanding and adherence through implementation of USP standards for patient-centered labels. *HARC X*. Boston, MA: Wisconsin Health Literacy.

Scott, D. M., & Wessels, M. J. (1997). Impact of OBRA '90 on pharmacists' patient counseling practices. *American Pharmacists Association*, NS37(4):401–406.

Shaver, E. F., & Wogalter, M. S. (2003). A comparison of older vs newer over-the-counter (OTC) nonprescription drug labels on search time accuracy. *Proceedings of the Human Factors and Ergonomics Society Annual Meeting* 47(5), 826, 830. Los Angeles, CA: SAGE Publications.

Shoemaker, S. J., Ramalho de Oliveira, D., Alves, M., & Ekstrand, M. (2011). The medication experience: Preliminary evidence of its value for patient education and counseling on chronic medications. *Patient Education and Counseling*, 83(3), 443–450.

Sojourner, R. J., & Wogalter, M. S. (1997). The influence of pictorials on evaluations of prescription medication instructions. *Drug Information Association*, 31(3), 963–972.

Sparks, S. W., Schellhase, K. G., Werner, L. B., Mott, D. A., Smith, P. D., Young, H. N., . . . . LaScala, K. N. (2018). Adopting patient-centered prescription medication labels in Wisconsin. *The Journal of the Pharmacy Society of Wisconsin*, 68, 30–36.

Stone, J. A., Lester, C. A., Aboneh, E. A., Phelan, C. H., Welch, L. L., & Chui, M. A. (2017). A preliminary examination of over-the-counter medication misuse rates in older adults. *Research in Social and Administrative Pharmacy*, 13(1), 187–192.

Stone, J., & Moskowitz, G. B. (2011). Non-conscious bias in medical decision making: What can be done to reduce it? *Medical Education*, 45(8), 768–776.

Tai, B. W., Bae, Y. H., LaRue, C. E., & Law, A. V. (2016). Putting words into action: A simple focused education improves prescription label comprehension and functional health literacy. *Journal of the American Pharmacists Association*, 56(2), 145-2.e3.

Tong, V., Raynor, D. K., & Aslani, P. (2014). Design and comprehensibility of over-the-counter product labels and leaflets: A narrative review. *International Journal of Clinical Pharmacy*, 36(5), 865–872.

Tong, V., Raynor, D. K., & Aslani, P. (2017). User testing as a method for identifying how consumers say they would act on information related over-the-counter medicines. *Research in Social and Administrative Pharmacy*, 13(3), 476–484.

Tong, V., Raynor, D. K., & Aslani, P. (2018). Developing alternative over-the-counter medicine label formats: How do they compare when evaluated by consumers? *Research in Social and Administrative Pharmacy*, 14(3), 248–261.

Trettin, K. W. (2015). Implementation of VA patient-centered prescription label and patient medication information. *Procedia Manufacturing*, 3, 1–5.

United Health Foundation. (2005). *Exceeding the recommended dosage can do more than just wipe out your pain. Just ask your major organs.* Retrieved from https://web.archive.org/web/20150511211923/http://www.fda.gov/downloads/Drugs/ResourcesForYou/Consumers/BuyingUsingMedicineSafely/UnderstandingOver-the-CounterMedicines/UCM290318.pdf.

United States Pharmacopeia. (2012). *USP-NF General Chapter <17> Prescription Container Labeling.* Retrieved from https://www.usp.org/health-quality-safety/usp-nf-general-chapter-prescription-container-labeling.

Vigilante Jr, W. J., & Wogalter, M. S. (1999). Over-the-counter (OTC) drug labeling: Format preferences. *Proceedings of the Human Factors and Ergonomics Society Annual Meeting*, 43(2)103–107. Los Angeles, CA: SAGE Publications.

Vredenburgh, M. J. (2009). Public Health: An epidemiological study to explore the relationship between literacy, language, aging, and familiarity on comprehension of health information. *Human Factors and Ergonomics Society Annual Meeting*, 2(2007), 744–748.

Wahlberg, D. (2017). *New prescription labels aim to curb confusion, errors.* Retrieved from Wisconsin State Journal: https://madison.com/wsj/news/local/health-med-fit/new-prescription-labels-aim-to-curb-confusion-errors/article_ac069348-f866-594e-ba7d-63d89d4a8e48.html.

Winterstein, A. G., Hatton, R. C., Gonzalez-Rothi, R., Johns, T.E., Segal, R. (2002). Identifying clinically significant preventable adverse drug events through a database of adverse drug reaction reports. *American Journal of Health-System Pharmacy*, 59(18):1742–1749.

Wogalter, M. S. (1999). Enhancing information acquisition for over-the-counter medications by making better use of container surface space. *Experimental Aging Research*, 25(1), 27–48.

Wogalter, M. S., & Vigilante, W. J. (2003). Effects of label format on knowledge acquisition and perceived readability by younger and older adults. *Ergonomics*, 46(4), 327–344.

Wogalter, M. S., Magurno, A. B., Scott, K. L., & Dietrich, D. A. (1996). Facilitating information acquisition for over-the-counter drugs using supplemental labels. *Proceedings of the Human Factors and Ergonomics Society Annual Meeting*, 40(14), 732–736. Los Angeles, CA: SAGE Publications.

Wolf, M. S., Davis, T. C., Curtis, L. M., Cooper Bailey, S., Pearson Knox, J., Bergeron, A., . . . Wood, A. J. (2016). A patient-centered prescription drug label to promote appropriate medication use and adherence. *Journal of General Internal Medicine*, 31(12), 1482–1489.

Wolf, M. S., Davis, T. C., Shrank, W., Rapp, D. N., Bass, P. F., Connor, U. M., . . . Parker, R. M. (2007). To err is human: Patient misinterpretations of prescription drug label instructions. *Patient Education and Counseling*, 67(3), 293–300.

# 6 Online Communities and Social Networks
## *Considering Human Factors and Patient Ergonomics*

*Annie T. Chen*
Department of Biomedical Informatics
and Medical Education
University of Washington School of Medicine

*Albert Park*
Software and Information Systems
University of North Carolina Charlotte

*Andrea L. Hartzler*
Department of Biomedical Informatics
and Medical Education
University of Washington School of Medicine

## CONTENTS

Online communities and social networks (OCSNs) are increasingly used by patients, informal caregivers, clinicians, and others for health-related purposes. Many terms refer to OCSNs, including social/online networks, virtual communities, online forums, and online communities. We consider OCSNs as community venues that are facilitated through electronic media where people with common interests gather virtually to share experiences, ask questions, and exchange support (Eysenbach et al., 2004). Consequently, OCSNs are important vehicles for *patient work*—the work that patients, family, friends, and caregivers perform to manage personal health. Patient work encompasses a myriad of tasks (e.g. finding and sensemaking about health information, implementing illness-related adjustments, coordinating resources) that take place within the social, technical, and environmental contexts of everyday life (Valdez et al., 2015). As a vehicle for patient work, OCSNs facilitate or enhance the performance of this wide range of tasks.

Patient work occurs in and is shaped by a Patient Work System, which includes three nested levels of abstraction: the triad of person–task–tools; the household; and the community (Holden et al., 2017). Both the household and the community are comprised of three contextual domains: the social environment, physical environment, and the organizational environment. The person–task–tools triad consists of persons engaged in health-related tasks and the tools they use. This triad is embedded in a household, which in turn is embedded in a community. Within the framework of the Patient Work System, OCSNs may therefore be conceptualized as a tool used by people to accomplish the tasks associated with patient work within their home and community settings. The information and support that participants receive can facilitate patient work across the domains of social, physical, and organizational environments. For example, an individual newly diagnosed with a severe illness might seek information about sharing such news with family and friends on an OCSN (social environment). Similarly, someone with a newly acquired disability may seek information about how to change their living space and what type of community resources to access for such modifications (physical environment). Finally, someone requiring new medications may engage with members of an OCSN to determine which pharmacies provide the lowest co-pays (organizational environment). In this chapter, we describe OCSNs, review relevant research and case studies, and then present design and practice recommendations for supporting patient work in and through OCSNs.

## 6.1  TYPOLOGY OF OCSNs

OCSNs vary substantially in terms of their characteristics (see Table 6.1), providing a range of ways to support patient work. First, OCSNs vary by subject matter, either generic or health-specific. Generic OCSNs, such as Google Groups, offer discussion forums which can focus on health topics. Health-specific OCSNs, such as PatientsLikeMe, are designed only for conversations about health. Whether or not the platform is designed for all conversations or only those that are health focused is important because health-specific platforms may offer particular features that support patient work. For example, PatientsLikeMe employs a faceted search to enable patients to filter their membership to identify patients with similar health concerns for peer support. Of course, it is still possible to identify others with similar health concerns on generic OCSNs, for example, by searching for content relating to a topic of interest and encountering a patient describing experiences similar to one's own. However, most generic platforms do not contain functionality to simplify this process.

Some OCSNs are dedicated to certain audiences. For example, the Caregiver Forum on AgingCare is designed to support informal caregivers in patient work.

## TABLE 6.1
## Typology of Online Community and Social Network Characteristics

| Characteristic | Category | Example |
|---|---|---|
| Subject matter | Generic | Google Groups (https://groups.google.com) |
| | Health-specific | PatientsLikeMe (https://www.patientslikeme.com/) |
| Participant type | Patient | Smart Patients (https://www.smartpatients.com/) |
| | Informal caregiver | Caregiver Forum on AgingCare: (https://www.agingcare.com/caregiver-forum) |
| | Clinician | Sermo (http://www.sermo.com/) |
| | Combination | Facebook (https://www.facebook.com/) |
| Functionality | Social networking | Facebook (https://www.facebook.com/) |
| | Discussion forum | Reddit (https://www.reddit.com/) |
| | Microblog/blog | Twitter (https://twitter.com/) |
| | Image/video sharing | Instagram (https://www.instagram.com/) |
| Intervention | Intervention | CHESS (https://chess.wisc.edu/) |
| | Not an intervention | DailyStrength (https://www.dailystrength.org/) |
| Content accessibility | Public | WebMD (https://www.webmd.com/exchanges/) |
| | Private | Closed groups in which only members are able to view content |
| | Combination | Reddit (https://www.reddit.com/) |
| Moderation | Expert-moderated | Clinician-led discussion forum within the context of a digital intervention |
| | Peer-moderated | UKFibromyalgia Forums (http://www.ukfibromyalgia.com/forums/) |
| | Unmoderated | Community section on patient (https://patient.info/forums/) |

Other OCSNs are accessible across patients, informal caregivers, and clinicians. For example, some Question & Answer forums allow clinicians and patients to interact around health-related questions.

A third characteristic of OCSNs is their functionality, ranging from social networking to image/video sharing. For example, patients can use YouTube (https://www.youtube.com/) to share and comment on health-related videos. Discussion-based platforms such as Reddit enable patients to ask questions, reply to questions, and exchange opinions. Social networking platforms such as Facebook enable people to connect with one another. Some OCSNs provide multiple functionalities. For instance, YouTube, Reddit, and Facebook can all facilitate media sharing, discussion, and social networking, but have different strengths. Discussion, sharing health-related videos and images, and connecting with others are all different ways to facilitate patient work.

OCSNs may also be part of an intervention. By intervention, we refer to an OCSN that is designed to help people perform patient work activities and is evaluated through research. In the context of this testing, interventions may be monitored by health professionals or researchers to assess whether they provide support as intended. Interventions can be stand-alone OCSNs, or an OCSN can form a part of a broader intervention. An example of the latter is the Comprehensive Health

Enhancement Support System (CHESS), which was designed to support chronic disease health management and which contains a widely used discussion group (Han et al., 2009).

Content on OCSNs can be publicly accessible or private. For example, content on WebMD communities is publicly visible, whereas PatientsLikeMe is visible only to community members. Other OCSNs support both types of content accessibility. Reddit is known for its public nature. Anyone can participate and content is visible by default; however, it is also possible to create private subreddits. Although some individuals are selective in the health-related information they choose to share privately and publicly on OCSNs (Newman et al., 2011), sharing practices are diverse (Valdez et al., 2017). By offering patients an opportunity to communicate with others anonymously, OCSNs facilitate patient work by enabling individuals to discuss health concerns that they may not be comfortable sharing in an openly public venue.

Lastly, some OCSNs have moderators who facilitate the exchanges, whereas others are unmoderated. In unmoderated OCSNs, users who informally facilitate and self-police interactions can emerge. Moderators can serve in a professional capacity, such as a healthcare provider, therapist, or researcher; they can also be peers. Peer moderation can create a nurturing and empowering environment to perform and support patient work (Kaplan et al., 2017).

## 6.2   KEY CONSIDERATIONS OF OCSNs AS A VEHICLE FOR PATIENT WORK

### 6.2.1   SUPPORT RECEIVED THROUGH OCSNs

Seeking, giving, and exchanging social support is an important patient work task that is facilitated by OCSNs. Research on social support in OCSNs has often employed a typology developed by Cutrona and Suhr (1992). The most commonly studied types of support are informational support, emotional support, esteem support, network support, and tangible assistance. Emotional support and informational support are the most widely exchanged types of social support in OCSNs (Chen, 2014).

The availability of different types of support is helpful, as patients' needs vary over time and by health condition. For example, after diagnosis patients often need emotional support first, followed by informational support (Jacobson, 1986). Nurturant support is more common for issues that threaten personal relationships or carry the potential of death, whereas action-facilitating types of support are more common for managing chronic issues (Rains et al., 2015). OCSNs can also serve as venues for people with rare conditions and their families to connect, build community, and engage in patient work activities (Oprescu et al., 2013).

Use of OCSNs for communication and support can lead to empowering outcomes, such as feeling better informed, feeling more confident in treatment and in relationships with providers, improved illness acceptance, and improved quality of life (Algtewi et al., 2017; van Uden-Kraan et al., 2009). Psychosocial benefits associated with OCSNs include reduced depression (Zhang et al., 2017), anxiety (Setoyama et al., 2011), stress (Bartlett & Coulson, 2011), and improved emotional well-being (Batenburg & Das, 2014; Erfani et al, 2016). OCSNs have also been shown to have a positive effect on changing health behaviors (Laranjo et al, 2015). Patients can encounter difficulties in being understood by friends and family, and support from peers can make patients feel less alone (Allen et al., 2016). Recipients of social support often take comfort in and make connections with other patients because of common struggles and similar illness journeys. Use of OCSNs can result in people finding positive meaning, giving and receiving social support, and improved self-care efficacy—all of which facilitate adaptive coping and improved quality of life (Mo & Coulson, 2012).

Anonymous social support is also an important aspect of many OCSNs and especially important for individuals suffering from stigmatized conditions. For example, many individuals turn to OCSNs for social support from new social connections to manage weight (Hwang et al., 2010); others use OCSNs as a means to disclose transgender identification (Haimson, 2019). OCSNs can be a useful alternative to existing social ties for obtaining social support, due to negative stereotypes and discrimination. Another example is mental health conditions. Reddit has been widely studied for stigmatized conditions such as depression, anxiety, and post-traumatic stress disorder (De Choudhury & De, 2014; Park et al., 2018). For individuals with mental health conditions, long-term participation in OCSNs has been associated with improvement in emotional states (Park & Conway, 2017).

The design and integration of features to enhance social support is a valuable contribution of OCSNs. For example, identifying users with similar health histories through their profiles is one way that patients connect with other patients for peer support through OCSNs. OCSNs could offer functionality to assist patients to complete personal profiles, adding information that is helpful to facilitate connections, while at the same time, facilitating privacy preservation by providing cautionary messages if patients enter sensitive information that could be disclosed. Eliciting feedback from patients about the support features that they would like could also inform the design of OCSNs. For example, breast cancer survivors are interested in professional involvement/support and connecting with other survivors, but are wary of competitive social features such as progress boards (Lloyd et al., 2020).

### 6.2.2 The Value, Quality, and Interpretation of Information on OCSNs

Critical to patient work, OCSNs serve as an important source of experiential knowledge of the lived patient experience (Kingod et al., 2017). Although some OCSNs, such as WebMD, have medical experts who post information, the majority of health information across all OCSNs is generated by nonmedical experts (i.e. "peers"). Patients consistently emphasize the value of health information provided by peers (Gray et al., 1997; Zhao & Zhang, 2017). Learning about the health experiences of others through illness trajectories can be crucial in helping patients manage illness (Huh & Ackerman, 2012).

Peers provide different types of information compared with medical experts, including experiential advice to manage everyday health and social issues, whereas medical experts provide fact-oriented clinical information (Hartzler & Pratt, 2011). To utilize the expertise of peer patients, researchers have designed systems to connect cancer patients with cancer survivors based on user-generated content on OCSNs (Hartzler et al., 2016). Although this is an innovative method to support patients' needs, further research is needed to monitor the quality of information on OCSNs.

Despite the potential value of information contributed on OCSNs, there can also be concerns about information quality, including accuracy and reliability. Misinformation, disinformation, the usage of bots, and astroturfing on social media, including OCSNs, are increasingly common. Misinformation is inaccurate information, whereas disinformation has the intention to deceive readers with inaccurate information (Mingers & Standing, 2018). Bots are automated software-driven accounts that are designed to operate with no or minimal human intervention to disseminate information (Lokot & Diakopoulos, 2016) and/or persuade (Ferrara et al., 2016). Astroturfing occurs when individuals use multiple accounts to act as a larger crowd with the same opinion to promote an artificially created "social consensus" (Harris et al., 2014). All of these concerns can negatively impact OCSNs as vehicles for patient work.

Strategies to control the quality of information on OCSNs are important for facilitating patient work and include misinformation detection (Resnick et al., 2014), credibility of content assessment (Ciampaglia et al., 2015), and utilization of counterfactual prompts (Betsch & Sachse, 2013). A health-related example is the use of probabilistic graphical models to extract side effects of drugs and filter out false information that is prevalent in online communities (Mukherjee et al., 2017). Given the value of patient expertise and growing concerns for information quality on OCSNs, researchers and designers have an opportunity to computationally measure information quality and limit spreading of low-quality information.

Concerns about the quality of information on OCSNs has given rise to research on how people evaluate, or interpret, this content. For example, with regard to assessment of information quality on Yahoo!Answers (https://answers.yahoo.com/), librarians and nurses tend to rate answers similarly, whereas users of Yahoo!Answers generally believe the quality of health answers to be higher than librarians and nurses (Oh & Worrall, 2013). Other research reports that patients engage in hypothesis testing based on incorrect initial hypotheses (Keselman et al., 2008), calling into question how patients interpret and apply information from OCSNs in patient work activities.

However, still other studies suggest that patients are aware of the potential for inaccurate information in OCSNs, and they develop their own methods for credibility assessment as they engage in patient work activities such as information seeking. For instance, people employ different criteria for assessing scientific and experiential information (Lederman et al., 2014). As patients settle into a pattern of long-term health management, they also develop their own ways of assessing sources, including comparison across multiple sources, assessing the "mechanics" of explanations, and harboring skepticism of quick fixes (Chen, 2016).

In sum, there is an active body of research examining how patients and other non-health professionals use and evaluate OCSN content. How OCSNs might be designed to assist participants in evaluating and making use of this information is a fertile ground for future work.

### 6.2.3 Participation in OCSNs

People participate in OCSNs in various ways, including reading, contributing, and interacting with content, and otherwise employing OCSN features to express sentiment (e.g. "liking" content). Participation is important to consider for OCSNs because they provide a window into patient work activities, health behavior change, and outcomes. For example, engaging with online communities can be associated with better glycemic control, in the context of diabetes (Litchman et al., 2018).

Patients, family, friends, informal caregivers, and others participate in OCSNs in different ways. Health information sharing practices on OCSNs are diverse (Valdez et al., 2017). For example, "lurkers" never post or post infrequently but read the content produced by others, and "posters" participate actively by both reading and posting (Nonnecke et al., 2004). Lurkers do not differ significantly from posters in the ways that they may benefit from engaging in patient work, including becoming better informed, having greater confidence in treatment and patient–provider interactions, disease acceptance, and optimism (van Uden-Kraan et al., 2008). However, lurkers can also be less satisfied with OCSNs (van Uden-Kraan et al., 2008) and have a greater need for information than posters (Han et al., 2012). Posters may seek support online to compensate for lack of support from their offline environment (Han et al., 2012). Understanding that OCSNs may assist lurkers and posters to perform patient work in different ways can help patient ergonomics experts to design OCSNs to support their different needs.

The concepts of "lurking" and "posting" emphasize one way in which individuals may engage with OCSNs; however, research has cautioned against the use of this simple dichotomy (Malinen, 2015). OCSNs can also be thought of as consisting of individuals playing many different roles. Jones et al. (2011) identified different types of participative stances (e.g. "caretaker," "butterfly," "discussants," "here for you," "people in distress") in discussion forums focused on self-harm. Previous research on an online community for older adults proposes a taxonomy with six roles: moderating supporter, central supporter, active member, passive member, technical expert, and visitor (Pfeil et al., 2011). How these richly diverse online social roles compare with offline support for patient work, and how they need to be addressed accordingly, is an interesting question for future patient ergonomics research.

Over time in the management of a chronic condition, people may engage differently with OCSNs to perform patient work. At some points, they may engage in more information seeking about their own health management concerns and, at others, play a greater role in providing encouragement to others in their health and care activities (Wen et al., 2011). People may also come to believe that OCSNs have outlived their usefulness due to the lack of new information, but thereafter experience resurgences of information need and perceived relevance due to changes in health status (Chen, 2016). Thus, another potential consideration is how to support a person's interactions with OCSNs as their patient work practices evolve in response to disease progression and changing environmental conditions.

By providing mechanisms for people to engage with OCSNs in their own ways, we can encourage participation and enhance benefits. For example, OCSNs might enable members to contribute in nonverbal ways such as sharing photos (Kamel Boulos et al., 2016). Moderators might take an active role in fostering discussion to draw out different perspectives, which could in turn facilitate more meaningful dialogue. Bidirectional communication via messaging could be emphasized, in addition to engaging community members through discussion forums. Enabling members to engage with content and others through multiple modalities and interactive pathways can enable them to engage more successfully in patient work.

Participation is also an important consideration for those who manage OCSNs, as they impact community interactions and dynamics. Various factors including member characteristics, membership duration and transience, community size, and community activity may influence the dynamic. For example, sentiment can change in a positive direction due to interactions with others (Qiu et al., 2011), word choices in replies can affect future engagement (Park et al., 2015), and community members who are exposed to more nurturant, as opposed to informational, support are less likely to quit communities (Wang et al., 2012). Design features of an OCSN, such as the visibility of lurking and social presence, may also influence the community atmosphere, affecting whether people feel that they are valued members and supported by others. These are all important considerations for supporting patient work in OCSNs.

### 6.2.4   ETHICAL CONSIDERATIONS OF OSCNs FOR RESEARCH

Ethical use of OCSNs has been a long-standing interest of researchers. As OCSNs began to take root, Eysenbach and Till (2001) established guidelines for qualitative research that consider potential harms, perceptions of "private" versus "public" spaces, confidentiality, and informed consent. Much of early OCSN research focused on qualitative analysis of discussion forum posts. As health-related use of OCSNs has grown, the diversity and scale of research studies have also grown to include large secondary analyses for disease outbreak monitoring (Charles-Smith et al., 2015), surveillance of adverse events (Golder et al., 2015), discovery of treatment outcomes (Frost et al., 2011), and synthesis of public opinion about health behaviors (Larson et al., 2013). OCSNs are also fertile ground for intervention and research recruitment (Gelinas et al., 2017).

Despite the public accessibility of much OCSN content, the right to privacy, consent, and confidentiality are common ethical considerations in research. Conway (2014) expands on this list with a taxonomy of ethical concepts derived from reviewing public health research on Twitter. When asked about their attitudes toward the use of OCSNs for research, users, researchers, and other stakeholders expressed varied views depending on the purpose and quality of the research, researchers' affiliations, and potential harms (Golder et al., 2017). Research ethics relating to OCSNs are complex and we lack a consistent set of ethical guidelines (Golder et al., 2017). The ethical "pitfalls" may be less obvious than in traditional research and thus easier to fall into (McKee, 2013).

Although there exists limited formal research guidelines, a number of best practice strategies can guide researchers in the use of OCSNs. Whether OCSN research consists of observational studies of posts, interview/survey research of people who use OCSNs to perform patient work, interventional research, or recruitment, researchers should carefully assess potential risks and benefits to community members.

Key issues include whether OCSN data are considered public or private (Eysenbach & Till, 2001; McKee, 2013) and whether community members have a reasonable expectation of privacy (Moreno et al., 2013). Although intervention studies engage study participants in explicit use of OCSNs through informed consent, in a great portion of the research that analyzes existing OCSN content, members are passive data providers with whom researchers do not interact. Some OCSNs, such as Reddit, generate publicly accessible content. However, this does not mean ethical principles no longer apply. Despite the posting of data that a researcher may find relevant, such an act does not imply consent for research use. In other words, a researcher is not excused from ethical obligations and should not assume that consent has been provided for collation of data or use of identifiable information (McKee, 2013). For access to OCSN content that is not publicly accessible, researchers should obtain permission by contacting the participant for their consent to view and use that data (Eysenbach & Till, 2001; Roberts, 2015). Researchers should seek entry to an OCSN starting with the "owner" of the community and then actively engage with the community over time to facilitate trust, rapport, and mutual understanding (Lawson, 2004; Roberts, 2015). Some communities may be too large for these strategies to be feasible. In such cases, researchers should strongly consider alternative ways of conducting the research, as well as work closely with their institutional review boards to ensure that study procedures do not violate the principles of informed consent (Kramer et al., 2014).

Just as important as the right to privacy and consent in OCSN research is confidentiality—protecting the identity of OCSN users. Although anonymity of some OCSNs enhances confidentiality, it can limit researchers from characterizing data for research. To preserve confidentiality, researchers should remove usernames, IP addresses, and other personally identifying information, consider disguising individuals by using pseudonyms (Lawson, 2004), and exclude the name of the OCSN in reports. Avoid reporting direct quotes and instead paraphrase (McKee, 2013). If reporting a direct quote is necessary, it is best to obtain informed consent (Lawson, 2004), since direct quotes can be traced to individuals using Internet search engines. Even when data are de-identified, it may be possible to link variables in ways that reidentify individuals (McKee, 2013). Therefore, developing robust procedures to protect confidentiality of users is critical when conducting OCSN-based research.

In summary, OCSNs create research opportunities, which also necessitate ongoing review of ethical considerations (McKee, 2013). Although there is a need for agreed-upon ethical principles for secondary use of OCSN data (Golder et al., 2017), the best practice strategies we have discussed can help to address ethical concerns while ensuring research integrity of OCSNs.

## 6.3 CASE EXAMPLES: INTERVENTIONAL AND NON-INTERVENTIONAL OCSNs

In this section, we consider two use cases, OCSN interventions and non-interventional OCSNs, to explore patient ergonomics considerations for OCSN design, research, and practice.

### 6.3.1 OCSN INTERVENTIONS: AN EXAMPLE FOCUSED ON OLDER ADULTS

Few reports show that older adults increasingly adopt newer technologies, with 42% of adults aged 65 and older reporting that they own smartphones, and 67% that they use the internet (Anderson & Perrin, 2017). OCSNs are also used to address health-related issues that older adults face, including caregiving (Oliver et al., 2015) and depression (Tomasino et al., 2017).

Given the potential for OCSNs to assist older adults with personal health management, we consider them through the lens of the Patient Work System (Holden et al., 2017). *Person* factors experienced by older adults include limited vision, mobility, and hearing, which can detract from their user experience and their ability to use OCSNs. Although older adults perceive benefits to technology use, promoting technology acceptance is important (Mitzner et al., 2010). Older adults use *tools and technologies*, including OCSNs, for health-related *tasks* including finding health information, health monitoring, and maintenance, such as checking blood pressure and monitoring weight (Mitzner et al., 2010). Older adults can also use OCSNs to exchange information and support to facilitate health and wellness in various *physical and social environments*, such as retirement community living spaces (Hartzler et al., 2018).

We consider the example of the Virtual Online Communities for Aging-Related Experiences (VOCALE), an intervention to assist older adults with frailty symptoms to manage their health more effectively (Teng et al., 2019). This intervention employs a private Facebook discussion group to provide group members a venue for discussing aging-related experiences. We have employed an iterative design process to develop the intervention, refining the intervention design through multiple pilot studies. During each week of the intervention, we posed a new topic addressing aging-related experiences for participants to discuss. In our second iteration, we introduced problem-solving therapy and asked participants to help a fictional persona with frailty symptoms solve their health-related problems.

At study enrollment, research team staff trained participants to use the system, such as logging in and teaching participants how to post to the discussion forum. Participants also received access to training materials that were especially designed for older adults, employing minimal use of text, large font size, and graphics to illustrate how to use the system.

Although VOCALE served as a rich platform for older adults to share content concerning health issues and management strategies, participants also experienced difficulties. Participants occasionally forgot to press the "enter key" to submit their post (Teng et al., 2019). This led to the "loss" of their post, causing confusion and frustration. There was also difficulty with posting due to mobility and fine-motor issues. Potential solutions to these problems include encouraging participants to post video/audio, teaching participants how to make textual posts using voice recognition technology such as Google Assistant, providing additional training on how to compose and submit posts through the textual interface, and adding a prompt to remind users to submit their post if they have stopped typing or attempt to navigate away without submitting their post. In deciding upon the most appropriate solution(s), it is important to weigh the costs/benefits of installing additional software/equipment, training time, effort needed on the part of staff/developers, and potential issues with cognitive overload on the part of users to learn how to use new tools.

Participants found various aspects of the study platform confusing. Given that participants were able to respond to topics from previous weeks and the Facebook newsfeed ordered topics by recency, the topics would appear out of order, leading to confusion and distress on the part of participants. In the second iteration of VOCALE, we employed the "Units" feature of Facebook, which organizes the topics in sequence, and participants did not express confusion about how to find the topic that they wanted to post to. This example illustrates how, even in the use of readily accessible social media technologies, it may be possible to make adaptations that are more suited to target populations.

In our most recent iteration of VOCALE, analysis of feedback from exit interviews with participants showed that there were various aspects of the intervention that participants appreciated. Participants commented that the intervention had inspired them to take more active approaches to addressing health issues, and they appreciated being exposed to ideas that they could apply to their own health management. Some participants felt that they had trouble relating to some of the material because the health issues discussed did not apply to their own lives. However, other participants said they enjoyed learning about other people's health concerns, and doing so also helped them to keep their own health issues in perspective.

In summary, OCSNs can serve as a resource for older adults to connect with their peers to exchange information and social support. There are important concerns in the design of these interventions, including ensuring the fit of person, task, and technology factors—a triadic relationship highlighted in the Patient Work System (Holden et al., 2017) and Center for Research and Education on Aging and Technology Enhancement Model (Rogers & Fisk, 2010). The provision of training and support from study personnel, in addition to technological modifications, can mitigate participant frustration.

### 6.3.2 Non-Interventional OCSNs: An Example Focused on Topic Drift

In our second example, we consider information scatter that can be observed in OCSNs "in the wild" (i.e. without an intervention). A large established OCSN typically includes many concurrent conversations among different individuals with diverse interests. One consequence of such communication dynamics is *topic drift—* the change of topic with progression of discussion (Hobbs, 1990). Although topic drift can occur in any conversation, in online conversations it has been linked to incoherence (Herring, 1999) and conflict (Lambiase, 2010), thus discouraging participation and exchange of social support in OCSNs.

Although topic drift can make it challenging for users to find health information that could support patient work, topic drift has not been well studied in the context of health-related OCSNs. One exception is our observational study of WebMD discourse (Park et al., 2016). WebMD has forums for different health conditions, and we employed a mixed-method approach to study topic drift among seven topically focused forums within WebMD.

We found a gradual change of topic in all conversations we examined through manual content analysis. The majority of topics were related to health, including symptoms, treatments, side effects, insurance issues, and emotional support. Although the majority of conversations were relevant to the community, some conversations had abrupt topic shifts, which were associated with the expression of frustration among some community members. Abruptly changing the topic was generally viewed negatively, and community members explicitly discouraged topic shifts and made attempts to rectify topic discourse when they noticed those drifts occurring. Despite the community's effort to self-monitor discussions, topic drift was still expressed by some users as a major issue.

Instilling a strong culture around communication behavior, for example, by setting clear forum guidelines and reminding members of these periodically, could reduce the occurrence of topic drift. In addition, computational means could be used to identify and remove topic drifts from conversations. In our research, we detected topic shifts computationally by measuring the similarity between conversation sequences and overall topical discourse patterns. In practice, off-topic content could then be filtered or presented with similar types of content that could help patients, caregivers, and other users of OCSNs find information and support for patient work.

In summary, information scatter in OCSNs is problematic and can be mitigated with better design of the tools/technologies. This effort can minimize information overload, as it allows for concentrated communication on related topics. Doing so, in turn, can improve the user experience and enhance the exchange of information and social support. However, it is also important to be mindful of negative consequences that could emerge when making changes to successful OCSNs. For example, although some members of the WebMD communities we studied expressed frustration with topic drift, a few members commented upon the positive side of discussing off-topic issues such as nonmedical life issues.

## 6.4  DESIGN RECOMMENDATIONS AND IMPLICATIONS FOR PRACTICE

The preceding discussion paves the way for recommendations concerning the design of OCSNs for patient work. First, it is important to engage diverse stakeholders, including patients, family, friends, caregivers, and healthcare providers, in the design of OCSNs to facilitate patient work. Community-based participatory research methods can help ensure that stakeholders' perspectives are valued and incorporated. Human factors methods such as interviews, focus groups, and participatory design techniques can foster inclusivity and provide insight into how the OCSN being developed could facilitate or hinder patient work.

In addition, OCSNs can help patients to find and retrieve relevant health information by integrating extant research literature, computational techniques, and human-centered design principles. Extant research literature pertaining to patient information needs at different temporal points and in different patient work contexts could inform the selection of topics of interest. Systems can be designed to weave expert opinions from health professionals into OCSNs discussions (Huh & Pratt, 2014). Computational techniques could be used to identify content containing potentially unreliable or inaccurate information (Starbird et al., 2016; Hou et al., 2019). Cluster analysis could be used to identify and present topics of interest to patients (Chen, 2012). In addition, human-centered design techniques could be employed to iteratively develop visual indicators that facilitate patients' interpretation of information quality and relevance.

It is also important to be persistent about threats to privacy and confidentiality and to promote users' awareness of the open nature of OCSN data. Although some OCSN members carefully balance information sharing to support patient work with the desire to manage self-presentation (Newman et al., 2011), all users may not be so strategic (Valdez et al., 2017). A tool could be designed to remind users about an OCSN's privacy policies and caution them about the potential for disclosure of posts containing sensitive information. The community could also institute practices to automatically anonymize sensitive information.

Lastly, in the development and monitoring of an OCSN, attention to moderator support and training can be critical. By moderator support, we refer to the support that OCSN support staff may provide to participants during the course of an intervention. This might simply include deleting offensive posts, or it could involve more active interaction with participants, such as providing patients with information they seek and incorporating semiautomatic methods to help moderators identify posts that require their attention and response (Huh et al., 2013). In addition to moderator support, there is a need for training of OCSN members, instructional materials, and tools for moderators to facilitate effective OCSN use and ensure that patients, caregivers, and others are able to obtain the information and support they need to perform patient work activities.

## 6.5  CONCLUSION

In this chapter, we introduced ways that OCSNs can facilitate patient work. OCSNs used as a vehicle for patient work can vary in terms of many characteristics, including subject matter, participant type, functionality, intervention (or not), content accessibility, and moderation. OCSNs serve a critical function in the patient work of users. Individuals can exchange informational, social, and other forms of support with community members. This support has been associated with many empowering outcomes, including psychosocial benefits such as improved mood and well-being and other benefits such as being better informed, feeling more confident about treatment, and increased optimism. Participation and engagement can be a critical factor in the realization of these benefits. Thus, in recent years, there has been increased interest in understanding the factors that may be associated with increased engagement. Aside from their potential to directly facilitate patient work, OCSNs can also be used to extend our extant health management knowledge through research. Although careful consideration of ethical concerns is imperative, it is our hope that by applying human factors methods to design OCSNs, people can realize the potential of OCSNs to facilitate patient work in diverse settings.

## REFERENCES

Algtewi, E., Owens, J., & Baker, S. R. (2017). Online support groups for head and neck cancer and health-related quality of life. *Quality of Life Research, 26*(9), 2351–2362.

Allen, C., Vassilev, I., Kennedy, A., & Rogers, A. (2016). Long-term condition self-management support in online communities: A meta-synthesis of qualitative papers. *Journal of Medical Internet Research, 18*(3), e61.

Anderson, M., & Perrin, A. (2017). *Tech Adoption Climbs Among Older Adults*. Pew Research Center, Washington, DC.

Bartlett, Y. K., & Coulson, N. S. (2011). An investigation into the empowerment effects of using online support groups and how this affects health professional/patient communication. *Patient Education and Counseling, 83*(1), 113–119.

Batenburg, A., & Das, E. (2014). Emotional approach coping and the effects of online peer-led support group participation among patients with breast cancer: A longitudinal study. *Journal of Medical Internet Research, 16*(11), e256.

Betsch, C., & Sachse, K. (2013). Debunking vaccination myths: Strong risk negations can increase perceived vaccination risks. *Health Psychology, 32*(2), 146–155.

Charles-Smith, L. E., Reynolds, T. L., Cameron, M. A., Conway, M., Lau, E. H. Y., Olsen, J. M., Pavlin, J. A., Shigematsu, M., Streichert, L. C., Suda, K. J., & Corley, C. D. (2015). Using social media for actionable disease surveillance and outbreak management: A systematic literature review. *PLoS ONE, 10*(10).

Chen, A. T. (2012). Exploring online support spaces: using cluster analysis to examine breast cancer, diabetes and fibromyalgia support groups. *Patient Education and Counseling, 87*(2), 250–257.

Chen, A. T. (2014). What's in a virtual hug? A transdisciplinary review of methods in online health discussion forum research. *Library & Information Science Research, 36*(2), 120–130.

Chen, A. T. (2016). The relationship between health management and information behavior over time: A study of the illness journeys of people living with fibromyalgia. *Journal of Medical Internet Research, 18*(10), e269.

Ciampaglia, G. L., Shiralkar, P., Rocha, L. M., Bollen, J., Menczer, F., & Flammini, A. (2015). Computational fact checking from knowledge networks. *PLoS ONE, 10*(6), e0128193.

Conway, M. (2014). Ethical issues in using Twitter for public health surveillance and research: Developing a taxonomy of ethical concepts from the research literature. *Journal of Medical Internet Research, 16*(12), e290.

Cutrona, C. E., & Suhr, J. A. (1992). Controllability of stressful events and satisfaction with spouse support behaviors. *Communication Research, 19*(2), 154–174.

De Choudhury, M., & De, S. (2014). Mental health discourse on Reddit: Self-disclosure, social support, and anonymity. Proceedings of International Conference on Web and Social Media Papers, Association for the Advancement of Artificial Intelligence, 71–80.

Erfani, S. S., Blount, Y., & Abedin, B. (2016). The influence of health-specific social network site use on the psychological well-being of cancer-affected people. *Journal of the American Medical Informatics Association, 23*(3), 467–476.

Eysenbach, G., Powell, J., Englesakis, M., Rizo, C., & Stern, A. (2004). Health related virtual communities and electronic support groups: Systematic review of the effects of online peer to peer interactions. *The BMJ, 328*(7449), 1166.

Eysenbach, G., & Till, J. E. (2001). Ethical issues in qualitative research on internet communities. *The BMJ, 323*(7321), 1103–1105.

Ferrara, E., Varol, O., Davis, C., Menczer, F., & Flammini, A. (2016). The rise of social bots. *Communications of the Association for Computing Machinery, 59*(7), 96–104.

Frost, J., Okun, S., Vaughan, T., Heywood, J., & Wicks, P. (2011). Patient-reported outcomes as a source of evidence in off-label prescribing: Analysis of data from PatientsLikeMe. *Journal of Medical Internet Research, 13*(1).

Gelinas, L., Pierce, R., Winkler, S., Cohen, I. G., Lynch, H. F., & Bierer, B. E. (2017). Using social media as a research recruitment tool: Ethical issues and recommendations. *The American Journal of Bioethics, 17*(3), 3–14.

Golder, S., Ahmed, S., Norman, G., & Booth, A. (2017). Attitudes toward the ethics of research using social media: A systematic review. *Journal of Medical Internet Research, 19*(6), e195.

Golder, S., Norman, G., & Loke, Y. K. (2015). Systematic review on the prevalence, frequency and comparative value of adverse events data in social media. *British Journal of Clinical Pharmacology*, *80*(4), 878–888.

Gray, R., Fitch, M., Davis, C., & Phillips, C. (1997). A qualitative study of breast cancer self-help groups. *Psycho-Oncology*, *6*(4), 279–289.

Haimson, O. L. (2019). Mapping gender transition sentiment patterns via social media data: Toward decreasing transgender mental health disparities. *Journal of the American Medical Informatics Association*, *26*(8–9), 749–758.

Han, J. Y., Hawkins, R. P., Shaw, B. R., Pingree, S., McTavish, F., & Gustafson, D. H. (2009). Unraveling uses and effects of an interactive health communication system. *Journal of Broadcasting & Electronic Media*, *53*(1), 112–133.

Han, J. Y., Kim, J.-H., Yoon, H. J., Shim, M., McTavish, F. M., & Gustafson, D. H. (2012). Social and psychological determinants of levels of engagement with an online breast cancer support group: Posters, lurkers, and non-users. *Journal of Health Communication*, *17*(3), 356–371.

Harris, J. K., Moreland-Russell, S., Choucair, B., Mansour, R., Staub, M., & Simmons, K. (2014). Tweeting for and against public health policy: Response to the Chicago Department of Public Health's electronic cigarette Twitter campaign. *Journal of Medical Internet Research*, *16*(10), e238.

Hartzler, A. L., Osterhage, K., Demiris, G., Phelan, E. A., Thielke, S. M., & Turner, A. M. (2018). Understanding views on everyday use of personal health information: Insights from community dwelling older adults. *Informatics for Health & Social Care*, *43*(3), 320–333.

Hartzler, A. L, Taylor, M. N., Park, A., Griffiths, T., Backonja, U., McDonald, D. W., Wahbeh, S., Brown, C., & Pratt, W. (2016). Leveraging cues from person-generated health data for peer matching in online communities. *Journal of the American Medical Informatics Association*, *23*(3), 496–507.

Hartzler, A., & Pratt, W. (2011). Managing the personal side of health: How patient expertise differs from the expertise of clinicians. *Journal of Medical Internet Research*, *13*(3), e62.

Herring, S. C. (1999). Interactional coherence in CMC. *Journal of Computer-Mediated Communication*, *4*(4), JCMC444.

Hobbs, J. R. (1990) Topic drift, in B. Dorval (ed.) *Conversational Organization and Its Development* 38, pp. 3–22. Norwood, NJ: Ablex.

Holden, R. J., Valdez, R. S., Schubert, C. C., Thompson, M. J., & Hundt, A. S. (2017). Macroergonomic factors in the Patient Work System: Examining the context of patients with chronic illness. *Ergonomics*, *60*(1), 26–43.

Hou, R., Perez-Rosas, V., Loeb, S., & Mihalcea, R. (2019). Towards automatic detection of misinformation in online medical videos. *2019 International Conference on Multimodal Interaction on - ICMI '19*, 235–243.

Huh, J., & Ackerman, M. (2012). Collaborative help in chronic disease management: Supporting individualized problems. *Computer Supported Cooperative Work*, 2012, 853–862.

Huh, J., & Pratt, W. (2014). Weaving clinical expertise in online health communities. Proceedings of the 32nd Annual Association for Computing Machinery Conference on Human Factors in Computing Systems - Conference on Human Factors in Computing Systems '14, 1355–1364.

Huh, J., Yetisgen-Yildiz, M., & Pratt, W. (2013). Text classification for assisting moderators in online health communities. *Journal of Biomedical Informatics*, *46*(6), 998–1005.

Hwang, K. O., Ottenbacher, A. J., Green, A. P., Cannon-Diehl, M. R., Richardson, O., Bernstam, E. V., & Thomas, E. J. (2010). Social support in an Internet weight loss community. *International Journal of Medical Informatics*, *79*(1), 5–13.

Jacobson, D. E. (1986). Types and timing of social support. *Journal of Health and Social Behavior*, *27*(3), 250–264.

Jones, R., Sharkey, S., Smithson, J., Ford, T., Emmens, T., Hewis, E., Sheaves, B., & Owens, C. (2011). Using metrics to describe the participative stances of members within discussion forums. *Journal of Medical Internet Research*, *13*(1), e3.

Kamel Boulos, M. N., Giustini, D. M., & Wheeler, S. (2016). Instagram and WhatsApp in health and healthcare: An overview. *Future Internet*, *8*(3), 37.

Kaplan, S. J., Chen, A. T., & Carriere, R. M. (2017). De-constructing the co-construction: Researcher stance, the nature of data and community building in an online participatory platform to create a knowledge repository. *Proceedings of the Association for Information Science and Technology*, *54*(1), 203–212.

Keselman, A., Browne, A. C., & Kaufman, D. R. (2008). Consumer health information seeking as hypothesis testing. *Journal of the American Medical Informatics Association*, *15*(4), 484–495.

Kingod, N., Cleal, B., Wahlberg, A., & Husted, G. R. (2017). Online peer-to-peer communities in the daily lives of people with chronic illness: A qualitative systematic review. *Qualitative Health Research*, *27*(1), 89–99.

Kramer, A. D. I., Guillory, J. E., & Hancock, J. T. (2014). Experimental evidence of massive-scale emotional contagion through social networks. *Proceedings of the National Academy of Sciences*, *111*(24), 8788–8790.

Lambiase, J. J. (2010). Hanging by a thread: Topic development and death in an online discussion of breaking news. *Language@ Internet*, *7*, 1–22.

Laranjo, L., Arguel, A., Neves, A. L., Gallagher, A. M., Kaplan, R., Mortimer, N., Mendes, G. A., & Lau, A. Y. S. (2015). The influence of social networking sites on health behavior change: A systematic review and meta-analysis. *Journal of the American Medical Informatics Association*, *22*(1), 243–256.

Larson, H. J., Smith, D. M., Paterson, P., Cumming, M., Eckersberger, E., Freifeld, C. C., Ghinai, I., Jarrett, C., Paushter, L., Brownstein, J. S., & Madoff, L. C. (2013). Measuring vaccine confidence: Analysis of data obtained by a media surveillance system used to analyse public concerns about vaccines. *The Lancet Infectious Diseases*, *13*(7), 606–613.

Lawson, D. (2004). Blurring the boundaries: Ethical considerations for online research using synchronous CMC forums. *Readings in Virtual Research Ethics: Issues and Controversies*, *11*(3), 80–100.

Lederman, R., Fan, H., Smith, S., & Chang, S. (2014). Who can you trust? Credibility assessment in online health forums. *Health Policy and Technology*, *3*(1), 13–25.

Litchman, M. L., Edelman, L. S., & Donaldson, G. W. (2018). Effect of diabetes online community engagement on health indicators: Cross-sectional study. *Journal of Medical Internet Research Diabetes*, *3*(2), e8.

Lloyd, G. R., Hoffman, S. A., Welch, W. A., Blanch-Hartigan, D., Gavin, K. L., Cottrell, A., Cadmus-Bertram, L., Spring, B., Penedo, F., Courneya, K. S., & Phillips, S. M. (2020). Breast cancer survivors' preferences for social support features in technology-supported physical activity interventions: Findings from a mixed methods evaluation. *Translational Behavioral Medicine*, *10*(2), 423–434.

Lokot, T., & Diakopoulos, N. (2016). News bots: Automating news and information dissemination on Twitter. *Digital Journalism*, *4*(6), 682–699.

Malinen, S. (2015). Understanding user participation in online communities: A systematic literature review of empirical studies. *Computers in Human Behavior*, *46*, 228–238.

McKee, R. (2013). Ethical issues in using social media for health and health care research. *Health Policy*, *110*(2), 298–301.

Mingers, J., & Standing, C. (2018). What is information? Toward a theory of information as objective and veridical. *Journal of Information Technology*, *33*(2), 85–104.

Mitzner, T. L., Boron, J. B., Fausset, C. B., Adams, A. E., Charness, N., Czaja, S. J., Dijkstra, K., Fisk, A. D., Rogers, W. A., & Sharit, J. (2010). Older adults talk technology: Technology usage and attitudes. *Computers in Human Behavior, 26*(6), 1710–1721.

Mo, P. K. H., & Coulson, N. S. (2012). Developing a model for online support group use, empowering processes and psychosocial outcomes for individuals living with HIV/ AIDS. *Psychology & Health, 27*(4), 445–459.

Moreno, M. A., Goniu, N., Moreno, P. S., & Diekema, D. (2013). Ethics of social media research: Common concerns and practical considerations. *Cyberpsychology, Behavior and Social Networking, 16*(9), 708–713.

Mukherjee, S., Weikum, G., & Danescu-Niculescu-Mizil, C. (2017). People on drugs: Credibility of user statements in health communities. *Proceedings of the 20th ACM SIGKDD International Conference on Knowledge Discovery and Data Mining*, 65–74.

Newman, M. W., Lauterbach, D., Munson, S. A., Resnick, P., & Morris, M. E. (2011). It's not that I don't have problems, I'm just not putting them on Facebook: Challenges and opportunities in using online social networks for health. *Proceedings of the Association for Computing Machinery 2011 Conference on Computer Supported Cooperative Work*, 341–350.

Nonnecke, B., Preece, J., & Andrews, D. (2004). What lurkers and posters think of each other. *Proceedings of the 37th Annual Hawaii International Conference on System Sciences*, 1–9.

Oh, S., & Worrall, A. (2013). Health answer quality evaluation by librarians, nurses, and users in social Q&A. *Library & Information Science Research, 35*(4), 288–298.

Oliver, D. P., Washington, K., Wittenberg-Lyles, E., Gage, A., Mooney, M., & Demiris, G. (2015). Lessons learned from a secret Facebook support group. *Health & Social Work, 40*(2), 125–133.

Oprescu, F., Campo, S., Lowe, J., Andsager, J., & Morcuende, J. A. (2013). Online information exchanges for parents of children with a rare health condition: Key findings from an online support community. *Journal of Medical Internet Research, 15*(1), e16.

Park, A., & Conway, M. (2017). Longitudinal changes in psychological states in online health community members: Understanding the long-term effects of participating in an online depression community. *Journal of Medical Internet Research, 19*(3), e71.

Park, A., Conway, M., & Chen, A. T. (2018). Examining thematic similarity, difference, and membership in three online mental health communities from Reddit: A text mining and visualization approach. *Computers in Human Behavior, 78*, 98–112.

Park, A., Hartzler, A. L., Huh, J., Hsieh, G., McDonald, D. W., & Pratt, W. (2016). "How did we get here?": Topic drift in online health discussions. *Journal of Medical Internet Research, 18*(11), e284.

Park, A., Hartzler, A. L., Huh, J., McDonald, D. W., & Pratt, W. (2015). Homophily of vocabulary usage: Beneficial effects of vocabulary similarity on online health communities participation. *Annual Symposium Proceedings. American Medical Informatics Association Symposium, 2015*, 1024–1033.

Pfeil, U., Svangstu, K., Ang, C. S., & Zaphiris, P. (2011). Social roles in an online support community for older people. *International Journal of Human-Computer Interaction, 27*(4), 323–347.

Qiu, B., Zhao, K., Mitra, P., Wu, D., Caragea, C., Yen, J., Greer, G. E., & Portier, K. (2011). Get online support, feel better–sentiment analysis and dynamics in an online cancer survivor community. *2011 IEEE Third International Conference on Privacy, Security, Risk and Trust (PASSAT) and 2011 IEEE Third International Conference on Social Computing (SocialCom)*, 274–281.

Rains, S. A., Peterson, E. B., & Wright, K. B. (2015). Communicating social support in computer-mediated contexts: A meta-analytic review of content analyses examining support messages shared online among individuals coping with illness. *Communication Monographs, 82*(4), 403–430.

Resnick, P., Carton, S., Park, S., Shen, Y., & Zeffer, N. (2014). Rumorlens: A system for analyzing the impact of rumors and corrections in social media. *Proceedings of the Computational Journalism Conference.*

Roberts, L. D. (2015). Ethical issues in conducting qualitative research in online communities. *Qualitative Research in Psychology, 12*(3), 314–325.

Rogers, W. A., & Fisk, A. D. (2010). Toward a psychological science of advanced technology design for older adults. *The Journals of Gerontology Series B: Psychological Sciences and Social Sciences, 65B*(6), 645–653.

Setoyama, Y., Yamazaki, Y., & Namayama, K. (2011). Benefits of peer support in online Japanese breast cancer communities: Differences between lurkers and posters. *Journal of Medical Internet Research, 13*(4), e122.

Starbird, K., Spiro, E., Edwards, I., Zhou, K., Maddock, J., & Narasimhan, S. (2016). Could this be true? I think so! Expressed uncertainty in online rumoring. *Proceedings of the 2016 Conference on Human Factors in Computing Systems Conference on Human Factors in Computing Systems,* 360–371.

Teng, A. K., Han, S., Lin, S.-Y., Demiris, G., Zaslavsky, O., & Chen, A. T. (2019). Using an innovative discussion platform to give voice to aging-related experiences: A pilot study. *Journal of Gerontological Nursing, 45*(12), 33–40.

Tomasino, K. N., Lattie, E. G., Ho, J., Palac, H. L., Kaiser, S. M., & Mohr, D. C. (2017). Harnessing peer support in an online intervention for older adults with depression. *The American Journal of Geriatric Psychiatry, 25*(10):1109–1119.

Valdez, R. S., Guterbock, T. M., Fitzgibbon, K., Williams, I. C., Wellbeloved-Stone, C. A., Bears, J. E., & Menefee, H. K. (2017). From loquacious to reticent: Understanding patient health information communication to guide consumer health IT design. *Journal of the American Medical Informatics Association, 24*(4), 680–696.

Valdez, R. S., Holden, R. J., Novak, L. L., & Veinot, T. C. (2015). Transforming consumer health informatics through a patient work framework: Connecting patients to context. *Journal of the American Medical Informatics Association, 22*(1), 2–10.

van Uden-Kraan, C. F., Drossaert, C. H., Taal, E., Seydel, E. R., & van de Laar, M. A. F. J. (2008). Self-reported differences in empowerment between lurkers and posters in online patient support groups. *Journal of Medical Internet Research, 10*(2), e18.

van Uden-Kraan, C. F., Drossaert, C. H. C., Taal, E., Seydel, E. R., & van de Laar, M. A. F. J. (2009). Participation in online patient support groups endorses patients' empowerment. *Patient Education and Counseling, 74*(1), 61–69.

Wang, Y.-C., Kraut, R., & Levine, J. M. (2012). To stay or leave? The relationship of emotional and informational support to commitment in online health support groups. *Proceedings of the ACM 2012 Conference on Computer Supported Cooperative Work,* 833–842.

Wen, K.-Y., McTavish, F., Kreps, G., Wise, M., & Gustafson, D. (2011). From diagnosis to death: A case study of coping with breast cancer as seen through online discussion group messages. *Journal of Computer-Mediated Communication, 16*(2), 331–361.

Zhang, S., O'Carroll Bantum, E., Owen, J., Bakken, S., & Elhadad, N. (2017). Online cancer communities as informatics intervention for social support: Conceptualization, characterization, and impact. *Journal of the American Medical Informatics Association, 24*(2), 451–459.

Zhao, Y., & Zhang, J. (2017). Consumer health information seeking in social media: A literature review. *Health Information & Libraries Journal, 34*(4), 268–283.

# Section III

Patient Ergonomics Populations

# 7 Designing for Veterans

*Arjun H. Rao*
Flight Deck Research & Concept Development
Texas A&M University

*Farzan Sasangohar*
Wm Michael Barnes '64
Department of Industrial and Systems Engineering
Texas A&M University

## CONTENTS

Since 2001, the United States has deployed over two million service members to conflicts in Afghanistan (Operation Enduring Freedom [OEF]) and Iraq (Operation Iraqi Freedom [OIF]), with over half of them being deployed more than once (Hautzinger et al., 2015; Seal et al., 2007). Recent estimates from Brown University's Watson Institute of International & Public Affairs put the combined death toll of U.S. service members at 6,900. In addition, 970,000 veterans report either a physical or cognitive disability upon return (Hautzinger et al., 2015). Common physical injuries include burns, orthopedic injuries (including loss of limbs), and traumatic brain injury. Moreover, many veterans also experience operational stress and mental health disorders including post-traumatic stress disorder (PTSD; Church, 2009). In addition to addressing the health-related aspects of disability, veterans also face several micro- and macroergonomic challenges in reintegrating into society.

## 7.1 UNIQUE CHALLENGES FACED BY RETURNING VETERANS

### 7.1.1 PHYSICAL AND COGNITIVE CHALLENGES

Much attention has been paid to physical ergonomics issues faced by returning veterans (e.g. Robbins et al., 2009; Sherman & Sherman, 1983; Smurr et al., 2008). Studies have suggested that military personnel who have served in Afghanistan and Iraq are more likely to have physical impairments relative to those who have served in other conflicts owing to the increased exposure to improvised explosive devices (Wade, 2013). Commonly reported impairments include wounds to the extremities resulting in amputations, sensory impairments, and head injuries (Owens et al., 2007). Amputations and injuries to the spinal cord can result in reduced physical dexterity, difficulty with prolonged sitting or standing, and challenges with mobility. Sensory impairments can lead to difficulty in hearing, seeing, or reading content, and issues in accessing electronic resources.

Studies have shown deployment stressors and exposure to combat result in severe mental health issues including anxiety, depression, and PTSD. PTSD is considered one of the "signature wounds" of returning U.S. military veterans (Tanielian & Jaycox, 2008, p. iii) and is among the most prevalent and functionally disabling conditions (Lew et al., 2009). Research has shown veterans are 5%–25% more likely to be affected by PTSD based on when they served (e.g. Vietnam War, Gulf War, Operation Iraqi Freedom [OIF], Enduring Freedom [OEF], and New Dawn; Kessler, 1995; Rodriguez-Paras et al., 2017). A recent meta-analysis by Fulton et al. (2015) estimated PTSD prevalence at 23% among veterans who returned from OIF/OEF. Failure to treat PTSD can have severe monetary and societal consequences, highlighting the need to improve access and treatment-seeking opportunities (Institute of Medicine and National Research Council, 2007; Sledjeski et al., 2008). Despite the prevalence of treatment options, the absence of veteran-centered, evidence-based interventions grounded in human factors and ergonomics (HFE) design principles limits the effectiveness and outcomes of current treatment techniques.

### 7.1.2 SOCIOCULTURAL CHALLENGES

Social isolation is a major barrier for returning veterans to reintegrate into their communities, impacting loved ones and the society. A study on the occupational performance needs of young veterans showed that engaging in relationships, re-enrolling in school, driving, maintaining physical health, and establishing healthy sleep habits were among the top challenges (Plach & Sells, 2013). Similarly, an interview-based study by Thomas et al. (2014) showed that social isolation, loneliness, depression, and hopelessness were mentioned as frequent precursors to suicide events among veterans. Loneliness and social isolation combined with physical disability and mental disorders have resulted in 41%–61% higher risk of suicide among OEF and OIF veterans (respectively), compared to the general U.S. population (U.S. Department of Veterans Affairs, 2019).

Research has shown the prevalence of societal stigma against seeking access to mental health care. Stigma can be self-directed or public, leading to self-discriminatory behavior and lack of opportunities, which can in turn result in negative professional and personal consequences (Corrigan & Kleinlein, 2005). Unfortunately, over two-thirds of those suffering from mental illness do not seek treatment and suffer in private (Henderson et al., 2013). This is especially prevalent among military veterans (Hoge et al., 2004; National Council on Disability, 2009; Pietrzak et al., 2009). Consequently, approximately 50% of returning veterans who are screened positive for PTSD or other psychiatric conditions are not willing to seek help (Brown et al., 2011; Hoge et al., 2004; Tanielian & Jaycox, 2008).

### 7.1.3 Organizational Challenges

Research has shown that veterans have trouble navigating the complex care systems. Specifically, previous studies have highlighted barriers relating to veterans' interactions with the U.S. Veterans Affairs (VA). A study involving women veterans highlighted increased wait times, scheduling issues, as well as difficulties with administrative paperwork and navigating the complex care system (Vogt et al., 2006). Moon and colleagues have argued that the care system in itself may be a barrier as it has evolved into a highly complex system involving multiple stakeholders (Moon et al., 2017, 2018). A recent study by Bovin et al. (2018) investigated veterans' experiences navigating the VA-mental health system and highlighted the lack of information or correct guidance about accessing services. Therefore, there is a need to augment the existing veteran care system to one that: (1) enables patients to seek care more easily to manage their condition; (2) supports healthcare professionals and informal caregivers; and (3) leverages the advances in technology to provide tools for health-related education, engagement, and treatment.

## 7.2 PATIENT ERGONOMICS AND VETERAN CARE

"Patient work" consists of activities carried out by patients and informal caregivers in clinical, home, and community settings (Holden et al., 2013; Valdez et al. 2015). In recent years, "patient ergonomics" (or patient-centered human factors)—the application of HFE to study and improve patient work—has emerged as a new subdiscipline of HFE (Holden & Mickelson, 2013). Employing the systems approach, patient ergonomics applies HFE and related design techniques (e.g. usability engineering) to improve patients' and nonprofessionals' activities (in some cases with a healthcare professional) toward achieving health goals (Holden & Valdez, 2018). Given the complex and multifaceted nature of the challenges faced by returning veterans, a patient ergonomics approach shows promise.

Literature on veteran patient work has investigated the role of informal care providers for the veteran population. One study found that veterans with spinal cord injuries relied heavily on informal caregivers for their daily health activities (Robinson-Whelen & Rintala, 2003). Another study of 89 veterans showed higher intensity of informal care (~47 hours per week) relative to primary VA care (~5.6 hours; Van

Houtven et al., 2010). Social and technological factors also play an important role in the patient and informal caregiver performance (Holden et al., 2013). An analysis of 198 frail male veterans' informal caregiver networks indicated these veterans had on average three people they relied on for emotional support, instrumental aid, health appraisal, and health monitoring. These supports were primarily family members including adult sons and daughters (Abbott et al., 2007). In some cases, informal caregiving can have adverse effects on the care provider. A survey study involving 135 family care givers revealed that more than a third of the respondents reported high strain while providing care, while only reporting moderate levels of satisfaction (Wakefield et al., 2012). Further, this study showed that the number of veterans seeking counseling for mental health disorders was a predictor for caregiver burnout. Therefore, there is a need for further research into patient ergonomics that could be utilized to support such effortful work.

A recent macroergonomic model of patient work emphasized not only the patient and tasks but also associated tools or technologies as part of the "inner triad" of important interacting microergonomic components (Holden et al., 2017). The availability, accessibility, and usability of these tools are important factors to facilitate effective patient work (Holden et al., 2015). Studies have highlighted the need to use appropriate tools to support care givers and veterans when working toward health goals (Wakefield et al., 2012). Geographic and accessibility barriers could be mitigated through the use of technology-enhanced interventions such as the VA's care coordination and telehealth program (Darkins et al., 2008). Features such as alerts and alarms, in addition to other technology-enabled functionality, may further support veteran's self-care efforts. However, human-factors-based approaches should be used to create technologies that are well integrated with characteristics of these intended users, tasks and broader macroergonomic factors to avoid undesirable consequences stemming from use of technology-based support systems (Brewin et al., 2010).

A patient ergonomics approach could be used to address many of the challenges of the veteran population detailed earlier. Here, in the following case study, we illustrate the use of patient ergonomics to design a mobile health (mHealth)-based intervention to support veterans to self-manage PTSD.

## 7.3 CASE STUDY: PATIENT ERGONOMIC DESIGN OF INTERVENTIONS FOR VETERAN MENTAL HEALTH

This section details patient ergonomics efforts, being carried out by researchers in the Applied Cognitive Ergonomics (ACE) Lab at Texas A&M University, to address veterans' mental health. Specifically, this case study guides the reader through a user-centered design of an mHealth application (app) to enable continuous monitoring and self-management of mental health conditions. We detail our data collection efforts to better understand veterans' experiences with PTSD, the barriers they face, and app functionalities they believed would help them better manage their condition. In addition, we highlight important factors to consider for conducting participatory ergonomics with the veteran population. Figure 7.1 illustrates the timeline of events and the three-phased research approach employed by the team for the design of a veteran-centered intervention.

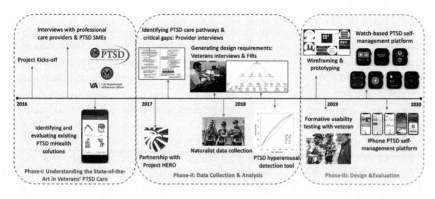

**FIGURE 7.1** Timeline and phases of research for the design of a veteran-centered intervention.

### 7.3.1 Phase I: Understanding the State-of-the-Art in PTSD Care

Our front-end analysis involved a comprehensive review of the available mHealth apps for PTSD, as well as a scoping review of literature to understand the extent of app usage and efforts toward mHealth app validation (Rodriguez-Paras et al., 2017). Findings revealed the scarcity of evidence-based apps that could be integrated with clinical PTSD treatment, as well as the need to consider stakeholders' (e.g. veterans, clinicians, caregivers) needs and characteristics while designing mHealth-based intervention bundles. Next, we carried out usability studies with *PTSD Coach*—the most downloaded PTSD support app developed by the VA. The findings from the study indicated that the educational material about PTSD was deemed informative, and self-assessments (e.g. PTSD Checklist [PCL-5]) were perceived by participants as useful in tracking veterans' mental well-being. Further, some of the mindfulness tools provided in the app helped alleviate stress (Rodriguez-Paras & Sasangohar, 2017). However, the study also highlighted several key usability issues. Participants in the study highlighted the app's poor color scheme, lack of personalization options, and unclear guidance on strategies to mitigate stressful situations.

We sought to understand patient needs from multiple perspectives. Consistent with this view, we interviewed 11 subject matter experts (SMEs) who were actively involved in PTSD care for veterans, including six clinical psychologists (two with expertise in biofeedback), one research psychiatrist, one veteran volunteer (three tours of duty) for peer support in the PTSD recovery program, two therapists (one with over 15 years of experience with the National Center for PTSD), one clinical social worker with expertise in cognitive processing therapy (CPT), and one researcher and clinical psychologist with over a decade of experience studying PTSD with the National Center for PTSD. The purpose of these interviews was to better understand the needs and barriers for mental health care, from a clinicians' perspective. The findings highlighted the lack of remote patient monitoring and absence of between-session support for veterans. In addition, the research indicated the need for a technology-driven approach to detect the onset of PTSD hyperarousal events from home and community settings. The SMEs also recommended more research on evidence-based, veteran-centered PTSD intervention bundles to help provide noninvasive, discreet, cost-effective, yet high-quality professional and remote care.

## 7.3.2   PHASE II: DATA COLLECTION AND ANALYSIS

To execute a veteran-centered design approach while creating an intervention for veterans with PTSD, a variety of quantitative and qualitative data were collected over a three-year period (2016–2019). Data collection methods spanned qualitative interviews, focus groups, usability tests, momentary self-reports, surveys, questionnaires, accelerometers, and heart rate monitors. The data were collected from 201 veterans at multiple bike riding events organized by Project Hero—a nonprofit organization dedicated to helping military veterans and first responders with PTSD.

Fifty combat veterans diagnosed with PTSD were recruited for interviews and focus groups that took place in hotel conference rooms in multiple cities across the United States, including California, Florida, Minneapolis, Texas, and Washington D.C. Participants were welcomed and provided with details about the study. The interviews and focus groups began shortly after researchers received participant consent to audio-record conversations and after participants were given a brief overview of the interview topic. Semistructured interviews were administered to elicit veterans' experiences dealing with PTSD. Follow-up questions were asked to better understand the nature of triggers for PTSD hyperarousal events, PTSD-related barriers and challenges in daily life, and preferred strategies for mitigating PTSD. In addition, veterans were asked about their expectation for a technology-based self-management tool.

The one-on-one and focus group interviews were transcribed and a hybrid Corbin & Strauss (2015) and Charmaz Qualitative Data Analysis method (Miles & Huberman, 1994) developed by Sasangohar and colleagues (2018) was used to systematically document the themes. Two coders completed the following steps, separately and sequentially, and met throughout to discuss any discrepancies: code creation; initial coding; and focused coding. A consensus coding process was used that entailed discussion of the themes and constructs that emerged from the analysis, and disagreements were resolved and changes made as necessary.

Heart rate measurements were collected with the intent of characterizing heart rate profiles for veterans with PTSD and to facilitate the development of a predictive algorithm. Data were collected using an app designed for smartwatches (MOTO 360 Gen 1 and Gen 2 [Motorola Inc.], and Apple iWatches series 2–4). The app allowed veterans to report hyperarousal moments (symptomatic of PTSD) through a simple "tap" on the watch face. In addition, the accelerometer and gyroscope data were collected to allow kinematic, linear, and angular acceleration data to be captured. Self-reports were recorded as time-stamped events and were used to build a machine learning tool to detect hyperarousal patterns (described in Section 7.3.2.2).

Data from multiple formative usability tests were collected to identify opportunities for incremental improvements to the design and to assess the overall user experience. Prototypes in different phases of design and implementation were evaluated using a combination of HFE and Usability Engineering (UE) methods to ensure compliance with human factors design principles. In order to understand the intended use workflow and identify potential interaction pain points, failure modes, and use errors, a hierarchical task analysis (HTA) was performed. The HTA included use cases derived from interviews and observational data. Cases include user goals for interaction with the system and steps taken to achieve those goals. Tasks such as setup, use, and troubleshooting were analyzed. Participant opinions were collected through a combination of cognitive walkthroughs and system usability scale (SUS).

The research team had to take into consideration some of the unique characteristics of the veteran population during the data collection process. For example, research team members learned to be patient and empathize with participants when they were narrating their combat experiences. The team also accounted for the interview venue configuration to accommodate veterans' requests. For instance, some of the veterans preferred being interviewed with their backs to the wall to minimize the risk of being startled from behind. The research team also streamlined the registration and consent process to avoid long wait times and exposure to crowds. Finally, when feasible, a member of the team accompanied the veterans on successive bike rides (data collection efforts), fostering a bond of friendship and trust. Consequently, some of the veterans were put at ease and were willing to share their experiences and opinions about the tool's design.

### 7.3.2.1 Veteran Experiences That Shaped Design Functionalities

The findings from the focus groups and interviews relating to veterans' experiences with PTSD yielded rich information on the challenges they faced in daily life, as well as the coping mechanisms they adopted to manage their condition. In addition to mentioning hyperarousal triggers such as loud sounds and crowds, they highlighted the challenges associated with interacting with loved ones and maintaining relationships.

> [...] the greatest frustration is trying to get like your family to understand because they don't, they're not in it, so they don't know. They can only see it from their point of view. And so you try to explain like, 'Hey, this is what's happening.' And they're like, 'oh,' they'll either be like, 'okay, we'll get you through it.' Or it'd be like, 'oh this again,' like that's the kind of vibe you get. So it makes it difficult and so then [you] don't want to share because then you know, you're like, well I don't want to inconvenience you.

Veterans also mentioned that they had trouble staying motivated to complete basic tasks, impacting their self-esteem and pride.

> So, um, motivation. Sometimes I don't even want to get up, get dressed, brush my teeth, take a shower, just simple things that normal people seem to be able to just do, and it's a chore so it's hard to do it.

To cope with their condition, some veterans mentioned using relaxation and focus techniques, peer support, and technology-based tools. Some of the methods they mentioned included completing the homework assigned to them in between therapy sessions or solving a Sudoku puzzle. Others mentioned the use of biofeedback to regulate their stress levels.

> I did a treatment, it was called biometric feedback, you sit down in a very comfortable chair and you watch a screen and depending [on] how well you focus, different things happen on the screen almost like a game, I have done that; that kind of helps [...]

Veterans also mentioned using different breathing techniques and recalling positive imagery to calm down after experiencing a trigger or entering a hyper-aroused state.

> […] I just try to concentrate on my breathing, slow my breathing down, slow my heart rate down and just try to think positive thoughts […]

When discussing desirable functionalities in a technology-based intervention, veterans highlighted the need to stay connected with individuals they trusted (e.g. family, friends, military unit members) when feeling low or stressed.

> There were some dark times in my life that if the tools are there, you know how much relief you get with the simple fact that you can talk to somebody.

Veterans admitted to not seeking help or reaching out, suggesting the need for a trusted individual or caregiver to be able to track/monitor them and reach out in times of need.

> I think the best scenario is somebody contacts me […] because we are the worst at reaching out for help […]

A key functionality that veterans desired was a predictive feature. Specifically, they wanted the self-management tool to predict the onset of a hyperarousal event. They believed that an early detection and warning system would greatly improve their ability to manage their PTSD. They added that the tool would need to consider contextual factors such as location, activity, and schedule to make accurate predictions.

> But maybe if this [tool] would give me advanced warning that you know okay so maybe my heart rate kicks up to 90 out there while I'm waiting but if it tells me that when I hit like 75 or 78 or whatever when I haven't quite started to notice it yet then giving me advanced warning then I can work on calming myself down prior to the point where I start getting worked up and having these huge conversations in my head, you know.

To facilitate better self-care and treatment adherence, veterans suggested the need to move away from a traditional patient–provider relationship, to a more proactive treatment regimen. Specifically, the veterans stated that professional caregivers could: send more activities in between therapy sessions; use remote monitoring to periodically inquire about their well-being; and personalize their treatment and offer coaching based on the data shared through the tool.

> It would almost make better relationship between us and our doctor because they almost kind of personalize it, like if they call us if we have too many hits. I like to feel like somebody cares, so if somebody were to call and ask if you are okay, it feels more like someone is actually out there who cares.

Figure 7.2 illustrates the design functionalities that resulted from the thematic analysis of veteran interviews and focus groups. The findings were documented using the Functional Information Requirements (FIR) method to design veteran-centered functions, features, and display interfaces (similar to the approach used in Khanade, Sasangohar, et al., 2018).

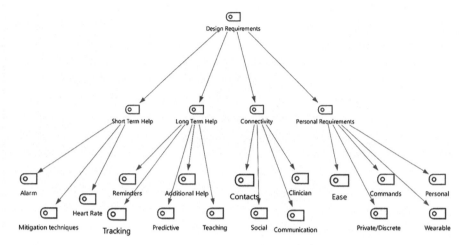

**FIGURE 7.2**   Illustrative map of the design functionalities identified.

### 7.3.2.2   Developing a Novel Stress Detection Algorithm

Our participatory ergonomics methods revealed that veterans consider continuous monitoring and detection of hyperarousals to be a major gap to enable self-management. Given the known correlation between elevated heart rate and the onset of PTSD-related hyperarousal events (Buckley et al., 2004; Dennis et al., 2016), as well as prevalence and accessibility of heart rate sensors, the team set out to develop a stress detection algorithm using the heart rate data collected. The heart rate data was preprocessed using the Kalman filter imputation approach to resolve missing data and was then used to train five machine learning algorithms: decision tree; support vector machine; random forest; neural network; and convolutional neural network. An assessment of the algorithms using the Area Under the receiver operating characteristic Curve (AUC) showed that the convolutional neural network, support vector machine, and random forests significantly outperformed a random classifier. Further analysis of the heart rate data and predictions suggested that the algorithms associate an increase in heart rate with PTSD trigger onset. Using this predictive algorithm, the device detected changes in heart rate not associated with athletics or normal activities and interacts with the wearer to help manage the onset of a PTSD trigger. Additional details regarding this algorithm can be found in McDonald et al. (2019).

### 7.3.3   Phase III: Design and Evaluation

Early in the design process, an Android watch-based prototype (Figure 7.3) that consisted of basic features, including "health status," "activity logs," "settings," and "stress reports," was used to guide users through system usage to collect subjective information on acceptance, satisfaction, and mental models. Cognitive walkthroughs were performed where intended users were encouraged to "think aloud" when interacting with the prototypes, thereby allowing the researchers to document the users' mental models. Initial feedback from usability studies suggested the need for an

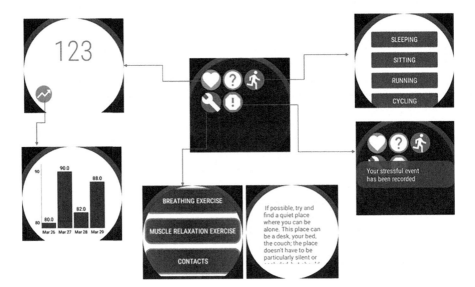

**FIGURE 7.3**   Initial prototype of PTSD support tool used in usability studies.

easier mechanism to report stressful or hyperarousal events using the watch-based app since the icon on the initial prototype was too small.

In a subsequent iteration of the interface design, a "single-tap" stress alert screen was added to facilitate quicker self-reporting. We observed increased frustration among the veterans when they accidentally tapped the stress-report screen, thereby registering a false alarm. To address this challenge the team modified the design, requiring users to tap twice in quick succession to report a hyperarousal event. This minor design change eliminated the possibility of incorrect reports, consequently improving user experience.

Given that a number of veterans in our previous studies owned Apple devices, the team also developed interfaces for iWatches (and accompanying iPhones). Figure 7.4 shows select screens from the latest version of the prototype developed for an iWatch. After several design iterations, the home screen (Figure 7.4a) for the watch provides the user the ability to access their health and heart rate information (symbolized by the heart), report stress events by tapping on the icon depicting a stressed individual, and access a suite of relaxation features shown in Figure 7.4d–7.4f. Consistent with suggestions from participants, a feedback message was provided to indicate successful stress reporting (Figure 7.4b). Further, designers leveraged the force touch option, permitting users to report a stress event without opening the app, but rather by pressing the app icon. Due to the severity of some hyperarousal events, veterans expected a way to let their loved ones know about their status with minimal efforts. Accordingly, a "broadcast location" feature was developed that allows the user to send a customized message with geographic location details to preset contacts (Figure 7.4c). Although participants in our study specifically requested a blue-color scheme (default color), users can customize the color theme.

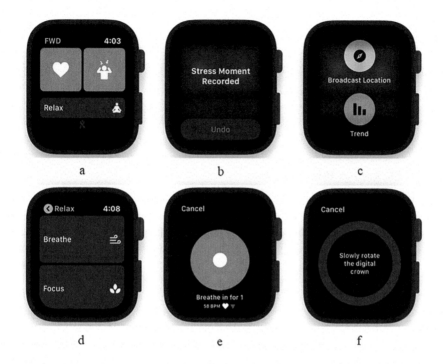

**FIGURE 7.4** Latest prototype of PTSD support tool deployed on an iWatch.

**FIGURE 7.5** Latest prototype of PTSD support tool deployed on an iPhone.

Figure 7.5 shows select screens from the latest version of the prototype designed for the companion iPhone app. The features on the home screen allow users to: access their heart rate data (depicted by the heart) and view trends over time (Figure 7.5c); take periodic self-assessments for PTSD (PCL-5), depression (PHQ-9), and anxiety (GAD-7); access contact details (depicted by the phone), as well as a customize trusted contact list (Figure 7.4b); and access relaxation features that include a suite of mindfulness exercises, as well as relaxing multimedia (Figure 7.5d). Similar to the watch, users have the option of using a two-step process to confirm broadcasting (Figure 7.5e) their location to loved ones by pressing the "Bell" button located at the bottom of Figure 7.5a–c.

## 7.4 DESIGN GUIDELINES FOR VETERANS

The case study revealed several important design considerations that should be made when designing interventions for veterans.

### 7.4.1 DESIGN FOR PERSUASIVENESS

Our studies showed that several veterans struggled to motivate themselves to perform routine self-care tasks including performing physical activities, adhering to their treatment, and communicating with professional caregivers and family. One approach we used in our studies to improve motivation levels was to incorporate "persuasive" design methodologies. Literature documents several behavioral change models that can be used to understand changes in human behavior in the context of interacting with interventions. For instance, the *Self-Efficacy* model explains how several variables including "performance accomplishments," "vicarious experience," "verbal persuasion," and "physiological states" can affect a person's beliefs as to how well they can achieve their goals. Digital behavioral change models such as Persuasive System Design (PSD) enable the designers to plan for the intended outcomes of an intervention, contexts in which users will interact with the persuasive system, and strategies to influence the user.

In the context of mHealth tools, we used personalized messaging or content tailoring (e.g. motivational message based on personality traits) and opportune timing (e.g. reminders based on user preference, activity, or usage patterns), all of which are important variables in persuasive design. Content such as motivational messages or reminders showed promise in our studies to improve utilization. These messages can also be tailored to specific user groups (e.g. military branches) to improve their effectiveness. In addition, content should be tailored to match individuals' personalities (Rammstedt & John, 2007). Research has shown that personality has a strong influence on behavior change, and adapting the messaging to an individual's personality is likely to improve engagement and compliance with the suggested (improved) behavior or lifestyle choice (Hirsh et al., 2012).

To ensure the efficacy of tailored content, it is critical to deliver this information in the appropriate context and opportune time. The decision to interact with users is triggered by the environmental context, as well as by emotional and physiological states, that can be captured by sensors on-board mobile technologies such as smartphones and smartwatches.

### 7.4.2 DESIGN FOR DISCREETNESS AND PRIVACY

Studies have shown that veterans experiencing mental health-related conditions face several challenges in reintegrating into civil society. Many of these challenges arise from difficulties related to social stigma. In particular, social stigma associated with seeking support prevents those affected from seeking formal and informal care and consequently causes them to suffer in isolation. Our patient ergonomic design study highlighted the need for discreetness. That is, veterans wanted to appear normal and did not want to attract attention to their condition. Overall, the veterans wanted a tool that would allow them to approach life without being exposed to stigma. This resulted in our approach to use off-the-shelf-products such as smartwatches and smartphones in contrast to alternative sensor arrangements or products that provided better sensitivity or bandwidth but were not discreet.

Mobile technology-based interventions such as the tool we designed are location-independent, eliminating the need for patients to travel to clinics. This may in turn reduce the feeling of stigma associated with the risk of being recognized when attending to treatment, especially in remote, rural communities. In addition, the integration of telehealth platforms with mHealth-based interventions can provide a discreet platform to interact with healthcare professionals (Ralston et al., 2019).

Several veterans, although intent on tracking their health data and sharing with care providers, expressed concerns about the security of their data both on-board the device and during transmission and storage. Therefore, designs need to account for important legal and ethical justifications for closely protecting mental health information. Although designs aim to reduce the stigmatization of mental health illness, individuals can still suffer social, psychological, and economic harm from the inappropriate use or disclosure of mental health information. Mental health information is also heavily regulated by federal and state laws. For example, the Health Insurance Portability and Accountability Act (HIPAA) restricts certain uses and disclosures of identifiable health information without an individual's authorization. Despite such challenges, voluntary participation in the exchange of health data should be enabled.

### 7.4.3 DESIGN FOR SUPPORT AND TRUST

Findings from our interactions with a wide range of veterans revealed that veterans tended to trust only a small network of "peers" and close family members. In a previous study by Rodriguez-Paras & Sasangohar (2017), participants indicated that their support group could be comprised of friends, family, members of the military, and other people in their geographic vicinity who shared similar experiences and challenges. For instance, one veteran highlighted this trust issue by saying, "Most military only trust military. And that's what I think people don't realize." This is in line with a 2006 RAND study, which found that veterans find talking with friends and colleagues more helpful in dealing with traumatic experiences and preferred to rely on other members of their unit when feeling stressed or depressed rather than turning to mental health professionals (Hosek et al., 2006). Therefore, to promote effective patient work for this population, it is imperative to allow personalization of peer groups and to facilitate access to such support system.

### 7.4.4 DESIGN OF SURROUNDINGS

Several variables related to indoor and outdoor living environments and space designs may affect veterans' mental health and poor designs may serve as triggers (Khanade,

Rodriguez-Paras, et al., 2018; Nuamah et al., 2020). For example, our studies show that maintaining situational awareness (SA) of surroundings is a key design consideration for veterans' mental health. For example, veterans expressed a strong desire to be aware of the people around them, both inside and outside the living spaces. This desire was expressed through multiple design attributes such as having access to windows or designing rooms with circular layouts. The role of architecture can be further defined by providing guidelines such as clearly labeling exits, providing appropriate window locations, and ensuring adequate ceiling heights. The construction materials need to be considered as well. For example, using clear material (e.g. glass) provides greater SA but reduces personal privacy.

### 7.4.5 DESIGN FOR ACCESSIBILITY

A term that is generally used in parallel with usability is accessibility. Accessibility is viewed as the relation between an individual and their environment and is particularly important in determining the degree to which one can independently carry out daily activities. Accessibility can have multiple dimensions including accessibility to the physical environment, to information, and to societal activities and services (Iwarsson & Ståhl, 2003). Due to the prevalence of physical disability among veterans, the need to consider physical ergonomics becomes apparent. For example, one of the veterans in our studies was an amputee (hand) and had a prosthetic limb. Despite the popularity of the reporting interface due to its simplicity, this individual reminded us about our assumption that all users can access this feature. In addition, the nature of the physical disability raises important questions about the placement of physiological sensors and the suitability of watch-based tools.

## 7.5  CONCLUSION

Almost two decades of conflicts have pushed veterans' health concerns to the forefront of public discussion. Returning combat veterans suffer from a myriad of physical and cognitive disabilities and face challenges reintegrating with the civilian society. Although traditional care approaches have provided some respite, the unique characteristics of this population (e.g. avoidance, emotional numbness, and distrust) require the pursuit of alternate care methods. A patient ergonomics approach, which accounts for micro- and macroergonomic factors, has shown promise in addressing veterans' needs. Our study illustrates the unique design challenges due to sensitivities associated with the psychosocial state of veterans with mental health or physical disability conditions. We employed a patient ergonomics approach that accounts for key factors pertinent to patient work. Through a case study, we illustrated how to systematically involve veterans and providers in the design and development of a self-management tool for PTSD by eliciting key barriers and enablers from multiple stakeholders. We defined a set of design guidelines that could further contribute to the tools that may enjoy sustainable perceived usability and acceptance among veterans. Our findings, while presenting key functionalities for a technology-based intervention, also identified key macroergonomic factors that affected veteran-centered design. During the course of this study, veterans alluded to complex relationships between the physical environment, social context, and organizational factors that impacted their self-care. Building on the current work, future research should establish the relationships between the interacting micro- and macroergonomic factors and how they affect veteran-centered design. Further, we recommend additional investigation into the roles and experiences of informal caregivers for veterans, particularly for those with mental health disorders.

## REFERENCES

Abbott, K. H., Stoller, E. P., & Rose, J. H. (2007). The structure and function of frail male veterans' informal networks. *Journal of Aging and Health, 19*(5), 757–777.

Bovin, M. J., Miller, C. J., Koenig, C. J., Lipschitz, J. M., Zamora, K. A., Wright, P. B., Pyne, J. M., & Burgess, J. F., Jr. (2018). Veterans' experiences initiating VA-based mental health care. *Psychological Services.* DOI: 10.1037/ser0000233.

Brewin, C. R., Gregory, J. D., Lipton, M., & Burgess, N. (2010). Intrusive images in psychological disorders: Characteristics, neural mechanisms, and treatment implications. *Psychological Review, 117*(1), 210.

Brown, M. C., Creel, A. H., Engel, C. C., Herrell, R. K., & Hoge, C. W. (2011). Factors associated with interest in receiving help for mental health problems in combat veterans returning from deployment to Iraq. *The Journal of Nervous and Mental Disease, 199*(10), 797–801.

Buckley, T. C., Holohan, D., Greif, J. L., Bedard, M., & Suvak, M. (2004). Twenty-four-hour ambulatory assessment of heart rate and blood pressure in chronic PTSD and non-PTSD veterans. *Journal of Traumatic Stress, 17*(2), 163–171.

Church, T. E. (2009). Returning veterans on campus with war related injuries and the long road back home. *Journal of Postsecondary Education and Disability, 22*(1), 43–52.

Corbin, J., & Strauss, A. L. (2015). *Basics of Qualitative Research.* Los Angeles, CA: SAGE.

Corrigan, P. W., & Kleinlein, P. (2005). The impact of mental illness stigma. In P. W. Corrigan (Ed.), *On the Stigma of Mental Illness: Practical Strategies for Research and Social Change* (pp. 11–44). Washington, DC: American Psychological Association.

Darkins, A., Ryan, P., Kobb, R., Foster, L., Edmonson, E., Wakefield, B., & Lancaster, A. E. (2008). Care coordination/home telehealth: The systematic implementation of health informatics, home telehealth, and disease management to support the care of veteran patients with chronic conditions. *Telemedicine Journal & E-Health, 14*, 1118–1126.

Dennis, P. A., Dedert, E. A., Van Voorhees, E. E., Watkins, L. L., Hayano, J., Calhoun, P. S., ... & Beckham, J. C. (2016). Examining the crux of autonomic dysfunction in PTSD: Whether chronic or situational distress underlies elevated heart rate and attenuated heart-rate variability. *Psychosomatic Medicine, 78*(7), 805.

Fulton, J. J., Calhoun, P. S., Wagner, H. R., Schry, A. R., Hair, L. P., Feeling, N., ... Beckham, J. C. (2015). The prevalence of posttraumatic stress disorder in Operation Enduring Freedom/Operation Iraqi Freedom (OEF/OIF) veterans: A meta-analysis. *Journal of Anxiety Disorders, 31*, 98–107.

Hautzinger, S., Howell, A., Scandlyn, J., Wool, Z. H., & Zogas, A. (2015). Costs of war. Retrieved from Watson Institute International and Public Affairs, Brown University website: https://watson.brown.edu/costsofwar/costs/human/veterans.

Henderson, C., Evans-Lacko, S., & Thornicroft, G. (2013). Mental illness stigma, help seeking, and public health programs. *American Journal of Public Health, 103*(5), 777–780.

Hirsh, J. B., Kang, S. K., & Bodenhausen, G. V. (2012). Personalized persuasion: Tailoring persuasive appeals to recipients' personality traits. *Psychological Science, 23*(6), 578–581.

Hoge, C. W., Castro, C. A., Messer, S. C., McGurk, D., Cotting, D. I., & Koffman, R. L. (2004). Combat duty in Iraq and Afghanistan, mental health problems, and barriers to care. *The New England Journal of Medicine*, *351*(1), 13–22.

Holden, R. J., Carayon, P., Gurses, A. P., Hoonakker, P., Hundt, A. S., Ozok, A. A., & Rivera-Rodriguez, A. J. (2013). SEIPS 2.0: A human factors framework for studying and improving the work of healthcare professionals and patients. *Ergonomics*, *56*(11), 1669–1686.

Holden, R.J., & Mickelson, R.S., (2013). Performance barriers among elderly chronic heart failure patients: an application of patient-engaged human factors and ergonomics. *Proceedings of the Human Factors and Ergonomics Society Annual Meeting*, *57*(1), 758–762.

Holden, R. J., Schubert, C. C., & Mickelson, R. S. (2015). The patient work system: An analysis of self-care performance barriers among elderly heart failure patients and their informal caregivers. *Applied Ergonomics*, 47, 133–150.

Holden, R. J., Valdez, R. S., Schubert, C. C., Thompson, M. J., & Hundt, A. S. (2017). Macroergonomic factors in the patient work system: Examining the context of patients with chronic illness. *Ergonomics*, *60*(1), 26–43.

Holden, R. J., & Valdez, R. S. (2018). Town hall on patient-centered human factors and ergonomics. *Proceedings of the Human Factors and Ergonomics Society Annual Meeting*, *62*(1), 465–468.

Hosek, J., Kavanagh, J. E., & Miller, L. L. (2006). *How Deployments Affect Service Members*. Santa Monica, CA: RAND Corporation.

Institute of Medicine and National Research Council. (2007). *PTSD Compensation and Military Service*. Washington, DC: The National Academies Press.

Iwarsson, S., & Ståhl, A. (2003). Accessibility, usability and universal design—Positioning and definition of concepts describing person-environment relationships. *Disability and Rehabilitation*, *25*(2), 57–66.

Kessler, R. C. (1995). Posttraumatic stress disorder in the National Comorbidity Survey. *Archives of General Psychiatry*, *52*(12), 1048.

Khanade, K., Rodriguez-Paras, C., Sasangohar, F., Lawley, S. (2018). Investigating architectural and space design considerations for post-traumatic stress disorder (PTSD) patients. *Proceedings of the Human Factors and Ergonomics Society Annual Meeting*, *62*(1), 1722–1726. Los Angeles, CA: SAGE Publications.

Khanade, K., Sasangohar, F., Sutherland, S. C., & Alexander, K. E. (2018). Deriving information requirements for a smart nursing system for intensive care units. *Critical Care Nursing Quarterly*, *41*(1), 29–37.

Lew, H. L., Otis, J. D., Tun, C., Kerns, R. D., Clark, M. E., & Cifu, D. X. (2009). Prevalence of chronic pain, posttraumatic stress disorder, and persistent postconcussive symptoms in OIF/OEF veterans: Polytrauma clinical trial. *Journal of Rehabilitation Research & Development*, *46*(6), 697–702.

McDonald, A. D., Sasangohar, F., Jatav, A., & Rao, A. H. (2019). Continuous monitoring and detection of post-traumatic stress disorder (PTSD) triggers among veterans: A supervised machine learning approach. *Institute of Industrial and Systems Engineers Transactions on Healthcare Systems Engineering*, *9*(3), 201–211.

Miles, M. B., & Huberman, M. (1994). *Qualitative Data Analysis: An Expanded Sourcebook*. Los Angeles, CA: SAGE.

Moon, J., Rodriguez-Paras, C., Sasangohar, F., Benzer, J. K., & Kum, H.-C. (2018). Modeling patient-centered pathways of the current PTSD care system. Abstract presented at *the HSPIC'18: The Healthcare Systems Process Improvement Conference*, Atlanta, GA.

Moon, J., Smith, A., Sasangohar, F., Benzer, J. K., & Kum, H.-C. (2017). A descriptive model of the current PTSD care system: Identifying opportunities for improvement. *Proceedings of the International Symposium on Human Factors and Ergonomics in Health Care*, *6*(1), 251.

National Council on Disability. (2009). *Invisible wounds: Serving service members and veterans with PTSD and TBI*. Retrieved from https://ncd.gov/rawmedia_repository/veterans.pdf.

Nuamah, J., Rodriguez-Paras, C., Sasangohar, F. (2020). Veteran-centered investigation of architectural and space design considerations for post-traumatic stress disorder (PTSD). *Health Environments Research & Design Journal*. Manuscript submitted for publication (HERD-19-0109). DOI: 10.1177/1937586720925554.

Owens, B. D., Kragh Jr, J. F., Macaitis, J., Svoboda, S. J., & Wenke, J. C. (2007). Characterization of extremity wounds in operation Iraqi freedom and operation enduring freedom. *Journal of Orthopaedic Trauma, 21*(4), 254–257.

Pietrzak, R. H., Johnson, D. C., Goldstein, M. B., Malley, J. C., & Southwick, S. M. (2009). Perceived stigma and barriers to mental health care utilization among OEF-OIF veterans. *Psychiatric Services, 60*(8), 1118–1122.

Plach, H.L., & Sells, C.H. (2013). Occupational performance needs of young veterans. *American Journal of Occupational Therapy, 67*, 73–81.

Ralston, A. L., Andrews, A. R. III, & Hope, D. A. (2019). Fulfilling the promise of mental health technology to reduce public health disparities: Review and research agenda. *Clinical Psychology: Science and Practice, 26*(1), e12277.

Rammstedt, B., & John, O. P. (2007). Measuring personality in one minute or less: A 10-item short version of the Big Five Inventory in English and German. *Journal of Research in Personality, 41*(1), 203–212.

Robbins, C. B., Vreeman, D. J., Sothmann, M. S., Wilson, S. L., & Oldridge, N. B. (2009). A review of the long-term health outcomes associated with war-related amputation. *Military Medicine, 174*(6), 588–592.

Robinson-Whelen, S., & Rintala, D. H. (2003). Informal care providers for veterans with SCI: Who are they and how are they doing? *Journal of Rehabilitation Research & Development, 40*(6), 511–516.

Rodriguez-Paras, C., & Sasangohar, F. (2017). Usability assessment of a post-traumatic stress disorder (PTSD) mHealth app. *Proceedings of the Human Factors and Ergonomics Society Annual Meeting, 61*(1), 1824–1828.

Rodriguez-Paras, C., Tippey, K., Brown, E., Sasangohar, F., Creech, S., Kum, H.-C., . . . Benzer, J. K. (2017). Posttraumatic stress disorder and mobile health: App investigation and scoping literature review. *Journal of Medical Internet Research mHealth and uHealth, 5*(10), e156.

Sasangohar, F., Peres, S. C., Williams, J. P., Smith, A., & Mannan, M. S. (2018). Investigating written procedures in process safety: Qualitative data analysis of interviews from high risk facilities. *Process Safety and Environmental Protection, 113*, 30–39.

Seal, K. H., Bertenthal, D., Miner, C. R., Sen, S., & Marmar, C. (2007). Bringing the war back home: Mental health disorders among 103 788 US veterans returning from Iraq and Afghanistan seen at Department of Veterans Affairs Facilities. *Archives of Internal Medicine, 167*(5), 476–482.

Sherman, R. A., & Sherman, C. J. (1983). Prevalence and characteristics of chronic phantom limb pain among American veterans. Results of a trial survey. *American Journal of Physical Medicine, 62*(5), 227–238.

Sledjeski, E. M., Speisman, B., & Dierker, L. C. (2008). Does number of lifetime traumas explain the relationship between PTSD and chronic medical conditions? Answers from the National Comorbidity Survey-Replication (NCS-R). *Journal of Behavioral Medicine, 31*(4), 341–349.

Smurr, L. M., Gulick, K., Yancosek, K., & Ganz, O. (2008). Managing the upper extremity amputee: a protocol for success. *Journal of Hand Therapy, 21*(2), 160–176.

Tanielian, T., & Jaycox, L. H. (Eds.). (2008). *Invisible Wounds of War: Psychological and Cognitive Injuries, Their Consequences, and Services to Assist Recovery*. Santa Monica, CA: RAND Corporation.

Thomas, L. P. M., Palinkas, L. A., Meier, E. A., Iglewicz, A., Kirkland, T., & Zisook, S. (2014). Yearning to be heard: What veterans teach us about suicide risk and effective interventions. *Crisis: The Journal of Crisis Intervention and Suicide Prevention*, 35(3), 161–167.

U.S. Department of Veterans Affairs. (2019). Suicide risk and risk of death among recent veterans - Public health. Retrieved July 28, 2019, from https://www.publichealth.va.gov/epidemiology/studies/suicide-risk-death-risk-recent-veterans.asp.

Valdez, R. S., Holden, R. J., Novak, L. L., & Veinot, T. C. (2015). Transforming consumer health informatics through a patient work framework: Connecting patients to context. *Journal of the American Medical Informatics Association*, 22(1), 2–10.

Van Houtven, C. H., Oddone, E. Z., & Weinberger, M. (2010). Informal and formal care infrastructure and perceived need for caregiver training for frail US veterans referred to home and community-based services. *Chronic Illness*, 6(1), 57–66.

Vogt, D., Bergeron, A., Salgado, D., Daley, J., Ouimette, P., & Wolfe, J. (2006). Barriers to Veterans Health Administration care in a nationally representative sample of women veterans. *Journal of General Internal Medicine*, 21(3), S19–S25.

Wakefield, B. J., Hayes, J., Boren, S. A., Pak, Y., & Davis, J. W. (2012). Strain and satisfaction in caregivers of veterans with chronic illness. *Research in Nursing & Health*, 35(1), 55–69.

Wade, M. (2013). Brain injury and stress disorder strong indicators of vision problems for veterans. *Insight (American Society of Ophthalmic Registered Nurses)*, 38(1), 22.

# 8 Patient Ergonomics in Pediatric Settings

*Siddarth Ponnala*
Center for Healthcare Quality and Analytics,
Children's Hospital of Philadelphia

*Orysia Bezpalko*
Center for Healthcare Quality and Analytics,
Children's Hospital of Philadelphia

*Ethan Larsen*
Center for Healthcare Quality and Analytics; Department
of Radiology, Children's Hospital of Philadelphia

*James Won*
Center for Healthcare Quality and Analytics, Children's
Hospital of Philadelphia; Department of Pediatrics,
Perelman School of Medicine, University of Pennsylvania

## CONTENTS

Patient ergonomics, or the study of work done by patients and their nonprofessional caregivers to support health-related goals (Holden et al., 2020), is particularly important to understand in the pediatric population due to the overwhelming involvement of patients' nonprofessional caregivers in health management. Compared to the adult population, pediatric patients have several constraints to self-management of health care such as cognitive capabilities, legal requirements, and rapidly evolving anatomies (Larcher, 2017; Stille et al., 2010). Pediatric patients typically cannot independently make healthcare decisions without the support of nonprofessional caregivers (i.e. family members or legal guardians). Therefore, family members of pediatric patients and other nonprofessional caregivers are an integral part of health management. Further, there are state and federal laws that require the active involvement of nonprofessional caregivers in pediatric health management. The combination of patient and work system factors that influence health management lends to the importance of considerations for patient ergonomics in the pediatric population. In this chapter, we discuss the following with respect to patient ergonomics: (1) differences between the adult and pediatric populations; (2) the relevant sociotechnical system context of pediatric health management; and (3) various roles and settings that present challenges in this domain. Further, we present four case studies to demonstrate the complexities of patient ergonomics in pediatric healthcare settings.

## 8.1 DIFFERENCES BETWEEN ADULT AND PEDIATRIC HEALTH CARE

There is a well-known adage in medicine: children are not small adults. Children differ from adults across multiple domains, including anatomy, physiology, and psychology, and as such have unique needs and risks when it comes to health care (Foster & Lyall, 2015; Klassen et al., 2008). As pediatric health care encompasses a wide range of services to an even broader population, commonly ranging from neonates to young adults, it is important to consider these different characteristics and how they impact the care provided.

### 8.1.1 COGNITIVE AND PSYCHOLOGICAL CHARACTERISTICS

Cognitive development occurs in a series of stages in children (Larcher, 2017), and as such, a broad range of cognitive and functional abilities are captured in the overall population of pediatric patients, including a significant portion that are not fully developed (e.g., infants). In the early years of their life, pediatric patients are unable to independently make decisions about their own health care and are therefore dependent on the active support of a parent or legal guardian. However, as children develop into adolescents, they typically take on more self-care responsibilities, relieving their caregivers of some care-related tasks.

In acute care settings for younger children, a parent or legal guardian serves as the firsthand source of information in constant communication with various healthcare professionals, recalling patient history and sharing relevant information to inform appropriate diagnosis and to ensure the highest quality care (Gallo et al., 2016). In adolescent populations, the patient may be increasingly involved and capable of communicating independently with healthcare professionals regarding their health history. In addition, patients and families take part in the biographical work associated with managing the trajectory of chronic illnesses (Corbin & Strauss, 1985), whereas in adult populations, nonprofessional caregivers may not be as involved. Parents and guardians can also serve as the interpreter of their child's feelings and behaviors to healthcare professionals, and in fact, studies have shown that the majority of dialogue in a pediatric primary care setting occurs between the physician and the adult nonprofessional care provider (van Staa, 2011).

Parents and legal guardians play a critical role in maintaining the health of their children within and beyond the acute care setting. Pediatric health care, thus, extends the concept of the patient-centered medical home and instead requires a vision of a family-centered medical home to ensure that the health and functioning of the entire family are maintained in order to provide high quality care for the child (Stille et al., 2010). In other words, pediatric healthcare providers must keep the family's health in mind as well as that of the child since the adult caregiver is typically highly engaged in the child's patient work as well as their own.

Children's dependency on the adults in their lives extends beyond the family unit to include other childcare providers such as teachers, creating a need for increased collaboration between the healthcare and education sectors that does not exist for adult populations (Larcher, 2017). Early education centers and schools are intrinsically linked to both the management of chronic health conditions and the ongoing emotional and psychological development of children, and so care coordination in pediatrics must also be extended to include those environments. These additional adults also become part of the patient work paradigm in pediatric health care—they engage actively in maintaining the health and well-being of the child, even if they are not directly present in the doctor's office or the hospital room. Although not always professionally trained to address health-related concerns, teachers and other nonprofessional care partners have to maintain a synchronous communication pattern with parents to manage care of a pediatric patient. In contrast, adult are likely to experience more autonomy in managing their health-related needs in school- or work-related settings.

Finally, pediatric health care is distinct from adult health care in that the patient's cognitive abilities grow and develop over time. Infants and toddlers have minimal autonomy and are heavily dependent on their parents and caregivers, but as children age and become adolescents and young adults, their cognitive development increases. As such, pediatric health care must recognize the increasing role that patients can play in their own care as they mature and must adjust care structures and expectations accordingly. The active role of the adult caregiver must adapt over time to not only support, but also include, pediatric patients in their own care as they grow and mature—in fact, there is evidence to suggest that children who are not involved in their medical care would like more say in the matter (van Staa, 2011).

When children grow into adolescents, their roles in self-care management may evolve (Shumow et al., 2009). Adult caregivers have the opportunity to redistribute care management tasks among their child or other caregivers. Adolescents have the ability to take on more self-care tasks that may no longer need to be supervised or guided by adult caregivers. In addition, adolescents who attend school outside their home settings do not always have the same surveillance they did as a young child, forcing them to take on certain basic responsibilities such as hydration and nutrition intake.

## 8.1.2 LEGAL REQUIREMENTS

A majority of pediatric patients are under the age of 18 and therefore are considered minors by law. As such, unemancipated minors rely on their parents or legal guardians for critical decision-making regarding their medical care; this differs significantly from adult care, in which the patient is legally independent and autonomous in their decision-making unless they have delegated that right to another adult (Jeremic et al., 2016; Kuther, 2003). Further, hospitals are charged with obtaining consent from parents/guardians to mitigate some of the risks and liabilities associated with provision of health care. For those reasons, much of the patient work in pediatric settings requires the involvement of parents or legal guardians, whereas it is typically self-managed in adult settings.

## 8.1.3 PATIENT ANATOMY AND PHYSIOLOGY

Pediatric patients have distinct and changing anatomical and physiological characteristics from their adult counterparts. These differing characteristics present several challenges to delivering health care and therefore require the support of patient ergonomics.

Size and anatomic development play important roles in the type of care provided and the manner in which that care is provided; for example, medication dosing varies greatly within different age and size groups in pediatric patients, and the impact of an improper dose can be catastrophic in a child as compared to an adult due to differing pharmacodynamics (Rowe et al., 1998). Another example includes pediatric characteristics such as narrow airways and disproportionate body masses (Scanlon et al., 2006). To support complex procedures with these physiological characteristics that are less common in the adult population, family caregivers take on a substantial amount of the coordination and communication work in the pediatric population.

Pediatric patient anatomies also play an important role in the self-management of simple tasks such as medication administration in the home environment. Imagine a five-year-old patient who needs cough syrup that can be purchased over-the-counter. The patient can neither drive themselves to the nearest store to buy the cough syrup, nor open the bottle of cough syrup and pour out the appropriate amount of syrup to be consumed. A pediatric patient's anatomy (in addition to their developing cognitive abilities) is a limiting factor in this scenario as they would not typically have the fine motor skills required to take the safeguard off the cough syrup bottle and precisely pour the correct amount of syrup into the cup for consumption. Given the anatomical limitations, the responsibility of administering cough syrup falls on a nonprofessional caregiver, whereas in the adult population this task can typically be self-managed.

## 8.2 PATIENT ERGONOMICS IN SOCIOTECHNICAL SYSTEMS

Sociotechnical work systems scholars have demonstrated success in modeling and understanding the complex interactions of modern health care and would be suitable to utilize for pediatric patient centric design (Carayon, 2006; Holden et al., 2015, 2017; Sittig & Singh, 2015; Valdez et al., 2014). Sociotechnical work systems models provide a means to categorize components of a complex work environment into specific domains and analyze the interactions that cross the domains. Although several versions of sociotechnical work systems models exist, the Systems Engineering Initiative for Patient Safety (SEIPS) model has seen significant use and subsequent modification in the healthcare domain (Carayon et al., 2006).

There are few studies holistically evaluating pediatric medicine from a sociotechnical perspective, which have examined specific components and interactions as they relate to pediatrics. Ratwani et al. (2016) found that improper design support for pediatric patients in the electronic health record (EHR) had a significant impact on correct dosing and identification of medication-related errors to avoid patient harm. However, this study and others using a sociotechnical systems approach in the pediatric population have primarily focused on professional work. Thus, there are several opportunities to understand the implications of EHR design on patient work.

On a larger scale, pediatric trauma care has been evaluated from a sociotechnical perspective. Although the study found that pediatric trauma care consists of a complex system of interactions across domains, roles, and technologies (Wooldridge et al., 2019), the study was predominantly focused on the providers of medical care in the professional sense. The patients and their families were acknowledged as not being included in the study, and their incorporation is recognized as areas for future work. The authors also acknowledge other findings that show parent involvement is often preferred and has a definite benefit to the quality of care and communication (Meeks, 2009; O'Connell et al., 2007; Wooldridge et al., 2019).

The literature on patient work in pediatrics is sparse and a developing area of ergonomics (Valdez et al., 2020). However, the geriatric population has characteristics similar to that of pediatrics. Given the potential commonalities between geriatric and pediatric care, some of the prior works examining the role of the geriatric patient in their care could be utilized as a foundation for exploration in the pediatric space. Unlike the pediatric space, the study of the role of geriatric patients within the sociotechnical work system has been established in 2015 and 2017 works by Holden et al. (2015, 2017). With a focus on both the patient and their informal caregivers, typically family, and their place within the sociotechnical work system, Holden et al. provide an initial model for the pediatric-oriented designer to follow. The key feature of the proposed patient-centric work system is the combination of the patient, healthcare provider, and the nonprofessional caregiver role at the center (Holden et al., 2015).

As noted in the previous sections, there have been studies examining the roles of parents and other nonprofessional caregivers in pediatric healthcare delivery. A bulk of studies have occurred primarily in high-risk pediatric environments such as intensive care units and operating rooms, as well as in high-risk procedures such as resuscitations (Bhat et al., 2016; Okonkwo et al., 2016; Sutherland et al., 2019). There have been studies conducted around usability testing and design of software and hardware in other contexts also (Cheng et al., 2020; Reid et al., 2017). However, there are several opportunities to understand the roles of patients and informal caregivers and how they shape patient care processes and outcomes.

A systematic review of Human Factors/Ergonomics (HF/E) interventions in the pediatric population revealed two studies that have touched on patient work (Ponnala & Rivera, 2019). One study examined patient and family members' experiences in an operating room waiting area (Margolies et al., 2015). This study aimed to understand the best placement of wall monitors in an operating room's waiting room. Patient status monitors continually communicate the progress of a patient in both simple and complex procedures to staff and family members. Readily having access to information on hand in convenient locations has been associated with improved anxiety levels and satisfaction of family members waiting for their loved ones in pediatric settings (O'neill et al., 2004).

Another study examined family-centered rounding with a multi-stakeholder collaboration inclusive of both clinicians and patients (Xie et al., 2015). This study found that it was important to have the voice of a parent in healthcare improvement projects, such as family-centered rounding, given their involvement in the healthcare delivery process. Family members of pediatric patients are able to fill in gaps of missing information, which can be crucial to inform appropriate clinical decision-making. Although it has been recognized that the roles of family members are important, there still remains opportunity to understand the patient work performed by nonprofessional caregivers to support family-centered rounds.

The opportunity to study and design for patient ergonomics expands across many healthcare services and a broad range of nonprofessional caregiver roles. Each service line in an acute care setting, ranging from the emergency department, to the operating room, to intensive care units, is designed to serve a unique purpose. All of the service lines in pediatric settings require some level of involvement from the patient's nonprofessional caregivers. However, the patient work done by nonprofessional caregivers may change based on the service line. In addition, there are several roles including parents, guardians, siblings, teachers, and childcare services that contribute to healthcare delivery outside the acute care setting. The interaction between the caregiver and patient may also be a source of variation for patient work. Therefore, using a sociotechnical systems approach to account for patient ergonomics in work system design has the potential to improve the quality of care delivered in pediatric settings and multiple outcomes of interest such as patient safety, equitable care, and satisfaction.

## 8.3  CASE STUDIES OF PATIENT ERGONOMICS

### 8.3.1  FAMILY-CENTERED ROUNDS

One specific example that highlights the importance of patient ergonomics is the implementation of Family-Centered Rounds (FCR) and the unique challenge in a pediatric setting of incorporating not only the patient, but in many cases, the parents and/or family of the patient into the process. FCR are defined as "interdisciplinary work rounds at the bedside in which the patient and family share in the control of the management plan as well as in the evaluation of the process itself" (Sisterhen et al., 2007, p. 320). Thus, FCR are a form of collaborative work between clinicians and family members. Many hospitals have embarked upon initiatives to develop FCR, in which the parent and/or family participates in the medical team rounding process as a partner to the team in order to provide the best care for patients. Although strategies have been developed for improving FCR (Xie et al., 2012), further work is needed to maximize its effectiveness.

At one children's hospital, HF/E was leveraged to provide insight into improving FCR. Observations and questionnaire data were used to identify barriers and challenges. These included physical constraints of the rounding environment, the short duration of rounds, the lack of formal training for providers on conducting FCR, and lastly, the willingness and ability of family members to participate in the daily rounds. Although families in general have indicated their satisfaction with the level of family-centered care at the hospital, no formal studies or surveys had been conducted to evaluate family involvement in the rounding process.

This study aimed to test the hypothesis that the reason for the low level of family involvement was due to a misalignment of expectations regarding the rounding process between clinicians and families. Observations and interviews with family members revealed that the rounding environment was not friendly to family participation in several aspects. First, since the rounds were conducted in the hallway, parents who did not want to or could not leave their child were not able to participate. Second, the clinical team used medical terminology throughout their discussion, except when the patient's parent, if present, was directly addressed. These brief moments of direct parent–clinician interaction were when the resident physician, acting as an intermediary, translated the medical verbiage used into layman terms that could be easily understood. These observations confirmed previous studies that showed FCR gives family members the opportunity to participate but does not guarantee their involvement, and the success of communication is often dependent on how much the professional care team uses real-world, understandable terminology (Subramony et al., 2014; Xie et al., 2012)

Focus groups and surveys were conducted concurrently with family members. Survey results revealed several information gaps, and family members in focus groups indicated that they did not fully understand both the rounding structure and the discussions during rounds. First of all, most families were neither familiar with the medical team caring for their child nor aware of the different roles of the members on the team. In addition, many were unaware of the FCR process and how their participation would improve their child's care and hence lacked incentive to participate actively in rounds. With respect to a potential knowledge gap, surveys with both families and clinicians showed a clear knowledge gap between families and clinicians on various items, such as the child's diet, vital signs, and the roles and experience levels of members of the clinical team.

Based on the data, two interventions were developed to improve communication between families and the rounding team: a standard family-centered rounding template and automated patient room screensavers. A simplified cognitive walkthrough process was conducted with both clinicians and family members to develop the rounding template, with the goal of better aligning their respective mental models. For clinicians, an automatically filled template with information retrieved from the EHR, and more specifically the progress notes, would be available to them in preparation of the rounding process. A simplified version of this same template, organized in the same structure, but with section headers and descriptions, would be given to families interested in attending FCR. This template would not only allow families to become familiar with the process, but also provide them a visual aid to follow along during FCR. Given that the template mirrored the current mental model of rounding for clinicians and would be automatically filled for the clinical team, the overall feedback was positive, and most clinicians expressed trust in the information as well as an inclination to use it. For families, the template as a handout would directly connect the information presented during rounds with their novice mental model of the rounding process. The template kept the families aligned with the discussions and prepared them to be more comfortable and able to speak up and provide input. Anecdotally, families had positive feedback regarding the template and indicated having a higher level of awareness and comfort during discussions.

In addition to revised templates, an automated patient room screensaver was proposed as a solution that could deliver information and messages to families without increasing the workload of the clinical team. Labor and time-intensive methods such as orientations and information sessions were assessed as infeasible, whereas traditional print media such as handouts were less than ideal with respect to usability and capturing attention. The automated patient room screensaver provided the following benefits. One, it is computer-based, which means algorithms can be built-in to automatically retrieve information from the hospital database. In this way, very little maintenance is required from the clinical team once the system is established. As the screen slides cycle through, families can choose to look at it at their leisure. Moreover, as a digital media tool, technology can be utilized to make the information easy to perceive and comprehend. Spatial layout of the information was designed to help families easily understand the process of rounds and introduce the clinical team. Slides contained various types of information, including pictures, roles, background, and fun facts about each member of the team. An animated visualization of FCR was developed to hold their attention and make it easier to understand. Lastly, font and text for all of the screensaver slides were designed with consideration of the typical visual angle for the patient and family members. Overall, the feedback was positive, and family members appreciated having the ability to easily view the information while waiting in the patient room.

### 8.3.2 Harm Prevention

There are several factors that make pediatric health care unique and challenging from a harm prevention standpoint. Pediatric patients engage in developmentally appropriate behaviors that create special considerations in the patient environment. Hospitalized children are still children and therefore engage in appropriate play using toys that are often brought into their hospital room and can be transported from room to room. Pediatric facilities typically have patient playrooms on inpatient units, as well as a number of activities such as music therapy or art therapy in which groups of children will participate. Furthermore, hospitalized children often have frequent visitors (family members, siblings, other children) who may shed viruses from the outside environment. These dynamics place hospitalized children at a high risk for health-care-associated viral infections (HAVIs), falls, and other hospital-acquired events of harm (DiGerolamo & Davis, 2017; Hei et al., 2018).

To reduce the risk of both HAVIs and falls, environmental cleanliness is key. Pediatric hospitals experience challenges to environmental cleanliness distinct from their adult counterparts due to the nature of pediatric health care. Although adult patients have family members and friends who visit with them in the hospital, they less frequently have someone staying with them for the entire duration of their stay—some adult hospitals only allow for overnight visitors when special exceptions are made. Pediatric patients, on the other hand, inherently require at least one adult caregiver to participate in the work of providing health care, and so it is much more common to have family members living in the hospital with the patient for the duration of their stay. Clothing, toys, and other family belongings may accumulate in the room and make it difficult for environmental services to do a thorough room clean. In addition, these improperly stored belongings may create an increased tripping hazard. The responsibility to maintain a clean, clutter-free environment is typically shared between clinical staff and the parent or guardian, adding another physical and cognitive task to their ongoing patient work in the healthcare environment.

To address barriers to environmental cleanliness on an inpatient oncology floor in a pediatric hospital, a human factors assessment was performed. First, real-time data were collected by the environmental services team through observations to understand which areas of the room they were unable to clean and for what reason. Observations were also performed on the unit to identify focal areas of clutter. Family feedback on perceptions of cleaning expectations and on challenges with maintaining room cleanliness was solicited via in-person conversations. Staff feedback on the same was collected using an online survey. Following this data collection phase, the central issue was validated: environmental services were unable to adequately clean many rooms due to both patient/family belongings and staff supplies. Contributing factors were also identified:

- Lack of identified space for families to store their belongings (many belongings were stored on windowsill as a result)
- Inconsistent education and communication for families regarding room clutter
- Lack of counter space for staff to keep supplies
- Computers in room that were unused and taking up counter space
- An excess of toys in the room when patients are on isolation precautions and unable to go to the playroom

Based on this assessment, several HF/E interventions were proposed, based on the concept of shared situation awareness. Situation awareness is defined as "perception of the elements in the environment within a volume of time and space, the comprehension of their meaning, and the projection of their status in the near future" (Endsley, 1987, p. 1389). The assessment showed that there was a lack of situation awareness for *all* members of the system: nursing, environmental services, and patients/families. Patient and family considerations were critical in this assessment. For example, due to room layout, families could not perceive which locations were available for them to store their belongings. In addition, due to inconsistent education, their understanding was not clear on what they could and could not do, and they could not project to future states, such as when cleaning would occur. This assessment led to HF/E interventions from three different perspectives:

1. *Environmental cues and design affordance* "Family storage zones" were developed for the windowsill, clearly marked off with a standard bin for storage. In addition, clear plastic totes were provided for storage, and unused desktop computers were removed to create more storage options for families.

2. *Education* Proposal to redesign the educational documentation for families to be more visual to account for potential language barriers and to facilitate comprehension of the policies.
3. *Technology* Proposal to develop an "open-table"-like mobile application, to allow shared situation awareness for families and environmental services with regard to cleaning time. Such a tool would allow parents to reschedule their cleaning time slot, and by allowing better prediction of the cleaning time, parents would be able to organize their belongings to allow more effective cleaning by environmental services.

These interventions took into account key pediatric-focused considerations from the physical, cognitive, and macroergonomic perspectives: education and signage needed to be designed in a way that it could be seen and understood by patients and families from a variety of backgrounds as they navigated the physical space of the hospital room; the physical environment needed to be altered such that policies could be easily followed by staff, patients, and families alike; and shared situation awareness needed to be facilitated among the staff, patients, and families via the mobile technology platform.

## 8.4 FUTURE DIRECTIONS

### 8.4.1 TELEHEALTH

Telehealth, or the use of technology to facilitate healthcare interactions between patients and providers (Tuckson et al., 2017), has been very useful for hospitals throughout the United States for optimizing staffing resources such as providers and staff to deliver timely healthcare services to patients remotely. Whereas in an adult care setting, the coordination work involved in scheduling a time for a telehealth consult, setting up the device, configuring the software, and participating in the telehealth visit mostly involves the clinicians and the patients, the pediatric population requires many more resources. To conduct a telehealth consultation for a pediatric patient, multiple nonprofessional caregivers such as one or more parents are involved in the visit. They are tasked with the coordination work involved in scheduling the appointment, which typically requires checking email, text messages, or taking phone calls. Nonprofessional caregivers also have to learn how to use hardware and software to actually attend the telehealth visit. Further, nonprofessional caregivers may also need to assist with a visual assessment of the patient during the telehealth consult and relay relevant clinical information to the providers, which they are not trained to do.

Specifically, telehealth has been useful in the context of pediatric neurology (Rametta et al., 2020). Often times in neurology, the clinical assessment can be done visually or without getting "hands on" with the patient and thus was well suited for the use of telehealth. The success of telehealth in neurology can be attributed to team efforts by the patient, caregivers, and providers. Although the provider remotely guided patients through certain motions for the visual assessment, informal caregivers were essential to the encounter. Caregivers were necessary to orient the camera or device toward the patient, restrict toddlers and younger children from moving around in the visit, and even communicate and motivate young children to cooperate with the tasks of the provider (e.g., opening/closing eyes, mouth, smelling various things). There are many opportunities in telehealth to streamline and support the processes to reduce the workload on patients and caregivers.

The complexity of tasks involved with telehealth-mediated healthcare delivery requires significant involvement of the patient and nonprofessional caregivers in the pediatric population. There may be several barriers such as technological proficiencies, distributed information, and clinical terminology that family members need to navigate through to ensure the success of a telehealth visit. There are many opportunities to consider the patient ergonomics of telehealth to deliver the highest-quality care to the pediatric population in a timely manner.

## 8.4.2 RADIOLOGY

A pediatric radiology department has several opportunities for patient ergonomics-centered improvement. Many of the care activities involve the parents playing an active role in preparing the patient for care and in some cases providing a calming presence during scans. As part of certain scans and some patients' ages and conditions, the patient needs to be sedated or under general anesthesia. These orders are often in place due to the requirement that the patient remains still during the scan. Home caregivers are relied upon to help prepare the patient for anesthesia, which includes fasting in the prescribed period before the exam. Parents will sometimes claim their child can remain still for the scan despite department age guidelines. If allowed and the patient becomes agitated, the entire day's schedule has to be rearranged to accommodate an unplanned anesthesia as the scan session runs longer than anticipated.

In cases such as magnetic resonance imaging scans, the patient needs to be physically screened for metal prior to being brought into the exam room. In both cases, the parents are relied upon to support the process. In the metal screening case, many common items used in childcare containing metal, such as safety pins, can be present and are often small enough to not trigger the metal detection wands and sensors. These items, however, will create image artifacts on the scan and there is risk of a metal object becoming a projectile. Any instance of a metal object entering the scanner room is also considered a serious safety event.

Throughout the hospital, portable imaging machines bring radiology services to patient rooms for patients who are unable to travel to the radiology department. Though the portable machines usually have a trade-off in image quality, their convenience makes them the best option for some patient populations. When the technologist arrives for the requested portable study, the parents or guardians present are again engaged in the care process to assist with positioning and identity confirmation of the patient.

Patient-centered operations are already present in pediatric radiology departments. However, they have not been examined or streamlined from a human factors perspective. At present, they are implemented ad hoc by the personnel of the department, and in many cases they are situationally implemented, not regulated, designs. Formal patient-centered human factors design could be highly beneficial to radiology processes.

## 8.5  CONCLUSION

HF/E is becoming rapidly integrated into healthcare quality/safety, but more attention needs to be paid on how to customize its application based on the patient population in question and its specific attributes and risk factors. In pediatrics, this process is already underway—Solutions for Patient Safety, a collaboration of over 100 pediatric hospitals working together to create safer care processes for hospitalized children, recently initiated a human factors-specific workgroup for HF/E practitioners in pediatric hospitals to come together to discuss how to better leverage the field in the pediatric healthcare setting. Through these efforts, HF/E applications in pediatric care will ideally become more commonplace and more targeted. Traditional human factors perspectives and methodologies, such as sociotechnical systems, knowledge elicitation, and cognitive task analysis, have been successfully used with clinicians and hospital staff in a variety of research settings and quality improvement projects. The aforementioned examples show the effectiveness and importance of applying these HF/E principles with the patient family. This participatory framework is essential in pediatric settings.

At Children's Hospital of Philadelphia (CHOP), systems are in place to further the concept of patient work involving families in the care of patients. CHOP has developed a robust Family Partners Program to ensure that the family voice is represented in every aspect of improvement and safety work, from discovery through implementation (Kratchman et al., 2015). Family consultants, parents of children who are cared for at CHOP, are staff members who provide the family voice and perspective by working strategically with clinical, operational, and improvement teams in identifying, developing, and implementing tests of change. This includes gathering feedback from families through the Family Partners Program and the hospital's Family Advisory Council.

Although these existing systems have been very effective at ensuring family participation, they have not yet been utilized to further the concept of patient work involving families. However, as HF/E initiatives become more embedded across all areas of the organization, it has been shown that there is a critical role for Family Partners in the HF/E process and in collectively building out the formal structure of patient work involving family in the care of patients. It is clear that the system infrastructure can, and should, evolve to support this next phase of family integration through the patient ergonomics approach.

## REFERENCES

Bhat, A., Bhat, M., Kumar, V., Kumar, R., Mittal, R., & Saksena, G. (2016). Comparison of variables affecting the surgical outcomes of tubularized incised plate urethroplasty in adult and pediatric hypospadias. *Journal of Pediatric Urology*, *12*(2), 108.e101–108.e107.

Carayon, P. (2006). Human factors of complex sociotechnical systems. *Applied Ergonomics*, *37*(4), 525–535.

Carayon, P., Hundt, A. S., Karsh, B., Gurses, A. P., Alvarado, C., Smith, M., & Brennan, P. F. (2006). Work system design for patient safety: The SEIPS model. *The BMJ Quality & Safety*, *15*(suppl 1), i50–i58.

Cheng, C. F., Werner, N. E., Doutcheva, N., Warner, G., Barton, H. J., Kelly, M. M., . . . Katz, B. J. (2020). Codesign and usability testing of a mobile application to support family-delivered enteral tube care. *Hospital Pediatrics*, *10*(8), 641–650.

Corbin, J., & Strauss, A. (1985). Managing chronic illness at home: Three lines of work. *Qualitative Sociology*, *8*(3), 224–247.

DiGerolamo, K., & Davis, K. F. (2017). An integrative review of pediatric fall risk assessment tools. *Journal of Pediatric Nursing*, *34*, 23–28.

Endsley, M. R. (1987). The application of human factors to the development of expert systems for advanced cockpits. *Proceedings of the Human Factors Society Annual Meeting*, *31*(12), 1388–1392.

Foster, C., & Lyall, H. (2015). Children are not small adults. *Journal of Virus Eradication*, *1*(3), 133.

Gallo, K. P., Hill, L. C., Hoagwood, K. E., & Olin, S.-c. S. (2016). A narrative synthesis of the components of and evidence for patient-and family-centered care. *Clinical Pediatrics*, *55*(4), 333–346.

Hei, H., Bezpalko, O., Smathers, S. A., Coffin, S. E., & Sammons, J. S. (2018). Development of a novel prevention bundle for pediatric healthcare-associated viral infections. *Infection Control & Hospital Epidemiology*, *39*(9), 1086–1092.

Holden, R. J., Cornet, V. P., & Valdez, R. S. (2020). Patient ergonomics: 10-year mapping review of patient-centered human factors. *Applied Ergonomics*, *82*, 102972.

Holden, R. J., Schubert, C. C., & Mickelson, R. S. (2015). The patient work system: An analysis of self-care performance barriers among elderly heart failure patients and their informal caregivers. *Applied Ergonomics*, *47*, 133–150.

Holden, R. J., Valdez, R. S., Schubert, C. C., Thompson, M. J., & Hundt, A. S. (2017). Macroergonomic factors in the patient work system: Examining the context of patients with chronic illness. *Ergonomics*, *60*(1), 26–43.

Jeremic, V., Sénécal, K., Borry, P., Chokoshvili, D., & Vears, D. F. (2016). Participation of children in medical decision-making: Challenges and potential solutions. *Journal of Bioethical Inquiry*, *13*(4), 525–534.

Klassen, T. P., Hartling, L., Craig, J. C., & Offringa, M. (2008). Children are not just small adults: The urgent need for high-quality trial evidence in children. *PLoS Medicine*, *5*(8), e172.

Kratchman, B., Barkman, M., Conaboy, B., de la Motte, M., & Biblow, M. (2015). The Children's Hospital of Philadelphia Family Partners Program: Promoting child and family-centered care in pediatrics. *Patient Experience Journal*, *2*(1), 50–60.

Kuther, T. L. (2003). Medical decision-making and minors: Issues of consent and assent. *Adolescence*, *38*(150), 343.

Larcher, V. (2017). Children are not small adults: Significance of biological and cognitive development in medical practice. In T. Schramme & S. Edwards (Eds.), *Handbook of the Philosophy of Medicine* (pp. 371–393). Dordrecht, Netherlands: Springer.

Margolies, R., Gurnaney, H., Egeth, M., Fink, N., Soosaar, J., Shames, A., & Rehman, M. (2015). Positioning patient status monitors in a family waiting room. *Health Environments Research & Design Journal*, *8*(2), 103–109.

Meeks, R. (2009). Parental presence in pediatric trauma resuscitation: One hospital's experience. *Pediatric Nursing*, *35*(6), 376.

O'Connell, K. J., Farah, M. M., Spandorfer, P., & Zorc, J. J. (2007). Family presence during pediatric trauma team activation: An assessment of a structured program. *Pediatrics*, *120*(3), e565–e574.

O'neill, E., Woodgate, D., & Kostakos, V. (2004). Easing the wait in the emergency room: Building a theory of public information systems. In the *Proceedings of the 5th Conference on Designing Interactive Systems: Processes, Practices, Methods, and Techniques,* 17–25.

Okonkwo, O., Simons, A., Nichani, J., & Collaborative, N. W. E. R. (2016). Paediatric airway foreign body: The human factors influencing patient safety in our hospitals. *International Journal of Pediatric Otorhinolaryngology*, *91*, 100–104.

Ponnala, S., & Rivera, A. J. (2019). Human factors engineering: Status, interventions, future directions in pediatrics. *Current Treatment Options in Pediatrics*, 5(2), 145–164.

Rametta, S. C., Fridinger, S. E., Gonzalez, A. K., Xian, J., Galer, P. D., Kaufman, M., . . . Melamed, S. E. (2020). Analyzing 2,589 child neurology telehealth encounters necessitated by the COVID-19 pandemic. *Neurology*, 95(9), e1258.

Ratwani, R. M., Wang, E., Fong, A., & Cooper, C. J. (2016). A human factors approach to understanding the types and sources of interruptions in radiology reading rooms. *Journal of the American College of Radiology*, 13(9), 1102–1105.

Reid, K., Hartling, L., Ali, S., Le, A., Norris, A., & Scott, S. D. (2017). Development and usability evaluation of an art and narrative-based knowledge translation tool for parents with a child with pediatric chronic pain: multi-method study. *Journal of Medical Internet Research*, 19(12), e412.

Rowe, C., Koren, T., & Koren, G. (1998). Errors by paediatric residents in calculating drug doses. *Archives of Disease in Childhood*, 79(1), 56–58.

Scanlon, M. C., Karsh, B.-T., & Densmore, E. M. (2006). Human factors engineering and patient safety. *Pediatric Clinics*, 53(6), 1105–1119.

Shumow, L., Smith, T. J., & Smith, M. C. (2009). Academic and behavioral characteristics of young adolescents in self-care. *The Journal of Early Adolescence*, 29(2), 233–257.

Sisterhen, L. L., Blaszak, R. T., Woods, M. B., & Smith, C. E. (2007). Defining family-centered rounds. *Teaching and Learning in Medicine*, 19(3), 319–322.

Sittig, D. F., & Singh, H. (2015). A new socio-technical model for studying health information technology in complex adaptive healthcare systems. *Cognitive Informatics for Biomedicine*, 19(3): i68–i74.

Stille, C., Turchi, R. M., Antonelli, R., Cabana, M. D., Cheng, T. L., Laraque, D., & Perrin, J. (2010). The family-centered medical home: Specific considerations for child health research and policy. *Academic Pediatrics*, 10(4), 211–217.

Subramony, A., Hametz, P. A., & Balmer, D. (2014). Family-centered rounds in theory and practice: an ethnographic case study. *Academic Pediatrics*, 14(2), 200–206.

Sutherland, A., Ashcroft, D. M., & Phipps, D. L. (2019). Exploring the human factors of prescribing errors in paediatric intensive care units. *Archives of Disease in Childhood*, 104(6), 588–595.

Tuckson, R. V., Edmunds, M., & Hodgkins, M. L. (2017). Telehealth. *New England Journal of Medicine*, 377(16), 1585–1592.

Valdez, R. S., Holden, R. J., Novak, L. L., & Veinot, T. C. (2014). Transforming consumer health informatics through a patient work framework: Connecting patients to context. *Journal of the American Medical Informatics Association*, 22(1), 2–10.

Valdez, R. S., Lunsford, C., Bae, J., Letzkus, L. C., & Keim-Malpass, J. (2020). Self-management characterization for families of children with medical complexity and their social networks: Protocol for a qualitative assessment. *Journal of Medical Internet Research Protocols*, 9(1), e14810.

van Staa, A. (2011). Unraveling triadic communication in hospital consultations with adolescents with chronic conditions: The added value of mixed methods research. *Patient Education and Counseling*, 82(3), 455–464.

Wooldridge, A. R., Carayon, P., Hoonakker, P., Hose, B.-Z., Ross, J., Kohler, J. E., . . ., Dean, S. M. (2019). Complexity of the pediatric trauma care process: Implications for multi-level awareness. *Cognition, Technology & Work*, 21(3), 397–416.

Xie, A., Carayon, P., Cartmill, R., Li, Y., Cox, E. D., Plotkin, J. A., & Kelly, M. M. (2015). Multi-stakeholder collaboration in the redesign of family-centered rounds process. *Applied Ergonomics*, 46, 115–123.

Xie, A., Carayon, P., Kelly, M. M., Li, Y., Cartmill, R., DuBenske, L. L., . . ., Cox, E. D. (2012). *Managing different perspectives in the redesign of family-centered rounds in a pediatric hospital.* Paper presented at the Proceedings of the Human Factors and Ergonomics Society Annual Meeting.

# 9 Understanding the Patient, Wellness, and Caregiving Work of Older Adults

*Abigail R. Wooldridge and Wendy A. Rogers*
University of Illinois at Urbana-Champaign

## CONTENTS

Patient work has been conceptualized very broadly to include any effortful activities in pursuit of health-related goals, which includes activities related to social determinants of health (Holden et al., 2020). Therefore, patient work for older adults can be conceptualized as the work an older person has to engage in to maximize their health. However, older adults participate in many facets of everyday activities to maintain their own wellness, including enhancing their quality of life and supporting their social well-being. Further, older adults may act as caregivers for others, a specific subtype of patient work. Therefore, in this chapter we consider three distinct types of work that older adults engage in to maximize their health:

- **Patient work**. activities directly tied to managing specific health conditions, including coordinating their own care network.
- **Wellness work**. activities directly tied to obtaining or enhancing social support, increasing social engagement, and improving quality of life.
- **Caregiving work**. activities directly tied to managing health conditions, coordinating care networks, and supporting wellness of another individual.

Specifying these three categories of work allows us to explore distinct challenges older adults face and potential solutions that vary between these types of work. Further, the term "patient" in patient work emphasizes work that is done explicitly when one is experiencing effects of a specific condition; our conceptualization of wellness work supports the idea that activities can be proactive, not tied to a specific illness or condition, and support a healthy social life in addition to physical and mental health (Mitzner et al., 2013). In addition, older adults are frequently caring for others as well as themselves, which encompasses different work activities (National Alliance for Caregiving (NAC) & AARP Public Policy Institute, 2015).

Consider a day in the life of a fictitious—but representative—couple, Justin and Nicki. Justin is a 78-year-old male with diabetes and multiple comorbidities (hypertension, insomnia) who was recently hospitalized due to a foot amputation. He has just transitioned back home in his rural community. He lives with his wife Nicki, age 76, who is his primary caregiver. She is a breast cancer survivor who is experiencing some social isolation due to the increasing demands on her as Justin's caregiver. Figure 9.1 presents a snapshot of their morning routine—how it should progress ideally, and how it often progresses in reality.

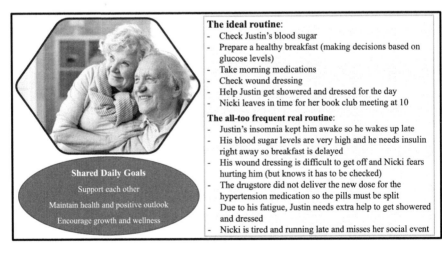

**The ideal routine:**
- Check Justin's blood sugar
- Prepare a healthy breakfast (making decisions based on glucose levels)
- Take morning medications
- Check wound dressing
- Help Justin get showered and dressed for the day
- Nicki leaves in time for her book club meeting at 10

**The all-too frequent real routine:**
- Justin's insomnia kept him awake so he wakes up late
- His blood sugar levels are very high and he needs insulin right away so breakfast is delayed
- His wound dressing is difficult to get off and Nicki fears hurting him (but knows it has to be checked)
- The drugstore did not deliver the new dose for the hypertension medication so the pills must be split
- Due to his fatigue, Justin needs extra help to get showered and dressed
- Nicki is tired and running late and misses her social event

**Shared Daily Goals**
Support each other
Maintain health and positive outlook
Encourage growth and wellness

**FIGURE 9.1** Snapshot of a morning routine for Justin and Nicki. This includes both the ideal routine and how it often actually occurs.

The complexities in this case study are myriad and illustrate the components of patient, wellness, and caregiving work. Justin is dealing with multimorbidity (i.e. managing multiple chronic conditions at once), which increases his patient workload. He has to manage his diabetes, insomnia, hypertension, and related medications; maintain his personal hygiene; come to terms with the loss of his right foot, and what that means for his future mobility; and cope with his increased reliance on his wife to support his health needs. For her part, Nicki has to manage her own patient work as a cancer survivor, e.g. medications (maintenance therapy for her cancer); perform caregiving work to coordinate care for Justin and help him as needed; and engage in wellness work to maintain her social support network to reduce her caregiver stress. As a couple, they have shared goals of supporting one another and maintaining their independent lifestyle in the home they built together 45 years ago in the rural community they love. Their two children have moved away, one across the state and one across the country. As such, the support they can provide is quite limited.

## 9.1 PATIENT, WELLNESS, AND CAREGIVING WORK OF OLDER ADULTS

Our case study of Justin and Nicki demonstrates the components of patient, wellness, and caregiving work considered in this chapter. These activities include care coordination, shared decision-making, use of technology, transportation, managing comorbidities, home maintenance (and perhaps remodeling for aging-in-place), addressing sleep challenges, preventing social isolation, and interacting with and coordinating home healthcare providers. This list is not exhaustive but it is illustrative of the variety of work tasks.

Moreover, there are well-documented age-related changes in sensory (e.g. vision, hearing), cognitive (e.g. working memory, processing speed), motor control (e.g. grip strength, movement precision) that may make these work tasks more challenging. Consequently, the older adult experience is unique from others who may have similar health diagnoses, wellness goals, and caregiving responsibilities.

All of the earlier highlighted activities have ergonomic aspects—perceptual, cognitive, physical, and organizational (see Volume I of this handbook). Cognitive ergonomics considers the cognitive abilities of humans including mental processes such as perception, memory, reasoning, and motor response. Physical ergonomics focuses on human anatomy, physiology, anthropometry, and biomechanics. Organizational ergonomics focuses on the optimization of sociotechnical systems, including the interactions between the people, tasks, tools, and environment. Our goal in this chapter is to provide an organizing framework to characterize the needs of older adults, emphasizing that multiple components and interactions between these components must be considered in the context of human factors/ergonomics (HFE) practice. We provide a general overview of older adult needs, illustrating the diversity of older adults. We then discuss the three types of work—patient, wellness, and caregiving—to provide a conceptual grounding for our framework, which we will detail in the context of older adults in the home and in formal care settings to demonstrate the range of challenges. Approaches to developing solutions include user-centered design and participatory design, which we illustrate with examples. We conclude with recommendations for future research and development efforts that can support patient, wellness, and caregiving work of older adults.

## 9.2  UNDERSTANDING THE HEALTH NEEDS OF OLDER ADULTS

### 9.2.1  Shifting Demographics of Older Adults

The demographics of the United States are changing quite dramatically. In 2000, the largest percentage of the population comprised middle-aged adults, and age groups older than 54 were dramatically smaller in size than younger age groups (Centers for Medicare and Medicaid Services [CMS], 2016). By 2030, however, the U.S. Census projects that the distribution of individuals among age groups will be more similar across age ranges until age 74. According to the Administration on Aging (2017), over one in every seven (15.2%) individuals living in the United States is over age 65, and older women outnumber older men (27.5 million to 21.8 million, respectively). Moreover, older adults are ethnically and racially diverse, with racial and ethnic minority populations projected to continue to increase from 11.1 million in 2016 to 21.1 million in 2030 (Administration on Aging, 2017). In 2016, 9% of older adults identified as African-Americans, 4% as Asian or Pacific Islander, 0.5% as Native American, 0.1% Native Hawaiian/Pacific Islander, and 0.7% as belonging to two or more races. Moreover, 8% of the older adult population were of Hispanic origin. This increase in diversity may result in varied personal and family/caregiver preferences, increased need for language translation, changes to provide services in a culturally sensitive way (Administration on Aging, 2017). Given the well-documented ethnic and racial disparities in health (Good et al., 2005), the rapid increase in demographic diversity of older adults makes addressing health inequity particularly important.

### 9.2.2  Living Arrangements of Older Adults

Although these trends may be changing, many older adults prefer to "age-in-place," to remain in their own homes for as long as they are able to take care of themselves (e.g. American Association Retired Persons [AARP], 2005, 2018; Shafer, 2000). The U.S. housing data suggest that the majority of older adults are indeed achieving this goal; nearly 80% of older adults live independently in their own homes (Houser et al., 2006; Joint Center for Housing Studies, 2018). Most live in private homes with a spouse; however, many live alone (approximately 30%) with close to 50% of women aged 75 and older living alone. Older adults living at home vary in their functional abilities and many receive assistance with everyday activities (Mitzner et al., 2014).

From a societal perspective, it is cost-effective to support aging-in-place. The median annual cost of a home health aide providing care at home is $33,540, whereas the median annual cost for a private room in a nursing facility is nearly $97,500 (Houser et al., 2018). Private residential living costs are estimated to be only 55% of the costs of full-time residential care (Tang & Venables, 2000). The burden and hardships of health care and aging are particularly high for those who have limited financial resources and limited family and community support (Felland et al., 2004).

In 2016, 37% of older adults lived below 250% of poverty level, i.e. with an income of less than $29,700 for one person or less than $40,050 for a family of two (Houser et al., 2018).

### 9.2.3 Health of Older Adults

Based on a cross-sectional survey, McLaughlin et al. (2012) estimated that only ~3% of older adults experience *healthy aging* as defined by Rowe and Kahn (1997), namely complete maintenance of physical and mental functioning, and avoidance of disease and disability. Indeed, the common experience of aging is managing conditions, diseases, and risk factors, yet hoping to age-in-place safely with intact autonomy. Healthcare value should be increased when older adults can safely and successfully age in their place of choice, reduce unintended care such as unnecessary emergency room visits and hospitalizations, and satisfactorily manage their chronic conditions at home, which for many enhances quality of life.

Two-thirds of older adults have diseases or risk factors (e.g. obesity, hypertension) requiring medications, procedures, surgeries, rehabilitative therapy, or resulting in functional limitations (McLaughlin et al., 2012). With longer life expectancy, the lifetime risk of a chronic condition increases (CMS, 2016); older adults are affected at higher rates than younger populations by: hypertension (55%), hyperlipidemia (45%), arthritis (29%), ischemic heart disease (27%), diabetes (27%), chronic kidney disease (CKD; 17%), depression (16%), heart failure (14%), and chronic obstructive pulmonary disorder (COPD; 11%). Having multiple chronic conditions impacts all aspects of healthcare outcomes, including medication management burden, recovery time, and hospital readmission (American Geriatrics Society [AGS] Expert Panel on the Care of Older Adults with Multimorbidity, 2012; Bayliss et al., 2014).

Older adults are increasingly asked to engage in health self-management that may involve the following activities: medication and diet adherence, exercise; use of medical devices and technologies (e.g. activity monitor, blood glucose meter); and interaction with the formal healthcare system, including hospitals, clinics, and specialists (Mitzner et al., 2013) (see also Volume I of this handbook). Comorbidities present special challenges related to overall increased number of tasks or discordant management tasks. For example, an older adult who has congestive heart failure and chronic kidney disease must navigate contradictory recommendations to restrict fluid intake, as part of managing their heart failure, and to drink plenty of water, as part of managing their kidney disease. This issue of navigating conflicting recommendations is not by any means unique to older adults, but it is a more prevalent concern in this population as older adults are more likely to manage multimorbidity (AGS Expert Panel on the Care of Older Adults with Multimorbidity, 2012; Bayliss et al., 2014).

Multiple clinicians may be involved in managing the health care of one older adult, particularly with the increased prevalence of multimorbidity, including geriatricians, internists, and specialists (e.g. nephrologists, endocrinologists, cardiologists) (National Research Council, 2011). Healthcare professionals providing care through home visits include nurses, rehabilitation therapists, and home health aides.

Older adults visiting emergency rooms and urgent care centers encounter additional providers who are not privy to their coordinated treatment plan. The large care network also includes family members and other informal caregivers.

At the care network's center is the older adult, who herself or himself plays a crucial role in the success of interventions and treatment plans. Yet older individuals are likely to experience sensory, cognitive, and motor changes that influence their capacity for understanding the complexity of the tasks facing them (see Czaja et al., 2019 for a review). The CREATE sociotechnical framework depicted in Figure 9.2 illustrates the factors that influence everyday activity in various domains, including health care.

The myriad patient work associated with self-management involves interactions of multimorbidity, medication management, use of technology, information requirements, and needs for coordination within the care network. An individual's ability to cope with work demands is one factor that determines success of self-management and can be characterized by their physical, sensory, cognitive, and social capabilities, or resources (Czaja et al., 2019). Forces in the environment place demands on individuals that may be physical, intellectual, or social in nature. If an individual's level of resources does not match the work and environmental demands, then maladaptive behavior may result, such as depression, increased levels of stress, and burnout. Patient work demands, just like demands of any other work, have the potential to exceed an individual's abilities, perhaps especially for persons with multimorbidity (Bayliss et al., 2014).

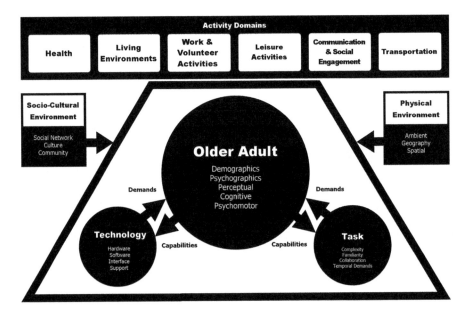

**FIGURE 9.2** CREATE sociotechnical model of design for older adults. (Reprinted with permission from Czaja et al., 2019.)

### 9.2.4 TECHNOLOGY TO SUPPORT THE HEALTH OF OLDER ADULTS

Technology has the potential to address both quality of life and cost containment, but currently falls short of addressing these challenges (see Volume I of this handbook). Some current technologies are not integrated in the processes and workflows of older adults and clinicians, resulting in duplicate effort, whereas others are inflexible, rendering them ineffective for diverse users. Innovative technologies may not be fully scalable for widespread use or disease-specific and not applicable beyond a small subset of potential users. Moreover, older adults with existing disabilities face challenges in utilizing technologies that may be unintentionally inaccessible to older adults with mobility, cognitive, vision, and hearing impairments (Harrington et al., 2015).

The growing trend of hospital-at-home programs, which care for certain acute medical conditions through monitoring and daily nursing and clinician visits, could potentially benefit from within-home monitoring given the enhancements in their efficiency (e.g. www.hospitalathome.org). In addition, technology innovations are fragmented, not validated with target older adult populations, and not integrated into either the healthcare ecology or the home itself (Sanford, 2010). When telehealth and home-based programs are implemented the technologies may be inflexible, unreliable, and unsustainable (Charness et al., 2011). Even well-designed products may fail because of insufficient attention paid to policy, acceptance, and ethical issues such as privacy (Hudson, 2014). Healthcare technologies are increasing at a rapid pace and older adults are expected to be able to integrate them into their daily health regimens. Societal needs for technologic facilitators of successful aging in place require an evidence-based system that is integrated, validated, deployed in context, tested with stakeholders, valuable for various chronic conditions and multimorbidity, and that can be scaled up to accommodate the needs of a rapidly increasing older adult population.

The potential for technology to support older adults' healthcare needs is illustrated in the TechSAge Technology Intervention Model (Figure 9.3; Mitzner et al., 2018). This model illustrates how age-related capacity limitations due to impairment and age-related changes can lead to functional disabilities that limit activity and participation if the context is not supportive. Well-designed technology interventions can change the barriers into facilitators, thereby increasing successful performance and hence activity and participation. For example, consider the case of Justin and Nicki. The blood glucose meter is a technology intended to support Nicki in her caregiving work and Justin in his patient work. However, the buttons give minimal feedback, and the text on the screen is too small to read. Thus, it becomes a barrier for effective use by older adults with reduced dexterity and visual acuity. An age-appropriate design could change that barrier into a facilitator. Alternatively, consider Justin's reduced mobility, a combination of age-related osteoarthritis and a leg amputation. His two-story farmhouse has become a barrier for navigation but a stair-lift in his home would mitigate that disability.

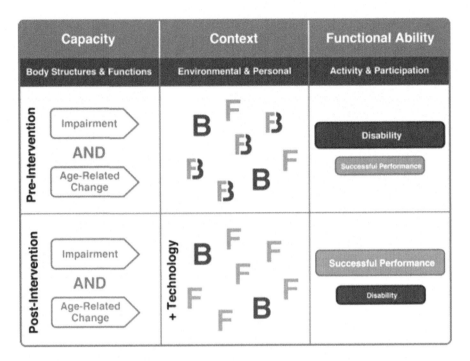

**FIGURE 9.3** The TechSAge Technology Intervention Model illustrates the value of a technology intervention. The top row illustrates individuals aging with a pre-existing impairment. Their reduced capacity results in contextual facilitators becoming barriers (symbolized by Fs transitioning to Bs in figure) and hence more disability. The bottom row illustrates how a technology intervention can turn the barriers (Bs) back into facilitators (Fs), which yields more performance that is successful. (Reprinted with permission from Mitzner, Sanford, and Rogers, 2018.)

## 9.3 UNDERSTANDING PATIENT, WELLNESS, AND CAREGIVING WORK OF OLDER ADULTS

HFE has proven valuable to understanding and improving the work and systems of health care. Outcomes of interest have included those that are patient-oriented such as patient safety and quality of care, as well as those that are clinician-oriented (Carayon et al., 2018). With the increasing focus and emphasis on patient engagement in health care, the idea that patients, their family, friends, and other nonprofessionals engage in effortful activities in the pursuit of health and well-being is increasingly accepted (Holden & Valdez, 2018; Valdez et al., 2015). In other words, all of those individuals engage in work (Hendrick, 2002). Thus, HFE professionals have begun to focus on the work of patients and their informal caregivers and have applied HFE methods to understand and improve this work.

Much of this research has taken a systems approach, as social, organizational, and physical factors shape patient work (Carayon, 2006; Holden et al., 2017). This approach, including the macroergonomic models utilized, has its foundation in sociotechnical systems theory and work system analysis and design (Kleiner, 2006; Wilson, 2014). Sociotechnical work systems can be described by five elements: (1) the people doing the work, (2) the tasks that make up the work, (3) the tools and technology they use to do the work, (4) the organizational context the work occurs in, such as cultural and social considerations, and (5) the physical environment the work occurs in. These are all influenced by the broader external environment the work occurs in, which is sometimes included as a sixth work system element (Carayon et al., 2006, 2014; Kleiner, 2008). Holden and colleagues (2015, 2017) proposed a consolidated model of the patient work system, which integrated aging-specific (Fisk et al., 2009; Rogers & Fisk, 2010) and healthcare-specific HFE systems models (Carayon et al., 2006; Holden et al., 2013). The patient work system model highlighted the triad of person(s) completing tasks using tools or technology within a household and community, which account for the physical, social, and organizational domains of macroergonomics.

These HFE systems models will continue to be a useful framework for future work in patient ergonomics, including work focused on older adults. The components of the systems models are likely similar across age groups but the weightings might differ. For example, age-related changes in perception, cognition, and movement control might increase the impact of a poorly designed environment. Moreover, older adults as a group have less experience with information and computer technology, which can influence their ability to utilize unfamiliar health technologies.

### 9.3.1 Patient Work

Older adults engage in work related to their own health, including management of acute and chronic illnesses (Mitzner et al., 2013). Older adults are more likely to have chronic conditions such as heart failure, COPD, stroke, and diabetes, which can be improved by patient engagement, patient self-management, shared decision-making, and peer support (Tapp et al., 2018), all of which entail patient work.

Mitzner and colleagues (2013) described several types of self-management activities of older adults that could be related to specific illness: adherence to diet, exercise regimen and medication schedule, coordination of a care network, and use of medical technologies such as blood pressure and blood glucose monitors. Corbin and Strauss (1988) identified four broad types of patient work in their studies of patients with chronic conditions, some of whom were older adults, although their work did not focus explicitly on this population. Two of the four types of work fall under our definition of patient work, whereas the others fall under wellness work:

1. Managing the illness, including tasks related to medications, obtaining and organizing care, following treatment regimens, as well as the self-management activities described by Mitzner et al. (2013).
2. Arrangement work to organize infrastructure and tools to maintain mobility and live with the illness.

Previous research has further specified tasks involved in self-management of chronic conditions. In diabetic patients (average age: 54, ranging from 22 to 75 years old), tasks include medication management, monitoring blood sugar, and general information management (Werner, Jolliff, et al., 2018). In heart failure patients, Willems and colleagues (2006) identified: organizing medications, managing fluid intake, and integrating recommendations for heart failure with recommendations based on other comorbidities (managing illness); organizing, partitioning day into chunks, especially due to fatigue, planning when to leave house due to medication side effects (everyday work); managing changes in ability to participate in activities and attend social gatherings, dealing with impact on self-image (biographical work); and managing mobility and organizing the infrastructure to live with severe heart failure such as house adaptations, getting walkers (arrangement work). In older patients with heart failure, the higher-level task of medication management has been described as drawing on five macrocognitive processes (sensemaking, planning, coordination, monitoring, and decision-making), which includes 15 subprocesses (Mickelson et al., 2016).

A major area of patient work is related to information management; many conditions result in demanding information needs and processes to manage that information (Arbaje et al., 2019). For example, one study found that cancer patients, including but not limited to older adults, need ten categories, with 64 subcategories, of information (Rutten et al., 2005). Information collection and interpretation are important parts of self-management (Bourbeau, 2008); given the vast amount of information needed, information storage and organization are also essential (Moen & Brennan, 2005). At times, older adults have struggled to organize and track information, such as medication history and cost at specific pharmacies (Mickelson & Holden, 2018). Ancker and colleagues (2015) studied the management of personal health information among patients with multiple chronic conditions aged 37–89 (average age: 64), finding that patients managed vast amounts of information, including correcting errors in their records and making decisions about what information to share with which physicians and healthcare organizations. This substantial information management work was largely unrecognized or unsupported by healthcare professionals.

In summary, many researchers have attempted to define and categorize the work of patients with various conditions, sometimes explicitly focusing on older adults and sometimes including older adults as well as younger patients. These activities are summarized in Table 9.1. Importantly, patient work changes depending on the setting of care (see Chapters 2–6 in this volume). At home, patients have more autonomy and responsibility for tasks. For example, in the hospital or a skilled nursing facility, patients complete work related to following recommended care regime such as taking medications provided by clinical staff, but at home they (or a caregiver) are responsible for managing medications themselves. Not all these studies focused exclusively on older adults, but those that did focused on specific conditions, leaving gaps in our understanding of how the patient work of older adults (i.e. work related to illness) differs from younger patients. Further, not all conditions have been studied, and therefore additional, unidentified activities could exist.

### 9.3.2 WELLNESS WORK

Older adults perform goal-directed activities in pursuit of overall wellness that may not be linked to a specific illness or condition. Activities of daily living (ADLs), instrumental activities of daily living (IADLs), and enhanced activities of daily living (EADLs) are three commonly described categories of activities completed by older adults (Rogers et al., 1998; Spector & Fleishman, 1998). ADLs include basic activities of hygiene and personal care, e.g. bathing, showering, toilet hygiene, grooming, dressing, self-feeding, functional mobility (Spector & Fleishman, 1998). IADLs include basic activities necessary to reside in the community, e.g. cleaning, maintaining the house, managing finances, preparing meals, shopping (Spector & Fleishman, 1998). EADLs include participating in social and enriching activities, learning new skills, and engaging in hobbies (Rogers et al., 1998, in press; Smarr et al., 2011).

Some IADLs relate to health conditions (e.g. medication management) but others are more general wellness activities such as preparing meals or maintaining the home. EADLs are most related to wellness, in general, as they represent activities in pursuit of social engagement, social support, and quality of life. Some of the activities described by both Mitzner and colleagues (2013) and Corbin and Strauss (1988) are not directly tied to specific illness, but rather a general pursuit of wellness and quality of life and are also related to IADLs and EADLs. For example, adherence to a diet or exercise regimen may not be tied to a specific condition (Mitzner et al., 2013). Everyday work to keep life going, including ADLs, and the biographical work of dealing with potential loss, disruption, or change of self-concept and engagement in activities, go beyond illness (Corbin & Strauss, 1988).

Many researchers have studied activities not directly tied to specific illness and conditions in which older adults participate to maintain their overall well-being (see Chapter 11 in this volume). Again, these activities change based on setting and are summarized in Table 9.1. ADLs, IADLs, and EADLs may not be specific to older adults, but they are often discussed and considered by researchers and clinicians in the context of older adults' needs and abilities. Thus, we have limited understanding of how this work differs from the work of younger individuals, beyond changes due to natural outcomes of the aging process described previously. Again, autonomy related to the completion of these activities is decreased in formal healthcare settings relative to home settings. Participation in some of these activities, particularly the EADLs, may be completely curtailed in formal healthcare settings.

### 9.3.3 CAREGIVING WORK

The terms patient and wellness work may lead to associations with work tied to managing one's own health as an individual. However, some older adults can also be informal (i.e. unpaid or nonprofessional) caregivers for others. In 2015, about 43.5 million adults in the United States provided unpaid care to another individual in the past year; nearly one in ten of those caregivers were 75 years or older (NAC & AARP Public Policy Institute, 2015). Caregivers over age 75 were mostly females taking care of a close relative, such as a spouse, adult child, or sibling, needing care due to a chronic condition (NAC & AARP Public Policy Institute, 2015).

Informal caregivers often help manage technologies and the physical environment to support the health of another (i.e. care recipient; Bratteteig & Wagner, 2013). They may help manage aspects of life that the care recipient is unable to manage, such as cleaning, cooking, and shopping (Bratteteig & Wagner, 2013). Informal caregivers may be more directly involved in the patient work activities described previously, such as making and coordinating appointments, providing or arranging transportation to and from those appointments, managing information, and advocating for the care recipient (Bratteteig & Wagner, 2013; NAC & AARP Public Policy Institute, 2015).

Clark and colleagues (2008) described caregivers monitoring symptoms and participating in decision-making with the care recipient and healthcare professionals. Other tasks could include basic nursing care, such as cleaning a wound, or work that aims to minimize or prevent the discomfort of the care recipient (Bratteteig & Wagner, 2013). Caregivers over age 75 typically had been performing this work for 5.6 years on average, which required about 34 hours per week to complete, without any paid assistance (NAC & AARP Public Policy Institute, 2015). Caregivers may also support the wellness work of the care recipients, encouraging them to exercise, eat well, continue their hobbies, and remain engaged in social/community activities.

In short, caregiving work can represent a significant demand, leading to work investigating the needs of and ways to support caregivers. High caregiver strain is associated with higher risk of emergency department (ED) utilization among older adults, supporting the argument that better caregiver support could reduce visits to the ED (Burgdorf et al., 2019). However, Wolff and colleagues (2020) found more than 40% of caregivers of older adults with dementia were never asked by healthcare professionals if they needed help or assistance (average age of caregivers was 59 years). Importantly, many interventions to support caregivers tend to focus on one individual caregiver. However, caregiving burden is often shared across a caregiving network or team; therefore, interventions to support caregivers may be more impactful if designed to support the entire team and their teamwork (Werner, Gilmore-Bykovskyi, et al., 2017).

### 9.3.4 THE DYNAMIC NATURE OF PATIENT, WELLNESS, AND CAREGIVING WORK

An important aspect of patient, wellness, and caregiving work is their dynamic nature. These work activities change as new health conditions and functional limitations arise. For example, a new health condition may necessitate a new medication, leading to new or different medication management tasks, and a disability could change the opportunity for social activities. Caregiving work may also be affected by changes to the caregiver's or recipient's individual health condition. For example, if the person they care for is hospitalized or develops a disability (Gill et al., 2004), the caregiver will likely take on additional caregiving tasks, such as managing information, assisting with activities of daily living, and so on.

Patient, wellness, and caregiving work also change across the spatiotemporal patient journey, in particular as the patient transitions from one care setting to another, and are impacted by changes related to space and time (Carayon et al., 2020; Carayon & Wooldridge, 2020). Transitions between care settings represent an important point when work systems can fail to adequately support the needs of patients and their caregivers, resulting in negative outcomes, but could also be opportunities for resilience and error recovery (see Chapter 3 in this volume).

Older adults are especially vulnerable to failures during care transitions (Werner et al., 2016; Werner, Malkana, et al., 2017). For example, when older adults transition from home to hospital and then back again, care responsibilities are also transferred from the patient and caregiver to the clinician and then back again, but often with adjustment (Werner, Tong, et al., 2018). Self-management includes goal selection, information collection and interpretation, decision-making, and action (Bourbeau, 2008); patients must identify their goals, which may shift over time, and then make decisions and take action to achieve those (Bodenheimer et al., 2002), often in conjunction with their informal caregivers.

## 9.4  A FRAMEWORK TO CHARACTERIZE NEEDS AND CHALLENGES

In this section, we synthesize and describe what is known about the patient, wellness, and caregiving work of older adults. We organize activities older adults engage in by the setting in which the work is done and by whether the work is related to management of health, activities beyond health care or caregiving. Table 9.1 presents this framework. Patient work includes the self-management activities described in the previous section, information management, and coordination of their own care network. Wellness work includes activities related to enhancing social support and engagement and maintaining a high quality of life. Although these activities may not be directly related to managing an illness, they are related to healthy aging and can influence health outcomes (Cohen, 2004). Caregiving work includes performing health management activities for a care recipient, especially those activities described previously.

In Table 9.1, we draw distinction between work done at home and work done in formal healthcare settings, such as a doctor's office, acute-care hospital, short-term rehabilitation facility, or long-term care facility. Health management activities in particular vary by setting. In formal healthcare settings, an older adult (or any patient, for that matter) may lose some autonomy as healthcare professionals "take over" some activities: for example, the older adult may no longer manage their own medications but be expected to comply with medication therapy as provided or recommended.

An important aspect in formal healthcare settings is advocating for self, especially by engaging in shared decision-making, to ensure one's own goals are considered in developing the care regimen (Barry & Edgman-Levitan, 2012). The patient and caregiver(s) as well as healthcare professionals should be cognizant of the importance of shared decision-making and should *all* focus on supporting it. Self-advocacy is a very important role but may represent a significant change for older adults who have been socialized to the paternalistic model of medicine where the clinician determines the treatment plan without consulting the patient. Some technologies and education materials (e.g. decision aids, question lists/prompts, and training for patients) have been developed to support self-advocacy and shared decision-making for other patient populations (Mann et al., 2010; Mathers et al., 2012). These tools could be useful for older adults, with or without adaptation (e.g. change in form or format), and other tolls may also be developed.

## TABLE 9.1
## Framework for Characterizing Patient, Wellness, and Caregiving Work of Older Adults

| Context | Home | Formal Healthcare Setting |
|---|---|---|
| Patient Work: Health management for self and coordinating own care network | Manage medication (e.g. get medications, follow regimen, deal with side effects, inform providers of changes made with other clinicians)<br>Follow diet and exercise requirements related to illnesses<br>Obtain and organize care (e.g. make appointments, arrange transportation to and from appointments, participate in appointments, coordinate information flow, arrange for "informal care")<br>Communicate with healthcare professionals and informal caregivers<br>Mange information (e.g. collect, interpret, organize, share, store information)<br>Correct errors in information about patient (e.g. EHR)<br>Reconcile competing recommendations and make decisions about care<br>Obtain tools/technology needed for self-care<br>Make/arrange modifications to home (e.g. handrails, ramp) | Follow recommended care regimen<br>Participate in making decisions about treatment, as possible and allowed<br>Advocate for self and engage in shared decision-making<br>Communicate with healthcare professionals<br>Mange information (e.g. collect, interpret, organize, share, store information)<br>Correct errors in information about patient (e.g. EHR, care plan)<br>Prepare for transition to home (e.g. arrange transportation, learn care routines, coordinate follow-ups) |
| Wellness Work: Activities beyond health care; social support and engagement; quality of life | Maintain independence and autonomy<br>Activities of Daily Living (ADLs)<br>Instrumental Activities of Daily Living<br>Enhanced Activities of Daily Living<br>"Everyday life to keep work going," including repair to home, job, housekeeping, marital work, child rearing, sentimental work<br>Participate in meaningful activities to maintain self-image—find them, get engaged, transport to/ from<br>Communicate and interact with family, friends, neighbors, others | Eat food as delivered, participate in other ADLs, but may not have to initiative or complete as many (e.g. healthcare worker will likely help with bathing, food will be prepared but may need to eat).<br>Communicate with family and friends |
| Caregiving Work: Activities specifically helping others manage their own health or wellness (i.e. completing patient and wellness work for someone else) | May include all activities in self-support category for a care recipient, in addition to:<br>Administer medical procedures (e.g. change wound dressing, check vitals, assist with medications)<br>Coordinate home care nurse visits<br>Coordinate other caregivers<br>Support care recipient's goals<br>Monitor progress<br>Ensure meals are consistent with health goals<br>Assist with transfers (e.g. bed to wheelchair)<br>Support care activities such as showering, dressing, eating<br>Support information management for care recipient | May include all activities in self-support category for a care recipient, in addition to:<br>Advocate for care recipient<br>Coordinate family visits<br>Coordinate other caregivers<br>Support care recipient's goals<br>Support information management for care recipient |

Activities beyond health management can change significantly by location. Again, at home, older adults have more autonomy—they can make more decisions and initiate more ADLs, IADLs, and EADLs. For example, at home they may select *and* prepare food before eating, whereas in an inpatient setting, they may select and eat only food that is provided. Whereas social activities that require physical presence may be limited in healthcare settings, older adults may still be able to communicate with family and friends, especially by using technology. New technologies could facilitate remote participation (e.g. telepresence). Interactions with family (spouse/partner, children) may occur in both home and formal healthcare settings. Couple and dyad (e.g. partners who are not romantically involved) issues can increase or change the work older adults do in pursuit of health and wellness (Fingerman, 1996; Landis et al., 2013; Whitlatch et al., 2006).

Caregiving activities may need to be redistributed when an older adult is in a formal healthcare setting, in particular as an inpatient, as the older adult may be unable to perform those activities. For example, if Nicki were hospitalized, she would not be at home to help Justin shower and dress. Technology could represent an important solution to help coordinate with other caregivers to ensure these activities are completed and to relieve stress associated with concern for the close family members older adults often care for. For example, there are websites that support organization of food delivery if an older adult (or anyone) is unable to shop or cook. Alternatively, if the caregiver is able and willing while in a formal healthcare setting, technology could support remote completion of activities, such as coordinating tasks, visits, and managing information.

There are other ways of specifying physical location that are not described in our framework but that do influence wellness work. One is the broader physical location—i.e. urban versus suburban versus rural environments—of the older adult. Being in very urban or very rural environments can introduce additional challenges. Approximately 19% of the rural population in the United States is older than 65 (Cromartie, 2018), and these older adults face geographic isolation and limited access to clinicians and report more unmet needs after hospital discharge (Rosenthal & Fox, 2000). Rural residents also experience a digital divide, impacting how consumer health information technology is used and should be designed (Greenberg et al., 2018).

Another way of specifying location in more detail than currently described in our framework is separating formal healthcare settings, as there is a broad continuum of care among acute-, ambulatory-, and community-care settings (see Chapters 2–6 in this volume). For example, in ambulatory settings, such as health clinics, there may be different communication and information management work done than in acute-care hospital settings. Both type of environment and further specification of formal healthcare setting (e.g. hospital, outpatient clinic, or long-term care facility) can impact the wellness work of older adults, including specific activities and need for support, and should be considered when developing solutions to meet their needs. Understanding differences in patient, wellness, and caregiving work in rural, suburban, and urban communities as well as along the continuum of formal healthcare settings represents an important opportunity for future research.

## 9.5 DEVELOPING SOLUTIONS THROUGH USER-CENTERED AND PARTICIPATORY DESIGN

Designers have increasingly accepted and embraced the idea that users must be considered during the design process. Nonetheless, how to operationalize consideration of the user remains open to interpretation (see Volume I of this handbook). In HFE, we tend to talk about making our designs and design processes user- (or human-) centered. Eason (1995) described two approaches to user-centered design ergonomists might take: first, use theories and knowledge about human capabilities, limitations, and behaviors to make design decisions on behalf of the end user (i.e. design *for* user); second, help the user participate in the actual design process (i.e. design *by* user).

In the design literature, there are two distinct terms for this approach: user-centered design (the first approach of Eason) and participatory design (the second approach of Eason). User-centered design (UCD) or human-centered design (HCD) involves the design team focusing on user needs and interests during the design process, usually in an iterative fashion using empirical measurements of usability (Norman & Draper, 1986). In some versions of HCD, the end user may not actually be involved in the design process at all, with their needs and interests represented by a usability expert, theories, and knowledge from HFE (Bekker & Long, 2000). Participatory design, on the other hand, emphasizes direct user involvement throughout all of the design process and as part of the design team (Bekker & Long, 2000).

Considering the user during the design process is the main goal we argue for here; we do not make a value judgment about which approach is better but seek to highlight the distinction. In fact, as argued by Eason (1995), the two design approaches are complementary and can be combined to develop more impactful solutions. In the remainder of this section, we will describe and discuss two example design processes—one HCD and one participatory—focused on designing technology solutions to support aging adults in wellness work. We have chosen to focus specifically on technology-based solutions in this chapter, but sociotechnical systems theory and macroergonomics frameworks highlight that technology-based solutions are not the *only* solutions. Technology-based solutions are promising on their own, but other ways of redesigning processes, environments, and roles are also promising and could be developed using both human-centered and participatory design processes.

### 9.5.1 HUMAN-CENTERED DESIGN EXAMPLE

An example of an HCD process to support older adults is the work done by Holden and colleagues to develop a consumer health information technology for aging adults with heart failure (e.g. Srinivas et al., 2017). In a multiphase process, a team of researchers first performed a needs analysis utilizing multiple methods of data collection, including observations in ambulatory clinic visits, surveys, review of medical records, and interviews, all of which were informed by macroergonomic frameworks. These data were subjected to 13 unique analyses, which identified six major themes and four design requirements that fed into the design phase. A design team, led by a PhD-prepared HFE principal investigator, and including human–computer interaction (HCI), computer science, and informatics experts, worked with clinical experts to develop the application design. Notably, whereas caregivers and clinicians were consulted by the design team, patients were not. The principal investigator made recommendations and revisions based on HFE principles, knowledge, and theories, i.e. Eason's (1995) design *for* user. The evaluation phase was partially concurrent with the design phase, with the HFE and HCI experts continually evaluating and making recommendations based on usability and user abilities and limitations. A formal heuristic evaluation was performed, followed by two rounds of laboratory-based usability testing with patients separated by periods of redesign. Despite the constant attention to HFE design principles, the first round of usability testing demonstrated that the application still had a below average score on the System Usability Scale (Brooke, 1996) and issues that resulted in confusion and errors during use. These issues were corrected before the second round of usability testing. For a full description of the design process, including references to individual reports in other publications, see Srinivas et al. (2017).

### 9.5.2 PARTICIPATORY DESIGN EXAMPLE

Participatory and co-design refer to involving the target users in ideation sessions of the design process, although participation can extend into other design phases, from defining the problem to be solved all the way through evaluation (see Volume I of this handbook). Participatory design can be a challenge, as people can be constrained by limited experiences and may have difficulty imagining a new approach to doing things. Thus, ideation may be particularly challenging for older adults who may have

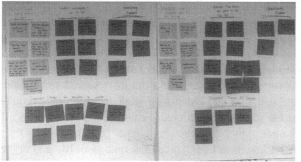

**Older Adults Engaging in Co-Design Activities:**

After several months of experience using a fitness app, they were asked to generate ideas about features they liked or disliked, and to generate ideas for a new and improved fitness app for older adults.

**FIGURE 9.4**  Co-design example from Harrington (2018). (Reprinted with permission from Czaja et al., 2019.)

long-standing approaches of performing certain activities. However, we found that older adults are willing participants in co-design activities, provided they are given the appropriate guidance and scaffolding (i.e. support throughout the design process) to be able to contribute. For example, in Harrington et al. (2018), we had older adults participate in a design session to develop a mobile fitness app (see Figure 9.4). They were able to generate many ideas, in large part because they had interacted with a mobile fitness app for 8 weeks prior to the design session. They knew what they did and did not like about existing apps; they had experiences with functions that were or were not supportive of their needs; and they were able to generate ideas for new mobile fitness apps specifically for older adults.

## 9.6   RECOMMENDATIONS AND FUTURE RESEARCH

In this chapter, we have described a range of activities that constitute work that older adults engage in, and we have highlighted different categories and locations where these activities are performed. Older adults experience some challenges, which are opportunities for various kinds of support, including technology-based solutions. These technologies should be designed in a way that fully considers the users; user-centered and participatory design processes are key to designing useful and usable solutions. Older adults have unique lifestyles, needs, preferences, and experiences that must be recognized during the design of any technological support (Rogers & Mitzner, 2017). Further specification of the intended users is required in the case of older adults, given the heterogeneous nature of the older adult population, as described in this chapter. The context in which the technology will be used must also be considered, including the physical environment, social environment, and personal factors (Mitzner et al., 2018).

One very important aspect of designing technological solutions is to consider how technology might reinforce inequities for some subgroups of users (see Chapter 10 in this volume). Technology interventions can produce or reinforce inequity if they are more accessible to, more frequently adopted by, more closely adhered to, or more effective for certain user subgroups (Veinot et al., 2018). For example, not all users have smartphones, and designing a mobile application may unintentionally exclude potential users (especially older adults; Czaja et al., 2019). User-centered and participatory design processes can help to ensure technological solutions do not create or increase inequity. Given that most designers are not older adults themselves, the involvement of the users is even more needed. See Veinot and colleagues (2018) for a more thorough discussion of inequity and informatics technology, as well as Rogers and colleagues (2005) for a discussion of considerations for designing technology for older adults.

This chapter highlighted two important areas for future research to increase understanding of the patient, wellness, and caregiving work in which older adults engage. First, as we noted at the start, we intentionally chose to use the three terms distinctly throughout this chapter, rather than the single term "patient work." Older adults engage in many everyday activities to enhance their quality of life and in the pursuit of wellness; not all of these activities are tied to specific illness or conditions. Thus, a major opportunity is to explore those other activities that fall into this health-related, but condition-nonspecific work (see Chapter 11 in this volume).

In keeping with the participatory ergonomics tradition, this work should focus on the perspective of older adults, likely drawing on the ethnographic example set by Corbin, Strauss, and colleagues (e.g. Corbin & Strauss, 1988).

The second major area for future research is related to the dynamic, changing nature of wellness work. As an older adult moves from one physical environment (e.g. hospital, home, doctor's office, retirement community), they experience changing patient, wellness, and caregiving work demands; for example, Werner, Tong, et al. (2018) identified changes in tasks as patients transitioned from hospital to home. These changes are related to the concept of the patient (or person) journey: "the spatio-temporal distribution of patients' interactions with multiple care settings over time" (Carayon & Wooldridge, 2019). It is imperative to understand the dynamic nature of the patient, wellness, and caregiving work of older adults, e.g. resulting from changes in health and functional status and transitions between healthcare settings. We should investigate what challenges they face and strategies they use to deal with those challenges (i.e. strategies related to adaptation and resilience). This knowledge can help identify additional unmet needs and opportunities to develop solutions to support older adults in their wellness work.

## ACKNOWLEDGMENTS

Wooldridge was supported in part by funding through the Jump ARCHES endowment through the Health Care Engineering Systems Center. Rogers was supported in part by grants from the National Institute on Aging (National Institutes of Health) Center for Research and Education on Aging and Technology Enhancement (CREATE; P01 AG17211); the National Institute on Disability, Independent Living, and Rehabilitation Research (Department of Health & Human Services, Administration for Community Living); Rehabilitation and Engineering Research Center on Technologies to Support Aging-in-Place for People with Long-Term Disabilities (TechSAge; 90REGE0006).

## REFERENCES

Administration on Aging, U.S.D.o.H.a.H.S.A. (2017). *A profile of older Americans: 2017*. Retrieved from http://www.aoa.gov/aoaroot/aging_statistics/Profile/2011/docs/2011profile.pdf.

American Association Retired Persons [AARP]. (2005). *Beyond 50.05 survey*. Retrieved from http://assets.aarp.org/rgcenter/il/beyond_50_05_survey.pdf

American Association Retired Persons [AARP]. (2018). *2018 home and community preferences survey: A national survey of adults age 18-plus*. Retrieved from https://www.aarp.org/content/dam/aarp/research/surveys_statistics/liv-com/2018/home-community-preferences-survey.doi.10.26419-2Fres.00231.001.pdf

American Geriatrics Society [AGS] Expert Panel on the Care of Older Adults with Multimorbidity. (2012). Guiding principles for the care of older adults with multimorbidity: An approach for clinicians. *Journal of the American Geriatrics Society, 60*(10), E1–E25.

Ancker, J. S., Witteman, H. O., Hafeez, B., Provencher, T., Van de Graaf, M., & Wei, E. (2015). The invisible work of personal health information management among people with multiple chronic conditions: Qualitative interview study among patients and providers. *Journal of Medical Internet Research, 17*(6), e137.

Arbaje, A. I., Hughes, A., Werner, N., Carl, K., Hohl, D., Jones, K., . . . Gurses, A. P. (2019). Information management goals and process failures during home visits for middle-aged and older adults receiving skilled home healthcare services after hospital discharge: A multisite, qualitative study. *The BMJ Quality & Safety, 28*(2), 111–120.

Barry, M. J., & Edgman-Levitan, S. (2012). Shared decision making — The pinnacle of patient-centered care. *New England Journal of Medicine, 366*(9), 780–781.

Bayliss, E. A., Bonds, D. E., Boyd, C. M., Davis, M. M., Finke, B., Fox, M. H., . . . Lachenmayr, S. (2014). Understanding the context of health for persons with multiple chronic conditions: Moving from what is the matter to what matters. *The Annals of Family Medicine, 12*(3), 260–269.

Bekker, M., & Long, J. (2000). User involvement in the design of human-computer interactions: Some similarities and differences between design approaches. In *People and computers XIV—Usability or else!* (pp. 135–147). Springer.

Bodenheimer, T., Lorig, K., Holman, H., & Grumbach, K. (2002). Patient self-management of chronic disease in primary care. *Journal of the American Medical Association, 288*(19), 2469–2475.

Bourbeau, C. (2008). Q&A with physician recruiter Christine Bourbeau. Interview by Gabriel Kiley. *Health Progress (Saint Louis, Mo.), 89*(6), 28–29.

Bratteteig, T., & Wagner, I. (2013). *Moving healthcare to the home: The work to make homecare work*, London.

Brooke, J. (1996). SUS: A "quick and dirty" usability scale. In P. W. Jordan, B. A. Werdmeester, & A. L. McClelland (Eds.), *Usability evaluation in industry* (pp. 189–194). London: Taylor & Francis.

Burgdorf, J., Mulcahy, J., Amjad, H., Kasper, J. D., Covinsky, K., & Wolff, J. L. (2019). Family caregiver factors associated with emergency department utilization among community-living older adults with disabilities. *Journal of Primary Care & Community Health, 10*, 2150132719875636.

Carayon, P. (2006). Human factors of complex sociotechnical systems. *Appled Ergonomics, 37*(4), 525–535.

Carayon, P., Hundt, A. H., Karsh, B. T., Gurses, A. P., Alvarado, C. J., Smith, M. J., & Brennan, P. F. (2006). Work system design for patient safety: The SEIPS model. *Quality & Safety in Health Care, 15*(Suppl 1), i50–58.

Carayon, P., Wetterneck, T. B., Rivera-Rodriguez, A. J., Hundt, A. S., Hoonakker, P., Holden, R., & Gurses, A. P. (2014). Human factors systems approach to healthcare quality and patient safety. *Appled Ergonomics, 45*(1), 14–25.

Carayon, P., Wooldridge, A., Hoonakker, P., Hundt, A. S., & Kelly, M. M. (2020). SEIPS 3.0: Human-centered design of the patient journey for patient safety. *Applied Ergonomics, 84*, 103033.

Carayon, P., & Wooldridge, A. R. (2019). Improving patient safety through the patient journey: Contributions from human factors engineering. In A. E. Smith (Ed.), *Women in industrial and systems engineering: Key advances and perspectives on emerging topics*. Switzerland: Springer.

Carayon, P., & Wooldridge, A. R. (2020). Improving patient safety in the patient journey: Contributions from human factors engineering. In A. E. Smith (Ed.), *Women in industrial and systems engineering: Key advances and perspectives on emerging topics* (pp. 275–299). Cham: Springer International Publishing.

Carayon, P., Wooldridge, A. R., Hose, B.-Z., Salwei, M., & Benneyan, J. (2018). Challenges and opportunities for improving patient safety through human factors and systems engineering. *Health Affairs, 37*(11), 1862–1869.

Centers for Medicare and Medicaid Services [CMS]. (2016). Retrieved from https://www.cms.gov/

Charness, N., Demiris, G., & Krupinski, E. (2011). *Designing telehealth for an aging population: A human factors perspective.* Boca Raton, FL: CRC Press.

Clark, A. M., Reid, M. E., Morrison, C. E., Capewell, S., Murdoch, D. L., & McMurray, J. J. (2008). The complex nature of informal care in home-based heart failure management. *Journal of Advanced Nursing, 61*(4), 373–383.

Cohen, S. (2004). Social relationships and health. *American Psychologist, 59*(8), 676.

Corbin, J. M., & Strauss, A. L. (1988). *Unending work and care: Managing chronic illness at home.* San Francisco, CA: Jossey-Bass.

Cromartie, J. (2018). *Rural America at a glance, 2018.* Retrieved from https://www.ers.usda.gov/webdocs/publications/90556/eib-200.pdf

Czaja, S. J., Boot, W. R., Charness, N., & Rogers, W. A. (2019). *Designing for older adults: Principles and creative human factors approaches, Third Edition.* Boca Raton, FL: CRC Press.

Eason, K. D. (1995). User-centred design: For users or by users? *Ergonomics, 38*(8), 1667–1673.

Felland, L. E., Felt-Lisk, S., & McHugh, M. (2004). Health care access for low-income people: Significant safety net gaps remain. *Issue Brief (Center for Studying Health System Change), 84*, 1–4.

Fingerman, K. L. (1996). Sources of tension in the aging mother and adult daughter relationship. *Psychology and Aging, 11*(4), 591.

Fisk, A. D., Rogers, W. A., Charness, N., Czaja, S. J., & Sharit, J. (2009). *Designing for Older Adults: Principles and creative human factors approaches.* Boca Raton, FL: CRC Press.

Gill, T. M., Allore, H. G., Holford, T. R., & Guo, Z. (2004). Hospitalization, restricted activity, and the development of disability among older persons. *Journal of the American Medical Association, 292*(17), 2115–2124.

Good, M. J. D., James, C., Good, B. J., & Becker, A. E. (2005). The culture of medicine and racial, ethnic, and class disparities in healthcare. In B.D. Smedley & A.Y. Stith (Eds.). *The Blackwell companion to social inequalities* (pp. 396–423). Malden, MA: Blackwell Publishing, Ltd.

Greenberg, A. J., Haney, D., Blake, K. D., Moser, R. P., & Hesse, B. W. (2018). Differences in access to and use of electronic personal health information between rural and urban residents in the United States. *Journal of Rural Health, 34*(Suppl 1), s30–s38.

Harrington, C. N., Mitzner, T. L., & Rogers, W. A. (2015). Understanding the role of technology for meeting the support needs of older adults in the USA with functional limitations. *Gerontechnology, 14*(1), 21–31.

Harrington, C. N., Wilcox, L., Connelly, K., Rogers, W. A., & Sanford, J. (2018). *Designing health and fitness apps with older adults: Examining the value of experience-based co-design.* Paper presented at the Proceedings of the 12th EAI International Conference on Pervasive Computing Technologies for Healthcare.

Hendrick, H. W. (2002). An overview of macroergonomics. In H.W. Hendrick & B.M. Kleiner (Eds.). *Macroergonomics: Theory, Methods, and Applications.* Hillsdale, NJ: Lawrence Erlbaum Associates Publishers, 1–23.

Holden, R. J., Carayon, P., Gurses, A. P., Hoonakker, P., Hundt, A. S., Ozok, A. A., & Rivera-Rodriguez, A. J. (2013). SEIPS 2.0: A human factors framework for studying and improving the work of healthcare professionals and patients. *Ergonomics, 56*(11), 1669–1686.

Holden, R. J., Cornet, V. P., & Valdez, R. S. (2020). Patient ergonomics: 10-year mapping review of patient-centered human factors. *Applied Ergonomics, 82*, 102972.

Holden, R. J., Schubert, C. C., & Mickelson, R. S. (2015). The patient work system: An analysis of self-care performance barriers among elderly heart failure patients and their informal caregivers. *Applied Ergonomics, 47*, 133–150.

Holden, R. J., & Valdez, R. S. (2018). *Town hall on patient-centered human factors and ergonomics.* Paper presented at the Proceedings of the Human Factors and Ergonomics Society Annual Meeting.

Holden, R. J., Valdez, R. S., Schubert, C. C., Thompson, M. J., & Hundt, A. S. (2017). Macroergonomic factors in the patient work system: Examining the context of patients with chronic illness. *Ergonomics, 60*(1), 26–43.

Houser, A., Fox-Grage, W., & Gibson, M. J. (2006). *Across the states 2006.* Washington, DC.

Houser, A., Fox-Grage, W., & Ujvari, K. (2018). *Across the states 2018.* Washington, DC.

Hudson, R. B. (2014). Aging and technology: The promise and the paradox. *Public Policy & Aging Report, 24*(1), 3–5.

Joint Center for Housing Studies. (2018). *Housing America's older adults.* In Jchs Cambridge, MA.

Kleiner, B. M. (2006). Macroergonomics: Analysis and design of work systems. *Applied Ergonomics, 37*(1), 81–89.

Kleiner, B. M. (2008). Macroegonomics: Work system analysis and design. *Human Factors, 50*(3), 461–467.

Landis, M., Peter-Wight, M., Martin, M., & Bodenmann, G. (2013). Dyadic coping and marital satisfaction of older spouses in long-term marriage. *Journal of the Gerontopsychology and Geriatric Psychiatry, 26*(1), 39–48.

Mann, D., Ponieman, D., Montori, V. M., Arciniega, J., & McGinn, T. (2010). The Statin Choice decision aid in primary care: A randomized trial. *Patient Education and Counseling, 80*(1), 138–140.

Mathers, N., Ng, C. J., Campbell, M. J., Colwell, B., Brown, I., & Bradley, A. (2012). Clinical effectiveness of a patient decision aid to improve decision quality and glycaemic control in people with diabetes making treatment choices: A cluster randomised controlled trial (PANDAs) in general practice. *The BMJ Open, 2*(6), e001469.

McLaughlin, S. J., Jette, A. M., & Connell, C. M. (2012). An examination of healthy aging across a conceptual continuum: Prevalence estimates, demographic patterns, and validity. *Journals of Gerontology Series A: Biomedical Sciences and Medical Sciences, 67*(7), 783–789.

Mickelson, R. S., & Holden, R. J. (2018). Medication management strategies used by older adults with heart failure: A systems-based analysis. *European Journal of Cardiovascular Nursing, 17*(5), 418–428.

Mickelson, R. S., Unertl, K. M., & Holden, R. J. (2016). Medication management: The macrocognitive workflow of older adults with heart failure. *Journal of Medical Internet Research Human Factors, 3*(2), e27.

Mitzner, T. L., Chen, T. L., Kemp, C. C., & Rogers, W. A. (2014). Identifying the potential for robotics to assist older adults in different living environments. *International Journal of Social Robotics, 6*(2), 213–227.

Mitzner, T. L., McBride, S. E., Barg-Walkow, L. H., & Rogers, W. A. (2013). Self-management of wellness and illness in an aging population. *Reviews of Human Factors and Ergonomics, 8*(1), 277–333.

Mitzner, T. L., Sanford, J. A., & Rogers, W. A. (2018). Closing the capacity-ability gap: Using technology to support aging with disability. *Innovation in Aging, 2*(1), 1–8.

Moen, A., & Brennan, P. F. (2005). Health@ Home: The work of health information management in the household (HIMH): Implications for consumer health informatics (CHI) innovations. *Journal of the American Medical Informatics Association, 12*(6), 648–656.

National Alliance for Caregiving (NAC), & AARP Public Policy Institute. (2015). *Caregiving in the U.S.* Retrieved from https://www.caregiving.org/research/caregivingusa

National Research Council. (2011). *Health care comes home: The human factors.* Washington, DC.

Norman, D. A., & Draper, S. W. (1986). *User-centered system design: New perspectives on human-computer interaction.* Hillsdale, NJ: Lawrence Erlbaum Associates.

Rogers, W. A., & Fisk, A. D. (2010). Toward a psychological science of advanced technology design for older adults. *Journals of Gerontology Series B: Psychological Sciences and Social Sciences, 65*(6), 645–653.

Rogers, W. A., Meyer, B., Walker, N., & Fisk, A. D. (1998). Functional limitations to daily living tasks in the aged: A focus group analysis. *Human Factors, 40*(1), 111–125.

Rogers, W. A., & Mitzner, T. L. (2017). Envisioning the future for older adults: Autonomy, health, well-being, and social connectedness with technology support. *Futures, 87,* 133–139.

Rogers, W. A., Mitzner, T. L., & Bixter, M. T. (2020). Understanding the potential of technology to support enhanced activities of daily living (EADLs). *Gerontechnology, 19*(2), 125–137.

Rogers, W. A., Stronge, A. J., & Fisk, A. D. (2005). Technology and aging. *Reviews of Human Factors and Ergonomics, 1*(1), 130–171.

Rosenthal, T. C., & Fox, C. (2000). Access to health care for the rural elderly. *Journal of the American Medical Association, 284*(16), 2034–2036.

Rowe, J. W., & Kahn, R. L. (1997). Successful aging. *The Gerontologist, 37*(4), 433–440.

Rutten, L. J. F., Arora, N. K., Bakos, A. D., Aziz, N., & Rowland, J. H. (2005). Information needs and sources of information among cancer patients: A systematic review of research (1980–2003). *Patient Education and Counseling, 57*(3), 250–261.

Sanford, J. (2010). The Physical Environment and Home Health Care. In N. R. Council (Ed.), *The role of human factors in home health care: Workshop summary* (pp. 201–246). Washington, DC: National Academies Press (US).

Shafer, R. (2000). *Housing America's seniors. Executive summary.* Cambridge, MA: Joint Center for Housing Studies, Harvard University.

Smarr, C.-A., Fausset, C. B., & Rogers, W. A. (2011). *Understanding the potential for robot assistance for older adults in the home environment.*

Spector, W. D., & Fleishman, J. A. (1998). Combining activities of daily living with instrumental activities of daily living to measure functional disability. *The Journals of Gerontology Series B: Psychological Sciences and Social Sciences, 53*(1), S46–S57.

Srinivas, P., Cornet, V., & Holden, R. (2017). Human factors analysis, design, and evaluation of Engage, a consumer health IT application for geriatric heart failure self-care. *International Journal of Human–Computer Interaction, 33*(4), 298–312.

Tang, P., & Venables, T. (2000). 'Smart' homes and telecare for independent living. *Journal of Telemedicine and Telecare, 6*(1), 8–14.

Tapp, H., Dulin, M., & Plescia, M. (2018). Chronic Disease Self-Management. In T. P. Daaleman & M. R. Helton (Eds.), *Chronic illness care: Principles and practice* (pp. 29–40). Cham: Springer International Publishing.

Valdez, R. S., Holden, R. J., Novak, L. L., & Veinot, T. C. (2015). Transforming consumer health informatics through a patient work framework: Connecting patients to context. *Journal of the American Medical Informatics Association, 22*(1), 2–10.

Veinot, T. C., Mitchell, H., & Ancker, J. S. (2018). Good intentions are not enough: How informatics interventions can worsen inequality. *Journal of the American Medical Informatics Association, 25*(8), 1080–1088.

Werner, N. E., Gilmore-Bykovskyi, A., Zenker, R., Pardell, C., & Kind, A. J. (2017). [P1–550]: Enhancing teamwork across informal Alzheimer's disease caregiving networks through novel health information technologies: A human factors engineering approach. *Alzheimer's & Dementia, 13*(7S_Part_10), P504–P504.

Werner, N. E., Gurses, A. P., Leff, B., & Arbaje, A. I. (2016). Improving care transitions across healthcare settings through a human factors approach. *Journal of Healthcare Quality, 38*(6), 328–343.

Werner, N. E., Jolliff, A. F., Casper, G., Martell, T., & Ponto, K. (2018). Home is where the head is: A distributed cognition account of personal health information management in the home among those with chronic illness. *Ergonomics, 61*(8), 1065–1078.

Werner, N. E., Malkana, S., Gurses, A. P., Leff, B., & Arbaje, A. I. (2017). Toward a process-level view of distributed healthcare tasks: Medication management as a case study. *Applied Ergonomics, 65*, 255–268.

Werner, N. E., Tong, M., Borkenhagen, A., & Holden, R. J. (2018). Performance-shaping factors affecting older adults' hospital-to-home transition success: A systems approach. *Gerontologist, 59*(2), 303–314.

Whitlatch, C. J., Judge, K., Zarit, S. H., & Femia, E. (2006). Dyadic intervention for family caregivers and care receivers in early-stage dementia. *Gerontologist, 46*(5), 688–694.

Willems, D. L., Hak, A., Visser, F. C., Cornel, J., & Van der Wal, G. (2006). Patient work in end-stage heart failure: A prospective longitudinal multiple case study. *Palliative Medicine, 20*(1), 25–33.

Wilson, J. R. (2014). Fundamentals of systems ergonomics/human factors. *Applied Ergonomics, 45*(1), 5–13.

Wolff, J. L., Freedman, V. A., Mulcahy, J. F., & Kasper, J. D. (2020). Family caregivers' experiences with health care workers in the care of older adults with activity limitations. *Journal of the American Medical Association Network Open, 3*(1), e1919866.

# 10 Underserved Populations
## *Integrating Social Determinants of Health into the Study of Patient Work*

Natalie C. Benda and Ruth M. Masterson Creber
Department of Population Health
Sciences Weill Cornell Medicine

## CONTENTS

*Underserved populations* have been defined as "groups whose demographic, geographic, or economic characteristics impede or prevent group members' access to healthcare services" (Blumenthal et al., 1995). *Social determinants of health* (SDoH), the conditions under which people live, grow, and work, have been found to explain 80% of health outcomes (McGovern et al., 2014). In other words, *social determinants* can impede the equitable attainment of health and wellness, specifically for underserved populations. Table 10.1 outlines six commonly accepted domains of SDoH and provides examples within each domain. Each of these factors can affect health outcomes, including mortality, morbidity, life expectancy, health expenditures, functional limitations, and health-related quality of life (Bennett et al., 2018). For example, in reviewing Table 10.1, it may be apparent that a person's physical environment affects the types and quality of healthcare patients can access. Consequently, healthcare facilities in poorer neighborhoods have been demonstrated to perform significantly worse in measures of quality and safety than the facilities in wealthier neighborhoods (Weiss et al., 2011). In part due to differences in SDoH, the life expectancy in different nations throughout the world ranges from 53 to 84 years and varies by over 20 years within different regions of the United States (Dwyer-Lindgren et al., 2017; World Health Organization, 2018). One study from the United States found determinants related to economic stability, including inability to work, unemployment, and lower income, were the strongest predictors of health-related quality of life (Jiang & Hesser, 2006).

The World Health Organization's Commission on SDoH (2008) argues that reducing health inequity and addressing SDoH are not only logical but also a moral, social justice imperative:

> This unequal distribution of health-damaging experiences is not in any sense a 'natural' phenomenon but is the result of a toxic combination of poor social policies and programmes, unfair economic arrangements, and bad politics. Together, the structural determinants and conditions of daily life constitute the social determinants of health and are responsible for a major part of health inequities between and within countries (p. 1).

The field of ergonomics also has founding tenets that make ergonomists uniquely situated for improving health and wellness in underserved communities by targeting SDoH as a part of the larger patient work system. In particular, ergonomists are trained to think about the ways multiple components of a system interact to produce health outcomes. There is an opportunity, therefore, for our studies of patient work to consider SDoH as within the bounds of the systems we analyze and design. Integration of SDoH into the study of patient ergonomics will advance health and wellness for underserved populations and holistically improve the scope and value of healthcare services. This chapter focuses on how SDoH may be integrated into patient ergonomics to improve health and wellness for *underserved populations* in each phase of the project life cycle (e.g. study conception, data collection, analysis, and interpretation).

Figure 10.1 presents a model of the patient work system that holistically considers needs of underserved populations. The model depicts the traditional elements of the patient work system described by Holden and colleagues (2017) highlighting person/individual and sociocultural components of the work system; this is also discussed by Kroemer (2006) as well as Smith-Jackson et al. (2013). The model also incorporates many of the domains of SDoH from Table 10.1 (physical environment, economic factors, social context) along with other systems-level factors (people, technology, organization, tasks). The figure demonstrates that inclusive design for patient work (i.e.

**TABLE 10.1**
**Domains and Examples of SDOH**

| Domain | Economic Stability | Physical Environment | Education | Food | Community, Social Context | Healthcare System |
|---|---|---|---|---|---|---|
| Examples | • Employment<br>• Income<br>• Expenses<br>• Medical bills | • Housing<br>• Transportation access<br>• Safety<br>• Parks/trees<br>• Pollution, environmental exposures | • Literacy<br>• Numeracy<br>• Language<br>• Early childhood education<br>• Higher education | • Hunger<br>• Access to fresh foods/ healthy options | • Social integration<br>• Support systems<br>• Discrimination | • Health coverage<br>• Provider linguistic and cultural competency<br>• Quality of care |

*Source:* Adapted from Bennett et al. (2018).

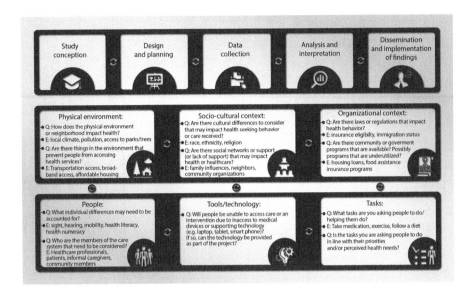

**FIGURE 10.1** A model for integrating SDoH into patient ergonomics. Bullets preceded by a "Q" signal questions to consider, whereas subsequent bullets preceded by an "E" signal example consideration related to the question. Not all questions have relevant examples related to SDOH.

inclusion of underserved groups) should be an integral part throughout the project life cycle as opposed to an add-on post-hoc subgroup consideration. In other words, it is more inclusive to begin the intervention design process considering how multiple groups may benefit from an intervention rather than to design the intervention for the "average user" and try to retrofit aspects for other groups later. The framework includes questions that may be helpful to ask (Q) and examples of factors to consider related to the question (E) in each component of the work system. Throughout the chapter, the model will serve as a framework for discussing past and future initiatives in this space.

## 10.1 REVIEW OF LITERATURE

### 10.1.1 ERGONOMICS LITERATURE FOCUSED ON UNDERSERVED POPULATIONS

Three works by ergonomists have addressed underserved populations in a broader context, but are not specific to patients. Kroemer's (2006) book *Extra-ordinary Ergonomics* highlights how design favors the "ordinary" user and ignores those who are traditionally underserved. This volume is of particular relevance for those designing patient work systems by providing strategies for inclusive design across a spectrum of psychological and physiological capabilities (Kroemer, 2006). Smith-Jackson et al.'s (2013) book *Cultural Ergonomics* conveys the importance of considering sociocultural factors in ergonomics research and design. The authors encourage researchers to combat their ethnocentric tendency to design solutions that disproportionately consider those similar to themselves. For example, some cultures may be more comfortable with risk and uncertainty than others, so in conversations related to prognosis or end-of-life, healthcare professionals may require guidance when discussing these issues with patients from different cultural backgrounds than their own (Periyakoil et al., 2015). Roscoe, Chiou, and Wooldridge's *Advancing Diversity, Inclusion, and Social Justice Through Human Systems Engineering* provides stories, methods, and practical applications for leveraging systems engineering to advance social justice (Roscoe et al., 2020). Although the majority of the book does not have a health-specific focus, the content is directly applicable to patient ergonomics efforts. In particular, the broad discussion of SDoH as related to ergonomics provides readers with a sense of the scope of factors that should be considered in design efforts. The section on healthy communities provides some additional guidance on linking these considerations to health-related application areas. Taken together, these works form a foundation for how ergonomists should approach understanding and supporting patient work with underserved populations.

### 10.1.2 Transition to Focus on Underserved Patient Populations

There has been an influx of human factors practitioners working in the healthcare domain over the past 30 years, in conjunction with the patient safety movement (Wears et al., 2014). Similar to other patient-centric work, initial research predominantly took place in the hospital environment (Wears et al., 2014). The work of ergonomists has since expanded to home and community environments (see also Chapter 4 of this volume), considering patient efforts related to wellness and self-care (see also Chapter 7 of Volume I) (Valdez & Holden, 2016). Ergonomists have also begun to address issues related to underserved patients (Benda et al., 2018; Valdez et al., 2019). They have helped consider the individual, organizational, sociocultural, and environmental contexts in the design of tools and technologies that support patients (Ezer et al., 2009; Harrington & Joines, 2011; Matalenas et al., 2016).

### 10.1.3 Applications to Health Information Technology (IT)
### and Medical Devices

Incremental progress has been made toward understanding and improving the use of health information among underserved groups, with a focus on personal health records. Previous work highlighted decreased use and benefits of health IT among older adults, racial and ethnic minorities, and those with limited English proficiency (Ancker et al., 2011; Montague & Perchonok, 2012). Others have developed design guidelines improving equity in the benefits derived from accessing personal health information with specific considerations for access, social/cultural appropriateness, and differences in cognitive abilities (e.g. limited literacy) (Barclay & Bowers, 2017; Valdez et al., 2012). Some researchers have also demonstrated that improving usability and devising more inclusive access policies can increase satisfaction and reduce disparities in the use of personal health records (Ali et al., 2018; Ancker et al., 2017). Despite these pockets of improvement, a recent review found that progress for widespread reduction of disparities related to benefits derived from personal health records remains slow (Grossman et al., 2019).

Ergonomists have also involved those from underserved groups in efforts to design and test health IT and medical devices. Many of these studies have focused on diabetes, a disease that disproportionately affects underserved populations. Story and colleagues (2009) completed usability tests and proposed design guidance for medical devices (e.g. glucometers) for those with physiological impairments, specifically limited vision. Zachary et al. (2017) utilized a participatory design process to develop a tool for diabetes self-management in low-income minority communities. The tool utilizes input from informal caregivers (family and friends) to support the patient's self-management needs (Zachary et al., 2017). Cage and colleagues (2014) combined approaches related to personal health records and a focus on diabetic patients in a multiphase effort to create a database of design preferences for minority patients. Valdez and Brennan (2015) and Valdez et al. (2017) describe support needs for patients with type 2 diabetes regarding health information communication and formulated recommendations for health IT design. Instead of targeting one specific demographic group, these studies used maximum variance and stratified sampling approaches to ensure inclusion of participants self-identifying across racial and ethnic identities (Valdez & Brennan, 2015; Valdez, Guterbock, et al., 2017).

### 10.1.4 CONCLUSION

Considering patient SDoH is far from embedded in our work as ergonomists, although the meaningful work previously described has aided progress toward integration. For example, the National Institutes of Health (NIH) had over 88,000 active grants in 2020. In a keyword search, over 1,322 had elements related to human factors and ergonomics, and 4,782 grants had elements related to health equity. However, only 117 of these grants coupled elements of human factors and ergonomics with work focused on underserved populations. In addition, Holden et al.'s (2020) review of over 200 proceedings papers of patient ergonomic work found fewer than ten that focused on underserved populations. There have, however, been several years of panels and town halls at the Human Factors and Ergonomics Society's Annual Meeting and Annual Healthcare Symposium demonstrating the growing consideration of SDoH and underserved populations taking a patient work approach (Benda et al., 2018; Holden & Valdez, 2018, 2019; Valdez et al., 2014, 2016; Valdez, Holden, et al., 2017; Valdez et al., 2019). This points to a growing effort to attend to this important intersection.

## 10.2 CASE STUDIES

We describe two case studies based on the project phases from Figure 10.1. Throughout each phase, we highlight how we accommodated (or were limited by) the interaction systems-level factors (from Figure 10.1), particularly as related to SDoH.

### 10.2.1 CASE STUDY 1 – COMMUNICATING WITH LIMITED ENGLISH PROFICIENT PATIENTS IN THE EMERGENCY DEPARTMENT

#### 10.2.1.1 Study Conception

*Selection of the patient population* in this case study was based on sociocultural SDoH that have been linked with health disparities. Namely, patients who speak a different language than the majority of the population, known in the United States as limited English proficiency (LEP), face disparities related to patient safety, quality of care, and reported satisfaction with their care (Divi et al., 2007; Ngai et al., 2016; Ramirez et al., 2008).

*Selection of the study environment*, the emergency department (ED), was based on organizational contexts that make patients with LEP more likely to seek care in the setting as well as physical, organizational, and people-based constraints that make caring for patients with LEP in the ED more challenging. Patients with LEP seek care in the ED at a higher rate compared with English-speaking patients (Timmins, 2002), in part due to reduced access to primary care services (Yu & Singh, 2009). The population's reduced access to care may stem from organizational reasons, such as economic constraints (e.g. underemployment, insurance costs) or legal constraints (e.g. legal status that permits them from obtaining insurance). Inclusion of professionally trained interpreters has been found to partly reduce the care disparities encountered by patients with LEP (Flores et al., 2012). However, several studies have demonstrated that clinicians underutilize professional interpreters due to physical, organizational, and social constraints, such as time and resource requirements as well as perceived loss of control over the encounter (Hsieh et al., 2010). Clinicians face particularly difficult organizational constraints using professional interpreters at the point of care in the ED because interpreters cannot be scheduled to arrive with the patient in advance, in contrast to the outpatient environment.

*Selection of the tasks to study* was based on gaps in previous research related to complexities of the organizational context of the ED and the different people that interact in the care system. Unsurprisingly, health disparities for patients with LEP have been linked to tasks related to communication with other people in the system (Divi et al., 2007). The case study addressed gaps in previous research by studying communication with Spanish-speaking patients with LEP throughout their entire stay in the ED. We also studied how different people (e.g. professional interpreters, family members, health professionals, patients) facilitate communication, expanding the focus of communication tasks above and beyond verbatim translation (Hsieh, 2016). Our research questions were as follows:

- How do different people (e.g. interpreters) communicate with LEP patients?
- What tasks (and associated strategies) are used for communication of information above and beyond verbatim translation?
- How do different contextual factors affect who facilitates communication (people) and how communication occurs (tasks and strategies)?

Considering the people aspect of the system is also important when selecting members of the project team. *Selection of the research team involved* considering the study environment (emergency medicine), relevant tasks/subject matters (communication, patient ergonomics), the patient population (Spanish-speaking patients with LEP), local organizational (clinicians employed by the health system), and sociocultural context (public/community health experts).

## 10.2.1.2 Design and Planning/Data Collection

In this study, we used a combination of patient tracing observations and member-checking interviews (see concluding two paragraphs of this section). We completed observations with LEP and English proficient participants throughout their stay in the ED until we had reached theoretical saturation of themes. Data collection occurred during any instance where participants (patients) communicated with hospital staff members. We elected to only record communicative information during these instances to preserve some privacy for patients and others accompanying them (e.g. family members). Notes were recorded in a transcript-style format using pen and paper and included the following elements: beginning and end time stamp of the communication exchange; hospital staff member role; strategy used for communicating with the patient (e.g. in-person interpreter, patient family); phase of care; and the content of the information exchanged (not included in this chapter). See Benda (2018) and Benda et al. (2019b) for further details. Our description here focuses on data collection considerations related to the interaction of SDoH and systems-level factors.

First, we included both the underserved group (i.e. patients with LEP) and the majority patient group, in this case, English proficient patients. Focusing solely on an underserved group may help reduce targeted disparities, whereas including majority groups can identify differences in design needs and facilitate creating solutions that are broadly inclusive, appropriate for multiple groups. In this case study, we noted the importance of understanding how communication occurred with English proficient patients, disentangling challenges related to language barriers from those that arose due to the intrinsic complexity of the patient communication in the ED environment. By including English proficient participants, our intent was to identify which strategies were used in the ED regardless of English proficiency.

Second, working with underserved patients specifically requires careful consideration in the design of research materials for different sociocultural needs and to accommodate the abilities of different people. For example, this study required the translation of all participant-facing materials into Spanish. Prior to translation, we also reviewed study materials (i.e. information and consent letter) with a health services researcher with extensive experience conducting research with various underserved patient groups. The consultations ensured the materials contained plain, simple language easily understandable by patients who may be unfamiliar with the research process. Failing to consider different abilities (e.g. health literacy) may cause a study to inadvertently self-select more advantaged patients. The Agency for Healthcare Research and Quality (AHRQ) (Agency for Healthcare Research and Quality, 2019) and the Centers for Disease Control and prevention (CDC) (Baur & Prue, 2014) have freely available guidance for creating plain language materials for patients.

Following plain language consultations, a paid professional service translated the information and consent letter. Institutional Review Boards (IRBs) often require translation of study materials by a paid service that provides a certificate of translation. It is important to consider additional resources related to including underserved groups in research, such as translation, so these costs may be planned in advance. As a further assurance that the participants understood the study and what they were consenting to, we built in a "teach-back" process, whereby the participant was asked to explain what they agreed to in their own words. The consent process took place with a researcher proficient in both English and Spanish. However, in the absence of bilingual research staff, interpreters may aid in the consent process if they are involved in an early stage and can ensure this does not interfere with their primary job of medical interpreting.

Third, we chose our data collection mechanism based on what may be the safest and most comfortable given organizational constraints for our participants. For example, some patients with LEP may be uncomfortable with questions related to personal information (e.g. name, date of birth) due to their immigration status. For this study, we elected not to collect demographic information in favor of protecting the participants and ensuring their comfortability. Data collection also occurred via pen and paper (in English, translated in real time by the investigator) due to the amount of sensitive personal and medical information that may be picked up using a recording device in an ED setting. Our research team made decisions regarding the data collection methodology following consultation with ED personnel and the IRB. We had also demonstrated the feasibility of collecting information related to communication in the ED using pen-and-paper notes in a previous study (Benda, Hettinger, et al., 2017).

Fourth, in the given case study, we also made an oversight regarding the groups of people we needed to involve. The study was approved by the ED staff as well as the IRB. We notified ED staff via emails and fliers in break spaces regarding the study. Our team, however, initially inadvertently failed to communicate with the hospital's interpreter service department. The research team did not recognize that the interpreters might be less accustomed to being shadowed than clinicians in an academic medical center who are frequently observed for teaching purposes. In order to ensure the interpreters working in the ED were comfortable with the study, we amended the IRB protocol to involve a voluntary consent for interpreters in addition to patients. Our initial failure to consider the unique needs of the interpreters involved slowed the study by multiple months. This experience highlights the criticality of considering *all* those who may be involved in a project, particularly those who fall outside of traditional clinician roles (e.g. nurse, physician, pharmacist). The interpreters became crucial allies throughout this project, and the subsequent work would not have been possible without their support.

### 10.2.1.3 Analysis and Interpretation

We utilized member-checking interviews with *ED clinicians*, which included nurses, physicians, advanced practice providers, and hospital-based interpreters, following the collection of observational data to improve the validity of the data interpretation related to this case study. Clinicians (from two hospitals) and interpreters (from one hospital) vetted key themes detected during the observations. Only one of the two hospitals from which we recruited clinicians employed professional interpreters, so we recruited interpreters from a single hospital. Feedback from participants in this stage did not greatly alter the themes themselves. However, member checking facilitated the presentation of exemplars related to the themes that most accurately reflected communication with patients with LEP in the ED. For example, one theme described how professional interpreters might anticipate issues in a patient's understanding of terms and provide an alternative word that may be more colloquial or understandable to the patient. The initial exemplar (in the interviews) involved an interpreter adding, "Are you married?" after interpreting that the clerical staff had asked for their "marital status." Clinicians noted that this type of action was more important for medical terminology. Therefore, a different example from the observations was included in the presentation of results to reflect this scenario. Specifically, at one point a nurse asked the patient about pain in their "abdomen" and the interpreter added "abdomen or stomach" to facilitate the patient's understanding.

Our research team decided not to complete member-checking interviews with patients based on organizational constraints (e.g. time, privacy), which was a limitation of the work. Following up with patients for interviews after their stay in the ED would have involved collecting their personal information (e.g. name and phone number). As described, patients with LEP in particular may be uncomfortable providing identifying information. In addition, analysis of data from interviews with Spanish-speaking participants presented a challenge as only one member of the research team spoke Spanish proficiently. As with any study, our project team needed to balance the feasibility of data collection and the inherent limitations of a project. Balancing these considerations is particularly necessary in patient ergonomics studies focused on underserved populations.

### 10.2.1.4  Dissemination and Implementation of Findings

Table 10.2 provides a summary of the dissemination plan related to this study based on the different clinical (emergency medicine), scientific (human factors), and patient population (health disparities researchers, interpreter service organizations) communities that may have interest in this work. We attempted to strike a balance between discussing methods and lessons learned with other ergonomists, providing insight to those who focus on improving health equity, and conveying findings to the frontline staff involved in caring for these patients (emergency medicine clinicians, interpreters). Gaining traction in clinically oriented journals may be challenging, but it

**TABLE 10.2**
**Dissemination Plan – Case Study 1**

| Outlet | Description | Citation |
|---|---|---|
| Human factors conference | Problem and methodological description using cognitive work analysis to understand and improve communication with LEP patients | Benda, Higginbotham, et al. (2017) |
| | Use of "prototypes" to represent conversations with patients in the emergency department | Benda and Bisantz (2019) |
| Emergency medicine-focused journal | Descriptive statistics related to patterns of interpreter use throughout the phases of care in the emergency department | Benda et al. (2019a) |
| Health equity or patient communication-focused journal | Qualitative differences in strategies used for communication by hospital staff and different types of interpreters | Benda et al. (2020) |
| Newsletter or magazine targeted at medical interpreters | Brief description of the role of professional interpreters in improving care for LEP patients above and beyond verbatim translation | To be developed |

provides an opportunity to disseminate the work to those who experience and can affect these issues on a daily basis.

## 10.2.2 Case Study 2 – Using Patient Reported Outcomes to Improve Care for Heart Failure Patients

### 10.2.2.1 Study Conception

For this second case study, we based *selection of the patient population* on people and disease-based factors as well as sociocultural and organizational contexts. The disease focus, heart failure (HF), is a large and growing global health concern that affects more than 26 million people worldwide (Ponikowski et al., 2014) and more than 6 million patients in the United States (Benjamin et al., 2018). Patients with HF experience progressively worsening symptoms that limit physical and social activities and have been linked to decreased quality of life (Green et al., 2000; Spertus, 2008). Previous work has demonstrated that environmental and sociocultural SDoH, including socioeconomic status, gender, age, and race significantly impact health outcomes among patients with HF (Erceg et al., 2013). It is also important for patients with HF to regularly engage in self-management activities. As a result, person and environmental factors, such as health literacy, education, and access to resources, play an important role in this population's health.

In this study, we took a patient work approach to improving symptom management among patients with HF, due to the critical role of the patient in managing their own condition. Furthermore, we created an intervention using an iterative participatory design approach with diverse samples of patients (across age, race, ethnicity, language, and socioeconomic status) to ensure the intervention is useful and usable across patients with varied SDoH.

We *selected the tasks/intervention* for this study to better link different people in the system (e.g. patients and providers) through tools/technology. This case study involves the design and evaluation of a mobile health (mHealth)-based application for collecting patient-reported outcomes (PROs) and then displaying them to patients and their care team to facilitate shared decision-making (Manemann et al., 2016). PROs can be particularly useful among older adults with multiple chronic conditions as they can help track overlapping symptoms and monitor health globally (e.g. health-related quality of life) (Lavallee et al., 2016). The long-term value of PROs will be realized when they are collected electronically and included into the patient health record, in ways that allow for integration into clinical care and decision-making. Inclusive design is particularly important for patient populations with HF as these patients are typically older and commercially available technologies (e.g. laptops, cell phones, tablets) are not frequently optimized for older adult users.

We *based selection of technology* on person, environmental, and sociocultural factors. In this study, we initially designed a mHealth-based application for collecting PROs from patients with HF, although we later made the tool available for tablets and laptops. Data from the Pew Research Center estimates that 79% of Hispanics and 80% of African Americans owned smartphones, levels which are comparable to smartphone ownership among Caucasians (82%) (Pew Research Center, 2019b).

African Americans and Hispanics, however, are twice as likely as Caucasians (23% and 25% vs. 12%, respectively) to be dependent on smartphones for internet access (Pew Research Center, 2019a) and not have access to broadband internet necessary for using tablets and laptops. Therefore, we elected to focus delivery of PRO symptom reporting using a mHealth-optimized web application called "mi.Symptoms," because it presents fewer barriers to access and use among diverse groups of patients.

Similar to case study 1, *selection of the research team involved* inclusion of individuals with relevant expertise related to: clinical domains (heart failure, nursing, cardiology); tasks/intervention (patient-reported outcomes, information visualization); tools/technology (mobile health technology, web applications); and a patient population that historically faces various health disparities (public health/health equity). The patient work approach was also integral to our study. We used a participatory, user-centered design approach to create an application for use by a diverse patient population.

### 10.2.2.2   Design and Planning, Data Collection, and Analysis and Interpretation

We designed multiple studies for the creation of *mi.Symptoms* to involve a process for iterative patient involvement. Table 10.3 summarizes our multistudy approach that culminates in a longitudinal feasibility study to assess the effectiveness of *mi.Symptoms* in improving physical symptoms, psychological symptoms, and quality of life.

We deliberately sampled a diverse and balanced group of patients related to age, gender, race, ethnicity, and language. In each study, at least 40% of our patients represented racial minorities and at least 20% included ethnic minorities. For age, we purposefully sampled across four generation groups (Millennials, Generation X, Boomers, and Silent Generation) (Pew Research Center). Generation group is a recommended metric for adequacy of a research sample on age because it is more informative of social context, secular trends in cohorts, and personal history than an arbitrary biological age category. The English version of the *mi.Symptoms* web application was also translated into Spanish, and some, but not all studies involved Spanish-speaking patients. Resultant samples also represented other groups that may not always be well represented in research with nearly half of participants reporting having trouble making ends meet financially, greater than 40% having a high school education or below, and greater than 45% having inadequate health literacy. Almost

---

**TABLE 10.3**
**Overview of Studies – Case Study 2**

| Study | Participants | Study Time Frame |
|---|---|---|
| Needs assessment (interviews) | 13 patients, 11 healthcare professionals | 2016 |
| Usability assessment | 12 patients | 2017 |
| Feasibility, cross-sectional pilot study | 168 patients | 2017–2018 |
| Visualization comprehension study | 40 patients | 2019 |
| Longitudinal feasibility study | 75 patients (ongoing) | 2020 |

a third of the sample did not have access to a computer at home and a quarter did not have access to the internet (Baik et al., 2019; Reading Turchioe, Grossman, Baik, et al., 2020). The subsequent paragraphs describe the purpose, sample, methods, results, and implications of each substudy in greater detail.

Prior to interacting with participants, we created an early prototype of *mi Symptoms* based on a systematic review of symptom self-monitoring tools for patients with HF (Masterson Creber, Maurer, et al., 2016). Our first user study involved (in 2016) an initial needs assessment eliciting qualitative and quantitative (survey-based) feedback from both patients with HF and healthcare professionals treating patients with HF (Grossman et al., 2018). We identified patient participants using purposeful sampling and recruited them from a cardiac inpatient unit and an ambulatory cardiac clinic at an urban academic medical center. The interviews involved having participants use *mi.symptoms* and provide feedback on semistructured questions including the usefulness of *mi.Symptoms,* helpful/unhelpful features, and recommended changes. A qualitative analysis of the interview transcripts revealed challenges related to use of *mi.symptoms* such as trouble understanding the PRO questions, lack of unstructured communication, and low technology literacy. Importantly, nearly half of the patients reported trouble understanding the PRO questions and reporting their symptoms. The findings of this initial study led to developing a series of design requirements, notably, that the design of the system should help patients understand the questions and that the design should educate the patients related to how their symptoms are linked with their disease. We revised *mi.Symptoms* based on these preliminary findings.

Next, we completed a usability assessment with a group of 12 new patients, purposefully sampled from a cardiac inpatient unit. During the usability study, participants executed tasks using *mi.Symptoms*, such as answering survey questions and interpreting survey results. Participants also provided preferences regarding different visualization options for presenting PROs and completed the eight-item Standardized User Experience Percentile Rank Questionnaire (SUPR-Q). The SUPR-Q assesses usability, credibility, loyalty, appearance, and overall quality (Sauro, 2015; Schnall et al., 2018). This set of patients rated the revised version highly across all constructs in the SUPR-Q (all > 0.9 out of 1). However, we discovered that half of the patients failed to interpret graphs of symptoms and others required multiple attempts to correctly interpret graphical information (Grossman et al., 2018). This finding led us to the create new PRO visualization options and to add an assessment of participant graph literacy in the future 2019 visualization comprehension study (Reading Turchioe, Grossman, Myers, et al., 2020).

Our 2017–2018 study involved a larger scale feasibility assessment of *mi.Symptoms*. We recruited 168 patients from an inpatient cardiac unit and an ambulatory cardiac clinic. The feasibility study also involved a Spanish version of *mi.Symptoms* evaluated by patients with a preferred language of Spanish. In the study, we assessed the correlation of the symptoms included in *mi.Symptoms* with a validated measure of health status. In addition, participants provided feedback on usefulness and ease of use using a modified Health Information Technology Usability Evaluation Scale (Health-ITUES) (Schnall et al., 2018). We found that it was feasible for patients with HF to complete the PRO questions in *mi.Symptoms* (i.e. there was no missing data) and participants rated the tool as both useful and easy to use. Furthermore, there were no differences in perceived usefulness or ease of use based on age, suggesting that the application was also suitable for older adults (Baik et al., 2019; Reading Turchioe, Grossman, Baik, et al., 2020).

In the 2017 usability study, we found that participants struggled to accurately interpret graphical presentations of symptoms (Grossman et al., 2018). To address this issue, we completed a visualization comprehension study (2019) with another group of 40 participants with HF. We purposively sampled 40 hospitalized patients with HF. In this study, we assessed participant performance interpreting PRO result information across four visualization conditions: text-only; text plus visual analogy; text plus number line; and text plus line graph (Reading Turchioe, Grossman, Myers, et al., 2020). The visual analogy compared patients' functioning using a colored gauge (signifying low, medium, and high) as shown in the bottom left of Figure 10.2. The visualization condition that had the highest comprehension was the visual analogy condition (83% correct). We also found that participants scored poorly on validated assessment of graph literacy, indicating that graphical visualizations, more specifically line graphs, may not support patient comprehension as much as other visualizations for this population. We also found that participants with worse cognition, lower education, and fewer financial resources had poorer comprehension of the visualizations presented, suggesting that failure to create appropriate graphical representations could have a particularly negative impact on already marginalized patients.

We have used the results of a series of usability studies with diverse groups of patients to design a validated PRO and shared decision-making application that was found useful and usable by participants. All studies involved purposive sampling across age and race, and the large-scale feasibility assessment included both English and Spanish-speaking participants. We also created a visual analogy for presenting PRO-based health information to patients that was well understood.

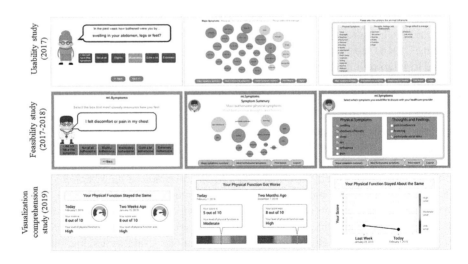

**FIGURE 10.2**  Depiction of the development of the *mi.Symptoms* interface across relevant studies.

Figure 10.2 illustrates the development of the *mi.Symptoms* interface over the previously described studies. We are currently enrolling patients in a longitudinal feasibility study to assess the feasibility of use over time with those participants in both an inpatient and outpatient setting. The next step is to conduct a randomized controlled trial to determine the effectiveness of *mi.Symptoms* in improving symptom management and quality of life among patients with HF as compared to usual care.

In addition to incorporating different people in the patient work system (e.g. patients, healthcare professionals) throughout the project life cycle, we also made study design considerations based on the patient's environment, assessment of patient abilities, and the sociocultural organizational contexts.

We partly attribute the ability to recruit a diverse sample of patients to our *choice of study location/recruitment*. Previous studies have demonstrated that those in underserved groups are less likely to reach out and volunteer for research studies (Ford et al., 2008). In each case, we recruited participants from currently hospitalized patients from urban academic medical centers, in addition to ambulatory patients in some cases. Recruitment of hospitalized patients ensured the participant pool more closely matches those with symptomatic HF, not just those who were getting out-patient follow-up for HF. Recruiting from within an in-patient setting also reduces barriers to participation, such as requesting time off of work and organizing transportation. In addition, in urban environments space may be a significant barrier to study participation. Often exam rooms are not available for conducting research studies. Consequently, there could be violations of patient privacy in crowded waiting rooms. Furthermore, if patients are paying for parking per hour in a city like New York, they are less likely to take the extra time to participate in a study. This approach to recruitment further allowed us to provide the technology for the study without having to purchase a device for every participant, which can be a cost-saving measure in the early phases of design.

Although the in-patient recruitment approach worked well for our purposes, it may not work well for all patient populations, for example, for diseases where hospitalization is not common or when a study requires a healthy population. Additionally, some patients may find it burdensome to be approached and asked to participate in a research study while hospitalized. There are also patient populations for which it may not be safe or feasible to participate. For example, our studies excluded patients with severe cognitive impairment and unstable psychiatric illnesses. These exclusion criteria were identified first through the patients' electronic medical records and second by the patients' healthcare providers, who we gained approval from prior to approaching patients to participate. In addition, we acknowledge the limitation that there is a loss of realism reporting symptoms while admitted to the hospital because patients do not face many of the complexities of their day-to-day lives outside of the hospital. On the other hand, we also found that it was a teachable moment, and patients who may not have considered there to be value in symptom monitoring now understood the consequences of letting the symptoms worsen into an acute exacerbation. To address the limitations of in-patient recruitment, we are completing a longitudinal feasibility study by recruiting from an outpatient setting. In this case, we also brought the study to the participants, completing initial recruitment in an outpatient heart failure clinic. Both approaches (inpatient vs. outpatient recruitment), however, have the limitation of missing patients who are *not* currently under the care of a provider at an academic medical center for their HF. In that way, we are likely missing the most vulnerable patients in need of intervention.

To understand person-related differences in perceptions and performance, we collected data related to *demographics, cognitive status, and abilities* at each stage of research. In our usability and feasibility studies, we collected demographic information as well as other SDOH-related data, such as socioeconomic status and insurance status. In each study, we also assessed the participants' health literacy. Health literacy dictates patient's and caregivers' ability to: find information and services; communicate their needs and preferences and respond to information and services; process the meaning and usefulness of the information and services; understand the choices, consequences, and context of the information and services; and decide which information and services match their needs and preferences so they can act (Centers for Disease Control and Prevention, 2019). Our iterative, multistudy approach allowed us to adapt later studies to incorporate findings from previous studies. For example, in our early usability study, we also found that patients had difficulty interpreting graphs, therefore in the later usability study where we compared visualizations, we added further assessments related to cognitive function and graph literacy. Our team in earlier studies also noticed that while participants with severe cognitive impairments had already been excluded (e.g. dementia) some participants did have trouble with things such as motivation and memory. Therefore, we included the Montreal Cognitive Assessment (MoCA) to be able to quantify cognitive impairment and evaluate whether that was driving differences in comprehension of symptom visualizations (Nasreddine et al., 2005; Reading Turchioe, Grossman, Myers, et al., 2020; Smith et al., 2007).

We did find that some patients started to fatigue as they completed the survey instruments. The most challenging survey for participants was the four-item graph literacy questionnaire. As a result of the response to the graph literacy survey, we conducted this last with participants. If participants said they no longer wanted to answer the questions, at that point the study was almost over and thus minimal data were lost. Had we included the measurement of graph literacy early in the survey instruments, we may not have had such strong study completion rates. Ultimately, the inclusion of graph literacy and cognition were critical for understanding patients' ability to utilize *mi.Symptoms* and especially for identifying which patient groups require additional support. Although the survey completion required some perseverance, it was well worth the effort in our use case.

We also utilized SDoH surveys and assessment of patient abilities to complete post-hoc *sub-group analyses*. Our subgroup analyses helped us identify important findings including high ratings of usability across age groups, and that despite our best efforts, some underserved groups still performed poorer than others in the final usability assessment. For instance, when we evaluated perceived ease of use and usability between English and Spanish speakers, there were statistically significant lower scores for both perceived ease of use and usefulness among Spanish speakers compared to English speakers. There were, however, no differences detected in perceived ease of use and usefulness by age.

**TABLE 10.4**
**Dissemination Summary – Case Study 2**

| Outlet | Description | Citation |
|---|---|---|
| Health informatics and mHealth | Review of current tools for collecting PROs in an HF patient population | Masterson Creber, Mauerer, et al. (2016) |
| | Initial needs assessment interviews and usability evaluation of *mi.Symptoms* prototype | Grossman et al. (2018) |
| | Comprehension assessment of different visualizations of PROs in *mi.Symptoms* | Reading Turchioe, Grossman, Myers, et al. (2020) |
| Heart failure journal focused | Patient activation among hospitalized patients with heart failure | Masterson Creber et al. (2017) |
| | Evaluation of PRO assessment questionnaire in relation to heart failure outcomes | Baik et al. (2019) |
| | Gerontechnologies for patients with heart failure | Masterson Creber, Hickey et al. (2016) |
| Population-focused (older adults) | Usability and feasibility assessment of *mi.Symptoms* for collection PROs from HF patients | Reading Turchioe, Grossman, Baik, et al. (2020) |

### 10.2.2.3   Dissemination and Implementation

Similar to case study 1, Table 10.4 provides a summary of the dissemination efforts related to the evaluation and testing of *mi.Symptoms*. We balanced publication across technology (informatics, mHealth), clinical domain/environment (heart failure), and patient population groups of interest (older adults). This strategy allowed us to disseminate findings to professionals who care for patients with HF, practitioners who create consumer health information technologies, and those who serve relevant populations (older adults, cardiology patients).

## 10.3   RECOMMENDATIONS FOR PRACTICE

Figure 10.1 presents a model of a patient work approach in which understanding SDoH and reducing disparities is an integral part of the approach as opposed to an add-on or afterthought. Table 10.5 presents a series of considerations for including underserved patients throughout the project life cycle. Recommendations are organized by study phase, and for each recommendation we summarize which components of the work system the recommendation involves. We have chosen the most relevant components of the work system for each recommendation, although any component may be involved depending on the scope of the project. The dependence of actions (recommendations) on multiple components of the work system highlights the complex, interconnected nature of patient work. The case studies presented included participatory design, but did not truly take a community-based approach. We recognize the importance of partnering with communities and those from other disciplines and provide related recommendations for integrating partners throughout

**TABLE 10.5**

**Recommendations for Patient Work That Incorporates Underserved Populations**

| | Relevant System Components | | | | | |
| Recommendations | Phys. Env. | Sociocultural Context | Org. Context | People | Tools/ Tech. | Tasks |
| --- | --- | --- | --- | --- | --- | --- |
| **Conceptualizing the Study** | | | | | | |
| Build community partnerships and establish champions to gain trust from different groups of people. | | X | X | X | | X |
| Choose an area of focus with community and patient needs in mind. | X | X | X | X | X | X |
| **Study Design and Planning** | | | | | | |
| Involve community partners in the study design. | X | X | X | X | X | X |
| Utilize advocacy and interest groups for feedback. | | X | X | X | | |
| Carefully consider your exclusion criteria, and try to safely include as many groups as possible. | X | X | X | X | X | X |
| Reduce barriers to participation by bringing the study to the participants, providing childcare/ eldercare, etc. | X | X | X | X | X | X |
| Create study materials (e.g. recruitment and consent documentation) that can be easily understood and are culturally appropriate. | | X | | X | X | X |
| Determine what subgroup analyses are necessary in advance and recruit accordingly. | | X | X | X | | X |
| **Data Collection** | | | | | | |
| Pilot data collection methods with different subgroups to ensure understandability and acceptability. | X | X | X | X | X | X |
| Monitor collection of data for potential issues (e.g. participant safety concerns) and make necessary adjustments related to the groups of patients involved. | | X | X | X | X | X |

*(Continued)*

**TABLE 10.5 (*Continued*)**

**Recommendations for Patient Work That Incorporates Underserved Populations**

| | Relevant System Components | | | | | |
|---|---|---|---|---|---|---|
| Recommendations | Phys. Env. | Sociocultural Context | Org. Context | People | Tools/ Tech. | Tasks |
| **Analysis and Interpretation** | | | | | | |
| Involve subject matter experts, community members, and/or patients in the data interpretation. | X | X | X | X | X | X |
| Convene a group to reflect on lessons learned and consider how your work could be even more inclusive in future iterations. Use this as an opportunity for fostering future collaborations. | | X | X | X | | X |
| **Dissemination and Implementation** | | | | | | |
| Strike a balance between preaching to the choir and gaining exposure in new areas—disseminate in human factors, as well as clinical specialty and policy-oriented journals, conferences, and other outlets. | | X | X | X | | |
| Focus on implementing in areas where you have champions. | | X | X | X | | |
| Implement findings where you can have the most impact by focusing on *upstream factors*[a] such the physical or organizational environment. | X | X | X | | | X |

[a]*See Siek et al. (2019) for further information on upstream factors.*

the project. See Wallerstein et al. (2017) and Valdez and Edmunds (2019) for further guidance on community-based work.

Considering SDoH in our work as ergonomists is both logical given the profound impacts of SDoH on health and a moral imperative for advancing social justice. In line with the last recommendation in Table 10.5, we should consider how we can impact "upstream factors" in our work. *Upstream factors* pertain to systemic drivers of inequity, such as how organizational and sociocultural constructs (governance, policies, and societal values) affect classism, power dynamics, and discrimination. Upstream issues lead to downstream SDoH such as safety challenges, housing insecurity, or food insecurity that affect health and create additional stressors for underserved groups (Siek et al., 2019). Therefore, focusing on these *upstream factors* will help us have more sustainable impacts on advancing health equity.

## ACKNOWLEDGMENTS

Dr. Benda's work presented in case study 1 was funded by the National Science Foundation's Graduate Research Fellowship Program (1117218) and the Charles and Mary Latham Foundation. Dr. Masterson Creber's work presented in case study 2 was funded by the National Institute of Nursing Research (K99 NR016275; R00 NR016275). The authors would like to acknowledge Lisa Grossman for her work in creating visualizations for case study 2.

## REFERENCES

Agency for Healthcare Research and Quality. (2019). AHRQ health literacy universal precautions. Retrieved from https://meps.ahrq.gov/data_files/publications/st354/stat354.pdf

Ali, S. B., Romero, J., Morrison, K., Hafeez, B., & Ancker, J. S. (2018). Focus section health IT usability: Applying a task-technology fit model to adapt an electronic patient portal for Patient Work. *Applied Clinical Informatics, 9*(1), 174–184.

Ancker, J. S., Barron, Y., Rockoff, M. L., Hauser, D., Pichardo, M., Szerencsy, A., & Calman, N. (2011). Use of an electronic patient portal among disadvantaged populations. *Journal of General Internal Medicine, 26*(10), 1117–1123.

Ancker, J. S., Nosal, S., Hauser, D., Way, C., & Calman, N. (2017). Access policy and the digital divide in patient access to medical records. *Health Policy and Technology, 6*, 3–11.

Baik, D., Reading, M., Jia, H., Grossman, L. V., & Masterson Creber, R. (2019). Measuring health status and symptom burden using a web-based mHealth application in patients with heart failure. *European Journal Cardiovascular Nursing, 18*(4), 325–331.

Barclay, P. A., & Bowers, C. A. (2017). Design for the illiterate: A scoping review of tools for improving the health literacy of electronic health resources. *Proceedings of the Human Factors and Ergonomics Society Annual Meeting, 61*(1), 545–549.

Baur, C., & Prue, C. (2014). The CDC Clear Communication Index is a new evidence-based tool to prepare and review health information. *Health Promotion and Practice, 15*(5), 629–637.

Benda, N. C. (2018). *Using cognitive work analysis to understand and improve communication between limited English proficient patients and emergency department care providers.* (Doctor of Philosophy), State University of New York at Buffalo.

Benda, N. C., & Bisantz, A. M. (2019). *Prototypical work situations: A robust, flexible means for representing activity in a work domain.* Paper presented at the Human Factors and Ergonomics Society's 63rd International Annual Meeting, Seattle, WA.

Benda, N. C., Bisantz, A. M., Butler, R.L., Fairbanks, R. J., Lin, L., & Higginbotham, D. J. (2020). The active role of interpreters in medical discourse – An observational study in emergency medicine. *Manuscript under review.*

Benda, N. C., Fairbanks, R. J., Higginbotham, D. J., Lin, L., & Bisantz, A. M. (2019a). Observational study to understand interpreter service use in emergency medicine: Why the key may lie outside of the initial provider assessment. *Emergency Medicine Journal, 36*(10), 582–588.

Benda, N. C., Fairbanks, R. J., Higginbotham, D. J., Lin, L., & Bisantz, A. M. (2019b). Observational study to understand interpreter service use in emergency medicine:

Why the key may lie outside of the initial provider assessment. *Emergency Medicine Journal, 36*(10), 582–588.

Benda, N. C., Hettinger, A. Z., Bisantz, A. M., Hoffman, D. J., McGeorge, N. M., Iyer, A., . . . Fairbanks, R. J. (2017). Communication in the electronic age: An analysis of face-to-face physician-nurse communication in the emergency department. *Journal of Healthcare Informatics Research, 1*(2), 218–230.

Benda, N. C., Higginbotham, D. J., Fairbanks, R. J., Lin, L., & Bisantz, A. M. (2017). Using cognitive work analysis to design communication support tools for patients with language barriers. *Proceedings of the Human Factors and Ergonomics Society 61st Annual Meeting, 61*(1), 120–124.

Benda, N. C., Thomas, A. T., Montague, E., Valdez, R. S., & Wesley, D. B. (2018). *Human factors approaches to improving health equity–Where have we been and where should we go next?* Paper presented at the Human Factors and Erognomics Society.

Benjamin, E. J., Virani, S. S., Callaway, C. W., Chamberlain, A. M., Chang, A. R., Cheng, S., . . . Deo, R. (2018). Heart disease and stroke statistics-2018 update: A report from the American Heart Association. *Circulation, 137*(12), e67.

Bennett, N. M., Brown, M. T., Green, T., Hall, L. L., & Winkler, A. M. (2018). *Addressing social determinants of health (SDOH): Beyond the clinic walls.* Retrieved from https://edhub.ama-assn.org/steps-forward/module/2702769

Blumenthal, D., Mort, E., & Edwards, J. (1995). The efficacy of primary care for vulnerable population groups. *Health Services Research, 30*(1), 253–273.

Cage, K., Santos, L., Scott, C., & Vaughn-Cooke, M. (2014). Personal health record design preferences for minority diabetic patients. In the *Proceedings of the Human Factors and Ergonomics Society Annual Meeting, 58*(1), 614–618.

Centers for Disease Control and Prevention. (2019). What is health literacy? Retrieved from https://www.cdc.gov/healthliteracy/learn/index.html

Divi, C., Koss, R. G., Schmaltz, S. P., & Loeb, J. M. (2007). Language proficiency and adverse events in US hospitals: A pilot study. *International Journal for Quality in Healthcare, 19*, 60–67.

Dwyer-Lindgren, L., Bertozzi-Villa, A., Stubbs, R. W., Morozoff, C., Mackenbach, J. P., van Lenthe, F. J., . . . Murray, C. J. L. (2017). Inequalities in life expectancy among US counties, 1980 to 2014: Temporal Trends and Key Drivers. *Journal of the American Medical Association Internal Medicine, 177*(7), 1003–1011.

Erceg, P., Despotovic, N., Milosevic, D. P., Soldatovic, I., Zdravkovic, S., Tomic, S., . . . Bojovic, O. (2013). Health-related quality of life in elderly patients hospitalized with chronic heart failure. *Clinical Interventions in Aging, 8*, 1539.

Ezer, N., Fisk, A. D., & Rogers, W. A. (2009). More than a servant: Self-reported willingness of younger and older adults to having a robot perform interactive and critical tasks in the home. *Proceedings of the Human Factors and Ergonomics Society Annual Meeting, 53*(2), 136–140.

Flores, G., Abreu, M., Barone, C. P., Bachur, R., & Lin, H. (2012). Errors of medical interpretation and their potential clinical consequences: A comparison of professional versus ad hoc versus no interpreters. *Annals of Emergency Medicine, 60*, 545–553.

Ford, J. G., Howerton, M. W., Lai, G. Y., Gary, T. L., Bolen, S., Gibbons, M. C., . . . Wilson, R. F. (2008). Barriers to recruiting underrepresented populations to cancer clinical trials: A systematic review. *Cancer: Interdisciplinary International Journal of the American Cancer Society, 112*(2), 228–242.

Green, C. P., Porter, C. B., Bresnahan, D. R., & Spertus, J. A. (2000). Development and evaluation of the Kansas City Cardiomyopathy Questionnaire: A new health status measure for heart failure. *Journal of the American College of Cardiology, 35*(5), 1245–1255.

Grossman, L. V., Feiner, S. K., Mitchell, E. G., & Masterson Creber, R. M. (2018). Leveraging patient-reported outcomes using data visualization. *Applied Clinical Informatics, 9*(3), 565–575.

Grossman, L. V., Masterson Creber, R. M., Benda, N. C., Wright, D., Vawdrey, D. K., & Ancker, J. S. (2019). Interventions to increase patient portal use in vulnerable populations: A systematic review. *Journal of the American Medical Informatics Association, 26*, 855–870.

Harrington, C., & Joines, S. (2011). Assessing user experience with crutch use: A review of literature. *Proceedings of the Human Factors and Ergonomics Society Annual Meeting, 55*(1), 1658–1662.

Holden, R. J., Cornet, V. P., & Valdez, R. S. (2020). Ergonomics: 10-year mapping review of patient-centered human factors. *Applied Ergonomics, 82*(102972).

Holden, R. J., & Valdez, R. S. (2018). Town hall on patient-centered human factors and ergonomics. *Proceedings of the Human Factors and Ergonomics Society Annual Meeting, 62*(1), 465–468.

Holden, R. J., & Valdez, R. S. (2019). 2019 town hall on human factors and ergonomics for patient work. *Proceedings of the Human Factors and Ergonomics Society Annual Meeting, 63*(1), 725–728.

Holden, R. J., Valdez, R. S., Schubert, C. C., Thompson, M. J., & Hundt, A. S. (2017). Macroergonomic factors in the patient work system: Examining the context of patients with chronic illness. *Ergonomics, 60*(1), 26–43.

Hsieh, E. (2016). *Bilingual health communication: Working with interpreters in cross-cultural care.* New York: Routledge.

Hsieh, E., Ju, H., & Kong, H. (2010). Dimensions of trust: The tensions and challenges in provider—interpreter trust. *Qualitative Health Research, 20*(2), 170–181.

Jiang, Y., & Hesser, J. E. (2006). Associations between health-related quality of life and demographics and health risks. Results from Rhode Island's 2002 behavioral risk factor survey. *Health Quality Life Outcomes, 4*, 14.

Kroemer, K. (2006). *"Extra-ordinary" ergonomics: How to accommodate small, and big persons, the disabled and elderly, expectant mothers and children.* Boca Raton, FL: CRC Press.

Lavallee, D. C., Chenok, K. E., Love, R. M., Petersen, C., Holve, E., Segal, C. D., & Franklin, P. D. (2016). Incorporating patient-reported outcomes into health care to engage patients and enhance care. *Health Affairs (Millwood), 35*(4), 575–582.

Manemann, S. M., Chamberlain, A. M., Boyd, C. M., Gerber, Y., Dunlay, S. M., Weston, S. A., . . . Roger, V. L. (2016). Multimorbidity in heart failure: Effect on outcomes. *Journal of the American Geriatrics Society, 64*(7), 1469–1474.

Masterson Creber, R. M., Chen, T., Wei, C., & Lee, C. S. (2017). Brief report: Patient activation among urban hospitalized patients with heart failure. *Journal of Cardiac Failure, 23*(11), 817–820.

Masterson Creber, R. M., Hickey, K. T., & Maurer, M. S. (2016). Gerontechnologies for older patients with heart failure: What is the role of smartphones, tablets, and remote monitoring devices in improving symptom monitoring and self-care management? *Current Cardiovascular Risk Reports, 10*(10), 30.

Masterson Creber, R. M., Maurer, M. S., Reading, M., Hiraldo, G., Hickey, K. T., & Iribarren, S. (2016). Review and analysis of existing mobile phone apps to support heart failure symptom monitoring and self-care management using the mobile application rating scale (MARS). *Journal of Medical Internet Research mHealth and uHealth, 4*(2), e74.

Matalenas, L. A., Hu, T., Veeramachaneni, V., & Muth, J. (2016). A cane for more than walking. In the *Proceedings of the Human Factors and Ergonomics Society Annual Meeting, 60*(1), 1063–1067.

McGovern, L., Miller, G., & Hughes-Cromwick, P. (2014). The relative contribution of multiple determinants to health outcomes. *Health Affairs Health Policy Briefs*, August, 1–9.

Montague, E., & Perchonok, J. (2012). Health and wellness technology use by historically underserved health consumers: Systematic review. *Journal of Medical Internet Research, 14*(3), e78.

Nasreddine, Z. S., Phillips, N. A., Bédirian, V., Charbonneau, S., Whitehead, V., Collin, I., . . . Chertkow, H. (2005). The Montreal Cognitive Assessment, MoCA: A brief screening tool for mild cognitive impairment. *Journal of the American Geriatrics Society, 53*(4), 695–699.

Ngai, K. M., Grudzen, C. R., Lee, R., Tong, V. Y., Richardson, L. D., & Fernandez, A. (2016). The association between limited English proficiency and unplanned emergency Department Revisit within 72 Hours. *Annals of Emergency Medicine, 68*(2), 213–221.

Periyakoil, V. S., Neri, E., & Kraemer, H. (2015). No easy talk: A mixed methods study of doctor reported barriers to conducting effective end-of-life conversations with diverse patients. *PLoS One, 10*(4), 1–13.

Pew Research Center. Generation and Age. Retrieved from https://www.pewresearch.org/topics/generations-and-age/

Pew Research Center. (2019a). Internet/Broadband Fact Sheet. Retrieved from https://www.pewresearch.org/internet/fact-sheet/internet-broadband/

Pew Research Center. (2019b). Mobile Fact Sheet. Retrieved from https://www.pewresearch.org/internet/fact-sheet/mobile/

Ponikowski, P., Anker, S. D., AlHabib, K. F., Cowie, M. R., Force, T. L., Hu, S., . . . Rohde, L. E. (2014). Heart failure: Preventing disease and death worldwide. *European Society of Cardiology Heart Failure, 1*(1), 4–25.

Ramirez, D., Engel, K. G., & Tang, T. S. (2008). Language interpreter utilization in the emergency department setting: A clinical review. *Journal of Health Care for the Poor and Underserved, 19*(2), 352–362.

Reading Turchioe, M., Grossman, L. V., Baik, D., Lee, C. S., Maurer, M. S., Goyal, P., . . . Masterson Creber, R. M. (2020). Older adults can successfully monitor symptoms using an inclusively designed mobile application. *Journal of the American Geriatrics Society. 68*(6), 1313–1318.

Reading Turchioe, M., Grossman, L. V., Myers, A. C., Baik, D., Goyal, P., & Masterson Creber, R. M. (2020). Visual analogies, not graphs, increase patients' comprehension of changes in their health status. *Journal of the American Medical Informatics Association, 27*(5), 677–689.

Roscoe, R., Chiou, E., & Wooldridge, A. (2020). *Advancing diversity, inclusion, and social justice through human systems engineering*. Boca Raton, FL: CRC Press.

Sauro, J. (2015). SUPR-Q: A comprehensive measure of the quality of the website user experience. *Journal of Usability Studies, 10*(2), 68–86.

Schnall, R., Cho, H., & Liu, J. (2018). Health information technology usability evaluation scale (Health-ITUES) for usability assessment of mobile health technology: Validation study. *Journal of Medical Internet Research mHealth and uHealth, 6*(1), e4.

Siek, K., Veinot, T., & Mynatt, B. (2019). *Research opportunities in sociotechnical interventions for health disparity reduction*. Retrieved from https://cra.org/ccc/wp-content/uploads/sites/2/2018/01/17602-CCC-Health-Disparities-ReportFinal.pdf

Smith-Jackson, T. L., Resnick, M. L., & Johnson, K. T. (2013). *Cultural ergonomics: Theory, methods, and applications*. Boca Raton, FL: CRC Press.

Smith, T., Gildeh, N., & Holmes, C. (2007). The Montreal Cognitive Assessment: Validity and utility in a memory clinic setting. *The Canadian Journal of Psychiatry, 52*(5), 329–332.

Spertus, J. A. (2008). Evolving applications for patient-centered health status measures. *Circulation, 118*(20), 2103–2110.

Story, M., Luce, A., & Rempel, D. (2009). Accessibility and usability of diabetes management devices for users with vision disabilities. *Proceedings of the Human Factors and Ergonomics Society 53rd Annual Meeting, 10*(6), 1382–1387.

Timmins, C. L. (2002). The impact of language barriers on the health care of Latinos in the United States a review of the literature and guide. *Journal of Midwifery and Women's Health, 47*(2), 80–96.

Valdez, R. S., & Brennan, P. F. (2015). Exploring patients' health information communication practices with social network members as a foundation for consumer health IT design. *International Journal of Medical Informatics, 84*, 363–374.

Valdez, R. S., & Edmunds, D. S. (2019). Reimagining community-based research and action in human factors: A dialogue across disciplines. In R. Roscoe, E. Chiou, & A. Wooldridge (Eds.), *Advancing diversity, inclusion, and social justice through human systems engineering.* Boca Raton, FL: CRC Press pp. 267–276.

Valdez, R. S., Gibbons, M. C., Siegel, E. R., Kukafka, R., & Brennan, P. F. (2012). Health and technology: Designing consumer health IT to enhance usability among different racial and ethnic groups within the United States. *Health & Technology, 2*(4), 225–233.

Valdez, R. S., Guterbock, T. M., Fitzgibbon, K., Williams, I. C., Wellbeloved-Stone, C. A., Bears, J. E., & Menefee, H. K. (2017). From loquacious to reticent: Understanding patient health information communication to guide consumer health IT design. *Journal of the American Medical Informatics Association, 24*(4), 680–696.

Valdez, R. S., & Holden, R. J. (2016). Health care human factors/ergonomics fieldwork in home and community settings. *Ergonomics in Design: The Magazine of Human Factors Applications, 24*, 4–9.

Valdez, R. S., Holden, R. J., Caine, K., Madathil, K., Mickelson, R., Lovett Novak, L., & Werner, N. (2016). Patient work as a maturing approach within HF/E: Moving beyond traditional self-management applications. *Proceedings of the Human Factors and Ergonomics Society Annual Meeting, 60*(1), 657–661.

Valdez, R. S., Holden, R. J., Hundt, A. S., Marquard, J. L., Montague, E., Nathan-Roberts, D., & Or, C. K. (2014). The work and work systems of patients: A new frontier for macroergonomics in health care. *Proceedings of the Human Factors and Ergonomics Society Annual Meeting, 58*(1), 708–712.

Valdez, R. S., Holden, R. J., Khunlerkit, N., Marquard, J., McGuire, K., Nathan-Roberts, D., . . . Ramly, E. (2017). Patient work methods: Current methods of engaging patients in systems design in clinical, community and extraterrestrial settings. *Proceedings of the Human Factors and Ergonomics Society Annual Meeting, 61*(1), 625–629.

Valdez, R. S., Holden, R. J., Madathil, K., Benda, N., Holden, R. J., Montague, E., & Werner, N. (2019). *An exploration of patient ergonomics in historically marginalized communities.* Paper presented at the Proceedings of the Human Factors and Ergonomics Society Annual Meeting, Seattle, WA.

Wallerstein, N., Duran, B., Oetzel, J. G., & Minkler, M. (2017). *Community-based participatory research for health: Advancing social and health equity.* San Francisco, CA: John Wiley & Sons.

Wears, R. L., Sutcliffe, K., & Van Rite, E. (2014). Patient safety: A brief but spirited history. In L. Zipperer (Ed.), *Patient safety: Perspectives on evidence, information and knowledge transfer.* Gower Publishing Ltd New York, NY, USA, pp. 1–21.

Weiss, C. C., Purciel, M., Bader, M., Quinn, J. W., Lovasi, G., Neckerman, K. M., & Rundle, A. G. (2011). Reconsidering access: Park facilities and neighborhood disamenities in New York City. *Journal of Urban Health, 88*(2), 297–310.

World Health Organization. (2018). Life expectancy and healthy life expectancy: Data by country. Retrieved from https://apps.who.int/gho/data/node.main.688

World Health Organization Commission on Social Determinants of Health. (2008). *Closing the gap in a generation: Health equity through action on the social determinants of health.* Geneva: World Health Organization.

Yu, S. M., & Singh, G. K. (2009). Household language use and health care access, unmet need, and family impact among CSHCN. *Pediatrics, 124*(Suppl 4), S414–419.

Zachary, W., Michlig, G., Kaplan, A., Nguyen, N., Quinn, C., & Surkan, P. (2017). *Participatory design of a social networking app to support type II diabetes self-management in low-income minority communities.* Paper presented at the International Symposium on Human Factors and Ergonomics in Health Care.

# 11 Health Promotion

## Patient Self-Management, Cognitive Work Analysis, and Persuasive Design

Jessie Chin
School of Information Sciences
University of Illinois at Urbana-Champaign

Catherine Burns
Department of Systems Design Engineering
University of Waterloo

## CONTENTS

The patient work of self-management is composed of self-activation, planning, and maintenance of a variety of health promotion behaviors, such as health information and service seeking, medication adherence, symptoms management, decision-making, and health habit formation (e.g. diet, physical activity (PA)) (Bodenheimer, 2002). These health promotion behaviors are complex and challenging, thus requiring significant cognitive resources and skills (Rich et al., 2015; Schwarzer et al., 2011). Hence, designing sociotechnical solutions to ease patients' demands and support patient self-management is important for patients' health promotion.

Human factors and ergonomics methods focus on analyzing current sociotechnical systems and enhancing their safety and efficiency (Vicente, 1999). Persuasive design may be seen as complementary, emphasizing behavioral change with the understanding that those behaviors help people reach longer-term goals (Fogg, 2009). The goal of this chapter is to bridge theories in health promotion, persuasive design, and a particular human factors and ergonomics method, cognitive work analysis (CWA), to demonstrate the potential approach to design new sociotechnical solutions for long-term health promotion. In this chapter, we will introduce: (1) theoretical foundations of health promotion, (2) the applications of persuasive design to health promotion, (3) the use of CWA to inform the persuasive design for health promotion, and (4) the implications of future work at this intersection for health promotion.

## 11.1  HEALTH PROMOTION MODELS

Health promotion models aim to explain and predict the processes and factors contributing to the change of existing behavior or adoption of new behavior. Such change encompasses the formation and stabilization of *intentions,* as well the planning, adoption, and maintenance of the *behavior.* In this section, we describe six prominent health promotion models, which highlight the role of a range of processes and factors of behavior change (see Table 11.1 for a summary).

### 11.1.1  HEALTH BELIEF MODEL

The Health Belief Model (HBM) explains the adoption of health behavior based on six factors related to risk assessments of both *the threats to prevent* and the *preventive (health) behavior to adopt.* The six factors include: (1) perceived susceptibility; (2) perceived severity of the threats to prevent; (3) motivations; (4) perceived benefits; (5) perceived barriers to adopt the prevention behavior; and (6) the cues to action (Janz & Becker, 1984; Rosenstock, 1974). For example, one study showed that the HBM can be used to explain the influenza vaccination behavior among adults, in that the likelihood of vaccination will increase if the perceived susceptibility to disease increases (Weinstein et al., 2007). Furthermore, meta-analyses have suggested that the HBM is able to explain the adoption of short-term health behavior such as cancer screening, medical test, and exam adoption (Carpenter, 2010; Harrison et al., 1992).

### 11.1.2  THEORY OF PLANNED BEHAVIOR

The Theory of Reasoned Action (Ajzen, 1985; Ajzen & Fishbein, 1977) emphasizes the crucial and immediate role of behavioral intentions to adopt a new behavior.

The Theory of Planned Behavior (Ajzen, 1991) further suggests that the behavioral intention is shaped by attitudes (the beliefs about the positive or negative consequences of the behavior), subjective norms (the motivations and beliefs to comply with the behavior from other peers and social norms), and perceived behavior control (the beliefs of control over one's behavior). The theory of planned behavior has been used to explain the adoption of health promotion behavior, such as PA (Hausenblas et al., 1997), smoking cessation (Topa & Moriano Leon, 2010), HIV prevention (Albarracín et al., 2001), and chronic illness treatment adherence (Rich et al., 2015).

### 11.1.3 SOCIAL COGNITIVE THEORY

The Social Cognitive Theory (Bandura, 1977, 1989; Schwarzer, 2001; Schwarzer & Renner, 2000) explains and predicts the changes of attitudes or behavior depending on the beliefs about the self to perform certain tasks or behavior, also called self-efficacy. Regardless of the levels of actual competence, the social cognitive theory suggests that an increase of self-efficacy could lead to increasing likelihood to adopt a behavior. In addition to self-efficacy, outcome expectancies are critical to the adoption of behavior: (1) action-outcome expectancy, the beliefs about the consequences resulted from the action; and (2) situation-outcome expectancy, the beliefs about the consequences resulted from other external environmental factors. Social cognitive theory proposed that the new behavior will be adopted if someone perceives control over their behavior, fewer external barriers, and more self-efficacy. Well-established evidence has shown the importance of self-efficacy and outcome expectancy in various health promotion behaviors, such as promoting quality of life and lifestyle change among cancer patients (diet and PA) (Graves, 2003; Stacey et al., 2015), promoting PAs (Young et al., 2014), and smoking cessation (Gwaltney et al., 2009).

### 11.1.4 PROTECTION MOTIVATION THEORY

The Protection Motivation Theory suggests that emotional appraisal (fear appeals) and reliance on the avoidance of harmful consequences of maladaptive behavior (smoking, binge drinking) are effective in changing the attitudes or intentions as related to health behavior adoption. The avoidance of harms is driven by three cognitive appraisal processes: perceived severity of the depicted harmful events, perceived vulnerability to a threat, and perceived effectiveness of the health behavior. The avoidance of harms, along with self-efficacy, is relevant to the intention to adopt health behavior (such as PA promotion, reduction of smoking behavior) (Maddux & Rogers, 1983; Prentice-Dunn & Rogers, 1986; Wurtele & Maddux, 1987; Floyd et al., 2000; Milne et al., 2000). For example, Pechmann et al. (2003) adopted protection motivation theory to analyze antismoking advertisements and suggested that using certain message themes, such as stressing the smoking-related consequences of endangering others, could increase the nonsmoking intentions of adolescents (Pechmann et al., 2003).

### 11.1.5 TRANSTHEORETICAL MODEL

The Transtheoretical Model defines behavior change as a process involving five stages, each associated with different levels of preparedness, intentions, and likelihood of behavioral change (Prochaska & DiClemente, 1982). These stages are qualitatively different. People at different stages will act differently and require different interventions to move closer to their goals. The five stages of behavior change are: (1) precontemplation, in which people have no intention to change within the next 6 months; (2) contemplation, in which people have intentions to change within 6 months; (3) preparation, in which people are ready to initiate changes; (4) action, in which people have just made a change in their health behavior within the past 6 months; and (5) maintenance, in which people made changes to their health behavior more than 6 months prior and are engaging in self-regulation to avoid relapse. Previous research has applied this model to design tailored communication and strategies at different stages of change for various health promotion behaviors, such as PA promotion, weight loss, smoking and substance cessation, cancer screening adoption, and HIV prevention, among others. (Hutchison et al., 2009; Marshall & Biddle, 2001; Mastellos et al., 2014; Prochaska & DiClemente, 1983; Prochaska et al., 1994; Spencer et al., 2002, 2005; Sutton, 2001).

### 11.1.6 HEALTH ACTION PROCESS APPROACH

The Health Action Process Approach divides patient self-regulated health promotion behavior into a pre-intentional phase (i.e. how individuals become motivated to change the behavior) and a post-intentional phase (i.e. how to maintain and regulate the behavior) (Schwarzer et al., 2011; Sniehotta et al., 2005). In the pre-intentional phase, action self-efficacy (i.e. how well people think they can carry out the health behavior), outcome expectancy (i.e. the expected consequences of adopting the behavior), and risk perceptions of the threats for not adopting this health behavior jointly affect the formation of intention. Once intention is stabilized, people then enter the post-intentional phase to decide where and when to adopt the new behavior. In order to translate the intention to behavior, there is a planning process. Planning includes (1) conducting detailed action planning to form the mental model to carry out the behavior (Lippke et al., 2004), and (2) coping planning, which is a self-regulatory process to avoid relapse for the prolonged pursuit of goals (Lippke et al., 2004; Schwarzer, 1999). Volitional, maintenance, and recovery self-efficacy (i.e. perceived competence to start the new behavior, continue the new behavior, and avoid relapse) jointly affect the planning process (Schwarzer & Renner, 2000). Compared to the Transtheoretical Model, the Health Action Process Approach proposed the "planning" process which is critical to fill out the intention-behavior gap. The Health Action Process Approach has shown some success to explain the adoption and *long-term* maintenance of health promotion behavior (e.g. rehabilitation, PA, lifestyle change) among various populations (e.g. patients with chronic illness, obesity and multiple sclerosis, pregnant women) (Chiu et al., 2011; Gaston & Prapavessis, 2014; Parschau et al., 2014; Schwarzer et al., 2011; Zhang et al., 2019).

### 11.1.7 COMPARISON OF MODEL TYPES

Although the continuum models (HBM, Theory of Planned Behavior, Social Cognitive Theory, and Protection Motivation Theory) each showed slightly different advantages to explain and predict different kinds of health promotion behaviors, they generally showed better success in explaining and predicting the formation of behavioral intentions and the adoption of certain health behaviors than stage models (such as vaccination uptake, medical tests, or exam use). However, the effectiveness of these models to predict long-term behavior change and habit formation has been mixed (such as in the cases of PA, diet change, treatment adherence). In contrast, the stage models (Transtheoretical Model and Health Action Process Approach) showed better success in addressing the intention–behavior gap, maintaining the behavior change, and supporting the formation of new habits. Despite different strengths, however, these two types of models are not exclusive. Stage models have adopted factors proposed in continuum models to explain and predict behavioral change processes (e.g. self-efficacy in Social Cognitive Theory, perceived severity and vulnerability of the threat in HBM and Protection Motivation Theory as risk perceptions, and subjective norm in Theory of Planned Behavior). Hence, depending on the kinds of health promotion behaviors and the goals of the patients (whether increasing motivations or adopting a new behavior), a combination of health promotion models may be useful in informing the design of sociotechnical solutions to promote preventive health behaviors.

## 11.2   DESIGNING FOR HEALTH PROMOTION

As summarized in Table 11.1, there are multiple factors and processes which are critical in health promotion. We will discuss different approaches to design sociotechnical solutions to support these factors and processes in health promotion

### 11.2.1   TAILORING AND NUDGING

Tailoring is a commonly used strategy to change attitudes or beliefs in health communication. Tailoring can be tied to the designing of different messages depending on unique factors in continuum models (e.g. stressing the perceived susceptibility of a threat in HBM to promote the adoption of health behavior), as well as depending on different stages of change, such as responding to specific factors in the stage models (e.g. promoting self-efficacy of patients in HAPA to increase the adoption and maintenance of a new behavior). Tailoring can also be used to design different messages depending on different characteristics of users. One of the important user characteristics that has been studied extensively in health behavior change is "regulatory focus," which describes individual differences in the tendencies to be motivated to adopt new health behaviors. Regulatory focus is achieved through either (1) promotion goals, seeking positive consequences on health (such as losing weight through exercise) or (2) prevention goals, avoiding negative consequences on health (such as lowering the likelihood of obesity through exercise) (Crowe & Higgins, 1997; Higgins, 1998; Lockwood et al., 2002). Previous research proposing "regulatory fit" has suggested that the promotion-focus messages are more effective to motivate health behavior among promotion-oriented people than prevention-oriented people. The promotion-oriented people would become more motivated to adopt a health behavior if they know that they will gain benefits to adopt this behavior

**TABLE 11.1**
**Health Promotion Models**

| Health Promotion Model | Behavior Change | Main Concept | Factors/Processes Contributing to Behavior Change |
|---|---|---|---|
| Health belief model (HBM) | Continuum model | Assess the risk of the threat for adopting prevention behavior | Perceived susceptibility and severity of the threat, motivations, perceived benefit and barriers of the behavior, and cues to action |
| Theory of planned behavior (TPB) | Continuum model | Attitudes determine behavior intentions, and then actual actions | Attitudes (consequences of the behavior), subjective norms, and perceived control over the behavior |
| Social cognitive theory (SCT) | Continuum model | Self-efficacy as the central component of behavior change | Self-efficacy, outcome expectancy |
| Protection motivation theory (PMT) | Continuum model | Negative affect drives the avoidance of maladaptive behavior | Perceived severity and vulnerability of a threat, and perceived effectiveness of the behavior |
| Transtheoretical model (TM) | Stage model | There are five qualitatively different stages in behavior change | Precontemplation, contemplation, preparation, action, and maintenance |
| Health action process approach (HAPA) | Stage model | The planning process is critical to move people from pre-intentional to post-intentional phase and sustain the change | Pre-intentional phase (action self-efficacy, outcome expectancy, intention, risk perceptions), post-intentional phase (volitional, maintenance and recovery self-efficacy, action planning, coping planning, adoption of health behavior) |

(such as improving their health); the prevention-oriented people would become more motivated to adopt a health behavior if they know they can prevent harms to adopt this behavior (such as reducing the likelihood to have obesity). Thus, prevention-focus messages are more effective in motivating health behavior among prevention-oriented people than promotion-oriented people (Higgins, 1998; Lockwood et al., 2002). However, the effects of regulatory fit on health promotion (e.g. diet change or PAs adoption) are mixed (Latimer et al., 2008; Rezai et al., 2019).

Nudging, defined as the effort to alter people's behavior in a desired direction without changing the availabilities or economic incentives of the choice architecture (Thaler & Sunstein, 2009), is an approach to promote the simple health choices in our everyday lives. Nudges have been applied to promote population health (Cioffi et al., 2015; Kraak et al., 2017) through directly manipulating health information (e.g. changing the nutrition labeling or packaging of the food), controlling accessibility or proximity of health choices (e.g. the position of healthy foods), and setting the desired choice as default (e.g. organ donation).

For example, manipulating the positioning of food (i.e. controlling proximity) has been shown to effectively guide food choice (Chapman & Ogden, 2012; Rozin et al., 2011). Researchers manipulated the positioning of food in a market and found that food items that were more difficult to reach (i.e. larger distance) showed a decrease in intake by 8%–16%. In another empirical study, researchers manipulated the food positioning in three grocery shops at the train station (Kroese et al., 2016). One store implemented the proximity nudge by having the healthy food located at the cashier. Another store implemented the proximity nudge with disclosure by having the healthy food put at the cashier with a sign stating that this nudge helps customers to make healthier choices. Lastly, the third store retained the original positioning of food to serve as the control condition. Findings showed that there was an increase in healthy food choices for both nudge groups (proximity and proximity with disclosure). In addition to the example provided, there are simpler versions of the proximity nudge. One previous study showed that items positioned at the beginning and end of a restaurant menu led to increased selection of those choices (20% higher) than items in the middle of the menu (Dayan & Bar-Hillel, 2011). Hence, health choice can be nudged through simple rearrangements within a given context.

## 11.2.2 FOGG BEHAVIOR MODEL AND PERSUASIVE SYSTEMS DESIGN FRAMEWORK

Persuasive design is an approach to design sociotechnical systems in order to motivate, initiate, and maintain the change of human behavior (Fogg & Fogg, 2003). In addition to usability, safety, or satisfaction, the goal of persuasive design is to motivate long-term behavioral change. The Fogg Behavior Model proposes three main factors, *motivation, ability, and triggers* in designing persuasive technologies (Fogg, 2009; Fogg & Fogg, 2003). Motivation, the intention to adopt the new behavior, has been addressed in all six health promotion models as a prerequisite to adopt the new behavior. Ability, the competence to conduct the behavior, has been mostly framed as the "perceived competence" in health promotion models (such as perceived control of the behavior in the Theory of Planned Behavior and action self-efficacy in the Health Action Process Approach). Trigger, the event which stimulates the adoption of behavior or the change of current behavior, has also been introduced in health promotion models in different formats (such as cues to action in the HBM, as well as volitional self-efficacy and planning processes in the Health Action Process Approach). By echoing the main factors/processes in health promotion models, Fogg proposed strategies to conduct a persuasive design through evaluating the motivation, ability, and trigger within a sociotechnical system.

According to this model, behavior change cannot occur without sufficient motivation and ability. As such, the design starts with boosting user motivation, assisting users' ability to pursue task goals, or both. "Spark" is a strategy to boost users' motivations, such as using tailoring messages to stress the positive consequence of PAs and showcasing the percentages of peers engaging in PAs daily (attitudes and subjective norms in the Theory of Planned Behavior). "Facilitator" is a strategy to persuade users that the task is easy to do through lowering the demands of the tasks, such as presenting optimal medication regimens to patients with chronic illness to promote their medication adherence (lowering barriers of the behavior in the HBM). Once the motivation and ability are addressed, we can implement "signal" as a trigger to remind people to take the actions, such as setting up automatic messages to remind medication uptake for patients (increasing maintenance self-efficacy and supporting action planning in the Health Action Process Approach). The Fogg Behavior Model has been applied to designing various sociotechnical systems for health promotion, such as mobile health applications for lifestyle management (Mohr et al., 2014; Rabbi et al., 2015).

## 11.3   COGNITIVE WORK ANALYSIS AS AN APPROACH TO IMPLEMENT AND EVALUATE PERSUASIVE DESIGN

CWA is a method from human factors engineering that takes a deep approach to the analysis of work processes (Vicente, 1999). CWA looks at the relationships that people must understand, the key tasks they must perform, and the analytical aspects of work they must consider. CWA creates a supportive information systems design that clarifies complex relationships for users, allows them to develop correct mental models, and encourages the development of effective strategies. CWA can be used more directly in order to understand the factors contributing to the adoption of a behavior, potential trigger points where the behavior could change, and what those changes would look like. Two of the methods in CWA will be introduced in this section, Work Domain Analysis (WDA) and Control Task Analysis (CTA). WDA is used to answer the two questions: (1) Why was the system designed? and (2) How does the system achieve its purpose? Abstract hierarchy is used to analyze the purpose, parts, and components of a sociotechnical system (Rasmussen, 1985). CTA is used to associate the system requirements with actors' decision. Decision ladders are used analyze the information processing activities and knowledge states of the users within the sociotechnical system (Rasmussen et al., 1994).

Designing technologies for behavior change is an emerging science. We focused on the following three main problems in behavior change. The first problem is how to influence user *motivation*; for example, designing ways to promote self-efficacy (Schwarzer & Renner, 2000). The second problem is *what behavior* to encourage the person to do. For example, researchers need to identify behavior with sufficient readiness to be initiated in terms of detailed action planning (Schwarzer et al., 2011). The third problem is *when* to trigger the new behavior. For example, to ensure that users have sufficient intention and complete detailed planning process (action and coping planning) (Prochaska & DiClemente, 1982; Sniehotta et al., 2005). WDA can provide insight into the first problem to trigger motivations, and CTA can inform the solution for the latter two problems of what and when to encourage new behaviors. We will introduce an example to show how to apply WDA and CTA to persuasive design (Rezai & Burns, 2014).

### 11.3.1   WORK DOMAIN ANALYSIS: UNDERSTANDING USER MOTIVATION

WDA is performed to represent the socotechnical system into five levels of abstractions, including (1) *functional purpose*, which states the main reason why the system exists; (2) *abstract function*, which shows the values that are important in the system;

**TABLE 11.2**

**A Work Domain Analysis for Blood Pressure Management**

| | Whole System (Patient) | Subsystem (Body Systems) |
|---|---|---|
| System purpose | Maintain blood pressure in normal range | Maintain blood pressure in normal range |
| Principles, priorities, and balances | Underlying laws and principles of human body for regulating blood pressure Valuing healthy life | Underlying laws and principles of patient's: circulatory system, nervous system, endocrine system, cognitive system, self-regulatory system |
| Processes (physiological and nonphysiological processes) | Taking medications according to the new prescription Following physicians' instruction regarding diet or physical activity | Physiological processes in patient's body (regulated by circulatory system, nervous system, endocrine system) Psychological processes (cognitive processes determining person's behavior and choices at each moment) Pharmacological processes of the prescribed drug (diuretic, beta-blocker, ACE inhibitor) Metabolism of food and processes associated with food nutrients |
| Physical function | Patient body Medication Food | Circulatory system (heart, blood, blood vessels) endocrine system, nervous system, active ingredients of medication, active ingredients of food |
| Physical form (patient and equipment) | Age, weight, gender, Race of the patient Patient's regulatory focus and mood Medication type and dose Food type and amount | Blood pressure level, heart rate and condition, blood vessel condition, psychological status, medication type and dose, food type and amount |

(3) *generalized function*, which describes the processes used to deliver the functional purpose; (4) *physical function*, which characterizes the componentes of the system; and (5) *physical form*, which states the attributes of the componenets in the system. Take blood pressure management for example, WDA can be used to identify the functions and relationships required to achieve the purpose of the system, in this case maintaining a normal blood pressure, as well as the values and processes associated with the blood measures management (Table 11.2) (Rezai & Burns, 2014).

## 11.3.2 Control Task Analysis: Understanding What New Behaviors to Establish

CTA is a strong analytical tool for exploring new behaviors. The decision ladder, the usual artifact of a control task analysis, shows different possibilities for information processing. Essentially the ladder is an information processing template that can be used to identify when people must undertake complex decision-making, where they may take advantage of rules and heuristics to decide the next course of action more

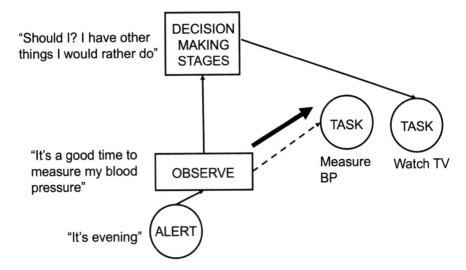

**FIGURE 11.1**   Changing a behavior path as discovered using the decision ladder.

quickly. Operating by these rules and heuristics is cognitively less effortful but is more typical of highly experienced users.

A CTA would identify the rules and heuristics of experienced users and, through design, try to encourage less experienced users to adopt these new pathways. Following the path of a more experienced user is one sort of path that might be accessible for behavior change (St. Maurice & Burns, 2015). In Figure 11.1, we give a simple example of blood pressure management. In this case, the user may be undergoing a process of assessing their options on whether they should measure their blood pressure (the solid black line from "observe" to "decision making stages"). It may be desirable to take this option consideration behavior away and instead build a habit (the dashed line from "observe" to "task"). The definition of habit we are using is from Merriam-Webster: "a settled tendency or usual manner of behavior" (Merriam-Webster, n.d.). In this case, the habit trajectory would look like "It's 7 pm, time to measure my blood pressure." This behavior path change is shown in Figure 11.1. The dashed line shows the behavior trajectory, avoiding the conscious decision-making stages of the previous pattern. This would be the first step of establishing a habit.

### 11.3.3   CONTROL TASK ANALYSIS: WHEN AND HOW TO ESTABLISH A NEW HEALTHY BEHAVIOR

The other problem is to identify where and when a trigger should be added (St. Maurice et al., 2018). The information system design can be tuned to add new information to encourage a particular path. Following the same example as before (Figure 11.2), the trigger can be strengthened and made more specific, "let's measure your blood pressure," and the cognitive process could be simplified—the user no longer needs to check the time and then remember to take action. This development of a trigger, to make the path even more persuasive, is shown in Figure 11.2. The trigger

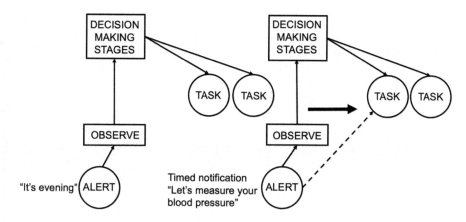

**FIGURE 11.2**   Creation of a notification to persuade behavior change further.

added here is a notification, which takes away the task of the user to monitor their time, to initiate the behavior of measuring their blood pressure.

In this case, we know that the "alert" stage must occur for the user to initiate the measurement of their blood pressure. We are taking advantage of this alert stage to refine it through design. Instead of expecting the user to monitor the time and alert themselves (the pattern on the left), a timed notification reduces the user's workload at the alert stage. The alert stage can be used further to provide a message that indicates the behavior pathway we want to encourage (i.e. "Let's measure your blood pressure").

### 11.3.4   AN EXTENDED EXAMPLE OF PERSUASIVE DESIGN

In this section, we discuss a hypothetical example in which persuasive design was used to promote PA of older adults with hypertension. 80% of older adults in the United States have been diagnosed with hypertension. Appropriate levels of PA have positive effects on heart health for older adults with hypertension (Stamatakis et al., 2007; Sun et al., 2013). To promote PA among older hypertensive patients, we propose to develop a mobile application with an evidence-based PA program from NIH (Go4Life) to help older adults become motivated about PA, start, and continue PA.

The first phase of this project involves an investigation of motivational triggers of PA for older adults with hypertension. An abstraction hierarchy can be built to identify key motivators of the PA adoption. Potential factors impacting older hypertensive patients' motivations to start engaging in PA include whether patients feel confident and competent to do PA and whether their family members and clinicians encourage them to do PA (Bethancourt et al., 2014; Lim & Taylor, 2005). Follow-up interviews with older adults with hypertension, their caregiver, and their clinicians may be used to support or challenge the assumptions that both PA self-efficacy and social support could be motivational triggers for older hypertensive patients to start PA.

The second phase consists of assessing what new behaviors to establish. Given that the "Go4Life" PA program is an evidence-based program, we will not modify the processes within the PA program to ensure the program's effectiveness. Rather, we will implement it as designed. This therefore leads us to the third phase.

The third phase focuses on exploring when and how to establish the new behavior (i.e. doing PA). We will follow theories in HAPA to measure the stages of change of the older hypertensive patients using the Physical Activity Stages of Change instrument (Chiu et al., 2011) and other instruments related to PA self-efficacy and perceived social support. The purpose of such measurements is to gauge the readiness of older adults with hypertension to start PA. Based on evidence supporting our assumptions related to motivation and overall findings from the three phases, we will then implement triggers to support PA self-efficacy and social support, including (1) tailored daily messages to promote the PA self-efficacy for older adults with hypertension in the mobile application, (2) a visualization of PA levels that people in their social networks (including family and peers) are achieving daily, and (3) a side panel to display awards and badges which people receive from their social networks for recognizing their progress in the PA program.

Assuming older adults start to do PA, we can conduct the further analysis on the current users to identify ways to help maintain PA after 6 months of use. We can use CTA to investigate how older adults with hypertension start their routine PA with the mobile applications, what problems they are encountering, when and why they stop doing PA, and what makes them resume PA if they do. The CTA will inform future designs of triggers to help sustain the new behavior.

## 11.4  IMPLICATIONS FOR THE FUTURE DESIGN OF HEALTH INFORMATION TECHNOLOGIES

This chapter demonstrated the use of CWA as an analytical framework to support the persuasive design for health promotion. In Table 11.3, we synthesize the main processes in health promotion models, the corresponding triggers in persuasive design, and the relevant analytic methods that fall under the umbrella of CWA. It is no longer acceptable design for health technologies to merely be usable. The patient of the future is no longer just a consumer of health care, but an active participant in their own health. Most health interventions require that patients understand their treatment, adhere to their treatment, and actively participate with other members of their healthcare teams. These requirements mean that technologies must be designed in a

**TABLE 11.3**
**The Synthesized Summary of Health Promotion Models, Persuasive Design, and Cognitive Work Analysis**

|  | Pre-Intention | Intention–Behavior | Post-Intention |
|---|---|---|---|
| Health promotion | Intention | Planning | Adoption, maintenance, recovery |
| Persuasive design | Boost motivation | Support the building of mental model | Maintain the behavior to avoid relapse |
| Cognitive work analysis | Work domain analysis | Control task analysis | Control task analysis |

way that help patients achieve their health goals. Thus, as discussed below, there are several important implications that derive from these ideas.

### 11.4.1 The Users' Existing Behavior Context Must Be Well Understood

Everyone uses new technologies within a context of already existing behavior patterns. A technology that disrupts these patterns is very unlikely to be adopted. By understanding the existing context, new behaviors can be carefully designed to fit within them. Technologies designed this way increase their likelihood of adoption as they are lower effort for users and less disruptive. Particularly, technologies that seek to establish new health behaviors must be responsive to a broad range of extant user behaviors in order to insert new behaviors successfully.

### 11.4.2 There Are Tools That Can Support the Development of Health Promotion Behaviors but More Is Needed

We demonstrated how CWA can inform a Persuasive Design process, but this work is in its infancy. Empirical studies have applied CWA in persuasive design to improve the data entry in primary care (Burns et al., 2018; St. Maurice et al., 2018). However, this approach has not been systematically applied to patient health promotion. Health promotion requires more self-management, autonomy, and planning for long-term behavior change. Hence, our design will not end at building a sociotechnical solution that is feasible and acceptable for patients to adopt. Rather, challenges come from the continuous use of the sociotechnical solution to support their long-term behavior change. Therefore, we will need health promotion models to help inform the integration of these two approaches, CWA and persuasive design.

### 11.4.3 Theory-Driven Design in Health Promotion Is Required

We have shown that new behaviors can be planned and technology can be designed to encourage those behaviors. Existing theories in persuasive design, such as the Fogg Behavioral Model and a Persuasive System Design Framework (Fogg & Fogg, 2003; Oinas-Kukkonen & Harjumaa, 2008), often consider behavior change as a continuum with factors (such as motivation and ability) contributing to the change independently. In other words, these existing models put more focus on changing the "factors" associated with behavior change, rather than the "processes" within the behavior change. For example, we can design an app to send regulatory fit messages to adults to promote their behavioral intention to do exercise, but the messages solely cannot prepare adults to move from intention to behavior without supporting the "planning" process. Accounting for processes is particularly important to prepare adults to "plan" their new behavior if the health behavior is complex, such as designing to support the in-home physical rehabilitation for patients with spinal cord injuries or stroke after being discharged from the clinic. Health promotion models underscore the fact that behavior change (especially long-term behavior changes such as lifestyle habit change, rehabilitation, treatment adherence) in health promotion is complex and diverse. Hence, bridging theories in health promotion models with persuasive design could help us build more solid sociotechnical solutions to support both factors and processes contributing to the sustained change of health behavior. CWA will then serve as a robust tool to facilitate this bridging from health promotion models to persuasive design by identifying critical factors and processes to change. Therefore, future studies applying CWA to design sociotechnical solutions for supporting health promotion are at frontier for patient ergonomics research and practice.

## REFERENCES

Ajzen, I. (1985). From intentions to actions: A theory of planned behavior. In J. Kuhl & J. Beckmann (Eds.), *Action Control* (pp. 11–39). Springer, Berlin Heidelberg.

Ajzen, I. (1991). The theory of planned behavior. *Organizational Behavior and Human Decision Processes*, *50*(2), 179–211.

Ajzen, I., & Fishbein, M. (1977). Attitude-behavior relations: A theoretical analysis and review of empirical research. *Psychological Bulletin*, *84*(5), 888–918.

Albarracín, D., Johnson, B. T., Fishbein, M., & Muellerleile, P. A. (2001). Theories of reasoned action and planned behavior as models of condom use: A meta-analysis. *Psychological Bulletin*, *127*(1), 142–161.

Bandura, A. (1977). Self-efficacy: Toward a unifying theory of behavioral change. *Psychological Review*, *84*(2), 191–215.

Bandura, A. (1989). Human agency in social cognitive theory. *American Psychologist*, *44*(9), 1175–1184.

Bethancourt, H. J., Rosenberg, D. E., Beatty, T., & Arterburn, D. E. (2014). Barriers to and facilitators of physical activity program use among older adults. *Clinical Medicine & Research*, *12*(1–2), 10–20.

Bodenheimer, T. (2002). Patient self-management of chronic disease in primary care. *Journal of the American Medical Association*, *288*(19), 2469.

Burns, C., Rezai, L. S., & Maurice, J. S. (2018). Understanding the context for health behavior change with Cognitive Work Analysis and Persuasive Design. *Hawaii International Conference on System Sciences 2018 (HICSS-51)*. Retrieved from https://aisel.aisnet.org/hicss-51/hc/health_behavior/3.

Carpenter, C. J. (2010). A meta-analysis of the effectiveness of Health Belief Model variables in predicting behavior. *Health Communication*, *25*(8), 661–669.

Chapman, K., & Ogden, J. (2012). Nudging customers towards healthier choices: An intervention in the University Canteen. *Journal of Food Research*, *1*(2), 13.

Chiu, C.-Y., Lynch, R. T., Chan, F., & Berven, N. L. (2011). The Health Action Process Approach as a motivational model for physical activity self-management for people with multiple sclerosis: A path analysis. *Rehabilitation Psychology*, *56*(3), 171–181.

Cioffi, C. E., Levitsky, D. A., Pacanowski, C. R., & Bertz, F. (2015). A nudge in a healthy direction. The effect of nutrition labels on food purchasing behaviors in university dining facilities. *Appetite*, *92*, 7–14.

Crowe, E., & Higgins, E. T. (1997). Regulatory focus and strategic inclinations: Promotion and prevention in decision-making. *Organizational Behavior and Human Decision Processes*, *69*(2), 117–132.

Dayan, E., & Bar-Hillel, M. (2011). Nudge to nobesity II: Menu positions influence food orders. *Judgment and Decision Making*, *6*(4), 333–342.

Floyd, D. L., Prentice-Dunn, S., & Rogers, R. W. (2000). A meta-analysis of research on Protection Motivation Theory. *Journal of Applied Social Psychology*, *30*(2), 407–429.

Fogg, B. (2009). A behavior model for persuasive design. *Proceedings of the 4th International Conference on Persuasive Technology - Persuasive '09*, 1.

Fogg, B. J., & Fogg, G. E. (2003). *Persuasive Technology: Using Computers to Change What We Think and Do.* San Francisco, CA: Morgan Kaufmann.

Gaston, A., & Prapavessis, H. (2014). Using a combined protection motivation theory and health action process approach intervention to promote exercise during pregnancy. *Journal of Behavioral Medicine, 37*(2), 173–184.

Graves, K. D. (2003). Social cognitive theory and cancer patients' quality of life: A meta-analysis of psychosocial intervention components. *Health Psychology, 22*(2), 210–219.

Gwaltney, C. J., Metrik, J., Kahler, C. W., & Shiffman, S. (2009). Self-efficacy and smoking cessation: A meta-analysis. *Psychology of Addictive Behaviors, 23*(1), 56–66.

Harrison, J. A., Mullen, P. D., & Green, L. W. (1992). A meta-analysis of studies of the Health Belief Model with adults. *Health Education Research, 7*(1), 107–116.

Hausenblas, H. A., Carron, A. V., & Mack, D. E. (1997). Application of the theories of reasoned action and planned behavior to exercise behavior: A meta-analysis. *Journal of Sport & Exercise Psychology, 19*(1), 36–51.

Higgins, E. T. (1998). Promotion and prevention: Regulatory focus as a motivational principle. *Advances in Experimental Social Psychology, 30*, 1–46. Elsevier.

Hutchison, A. J., Breckon, J. D., & Johnston, L. H. (2009). Physical activity behavior change interventions based on the Transtheoretical Model: A systematic review. *Health Education & Behavior, 36*(5), 829–845.

Janz, N. K., & Becker, M. H. (1984). The Health Belief Model: A decade later. *Health Education & Behavior, 11*(1), 1–47.

Kraak, V. I., Englund, T., Misyak, S., & Serrano, E. L. (2017). A novel marketing mix and choice architecture framework to nudge restaurant customers toward healthy food environments to reduce obesity in the United States: A marketing and nudge framework for restaurants. *Obesity Reviews, 18*(8), 852–868.

Kroese, F. M., Marchiori, D. R., & de Ridder, D. T. D. (2016). Nudging healthy food choices: A field experiment at the train station. *Journal of Public Health, 38*(2), e133–e137.

Latimer, A. E., Williams-Piehota, P., Katulak, N. A., Cox, A., Mowad, L., Higgins, E. T., & Salovey, P. (2008). Promoting fruit and vegetable intake through messages tailored to individual differences in regulatory focus. *Annals of Behavioral Medicine, 35*(3), 363–369.

Lim, K., & Taylor, L. (2005). Factors associated with physical activity among older people— A population-based study. *Preventive Medicine, 40*(1), 33–40.

Lippke, S., Ziegelmann, J. P., & Schwarzer, R. (2004). Initiation and maintenance of physical exercise: Stage-specific effects of a planning intervention. *Research in Sports Medicine, 12*(3), 221–240.

Lockwood, P., Jordan, C. H., & Kunda, Z. (2002). Motivation by positive or negative role models: Regulatory focus determines who will best inspire us. *Journal of Personality and Social Psychology, 83*(4), 854–864.

Maddux, J. E., & Rogers, R. W. (1983). Protection motivation and self-efficacy: A revised theory of fear appeals and attitude change. *Journal of Experimental Social Psychology, 19*(5), 469–479.

Marshall, S. J., & Biddle, S. J. H. (2001). The transtheoretical model of behavior change: A meta-analysis of applications to physical activity and exercise. *Annals of Behavioral Medicine, 23*(4), 229–246.

Mastellos, N., Gunn, L. H., Felix, L. M., Car, J., & Majeed, A. (2014). Transtheoretical model stages of change for dietary and physical exercise modification in weight loss management for overweight and obese adults. *Cochrane Database of Systematic Reviews, 2*, CD008066.

Merriam-Webster (n.d.). Habit. In *Merriam-Webster online dictionary.* Retrieved from https://www.merriam-webster.com/dictionary/habit.

Milne, S., Sheeran, P., & Orbell, S. (2000). Prediction and intervention in health-related behavior: A meta-analytic review of Protection Motivation Theory. *Journal of Applied Social Psychology, 30*(1), 106–143.

Mohr, D. C., Schueller, S. M., Montague, E., Burns, M. N., & Rashidi, P. (2014). The Behavioral Intervention Technology Model: An integrated conceptual and technological framework for eHealth and mHealth Interventions. *Journal of Medical Internet Research, 16*(6), e146.

Oinas-Kukkonen, H., & Harjumaa, M. (2008). A systematic framework for designing and evaluating persuasive systems. In H. Oinas-Kukkonen, P. Hasle, M. Harjumaa, K. Segerståhl, & P. Øhrstrøm (Eds.), *Persuasive Technology* (Vol. 5033, pp. 164–176). Springer, Berlin Heidelberg.

Parschau, L., Barz, M., Richert, J., Knoll, N., Lippke, S., & Schwarzer, R. (2014). Physical activity among adults with obesity: Testing the health action process approach. *Rehabilitation Psychology, 59*(1), 42–49.

Pechmann, C., Zhao, G., Goldberg, M. E., & Reibling, E. T. (2003). What to convey in anti-smoking advertisements for adolescents: The use of Protection Motivation Theory to identify effective message themes. *Journal of Marketing, 67*(2), 1–18.

Prentice-Dunn, S., & Rogers, R. W. (1986). Protection Motivation Theory and preventive health: Beyond the Health Belief Model. *Health Education Research, 1*(3), 153–161.

Prochaska, J., & DiClemente, C. (1982). Transtheoretical therapy: Toward a more integrative model of change. *Psychotherapy: Theory, Research & Practice, 19*(3), 276–288.

Prochaska, J., & DiClemente, C. (1983). Stages and processes of self-change of smoking: Toward an integrative model of change. *Journal of Consulting and Clinical Psychology, 51*(3), 390–395.

Prochaska, J. O., Redding, C. A., Harlow, L. L., Rossi, J. S., & Velicer, W. F. (1994). The Transtheoretical Model of change and HIV prevention: A review. *Health Education Quarterly, 21*(4), 471–486.

Rabbi, M., Aung, M. H., Zhang, M., & Choudhury, T. (2015). MyBehavior: Automatic personalized health feedback from user behaviors and preferences using smartphones. *Proceedings of the 2015 Association for Computing Machinery International Joint Conference on Pervasive and Ubiquitous Computing - UbiComp '15*, 707–718.

Rasmussen, J. (1985). The role of hierarchical knowledge representation in decisionmaking and system management. *Institute of Electrical and Electronics Engineers Transactions on Systems, Man, and Cybernetics, SMC, 15*(2), 234–243.

Rasmussen, J., Pejtersen, A. M., & Goodstein, L. P. (1994). *Cognitive Systems Engineering.* New York, NY: John Wiley & Sons, Inc.

Rezai, L., & Burns, C. (2014). Using Cognitive Work Analysis and a Persuasive Design Approach to create effective blood pressure management systems. *Proceedings of the International Symposium on Human Factors and Ergonomics in Health Care, 3*(1), 36–43.

Rich, A., Brandes, K., Mullan, B., & Hagger, M. S. (2015). Theory of planned behavior and adherence in chronic illness: A meta-analysis. *Journal of Behavioral Medicine, 38*(4), 673–688.

Rosenstock, I. M. (1974). Historical origins of the Health Belief Model. *Health Education Monographs, 2*(4), 328–335.

Rozin, P., Scott, S. E., Dingley, M., Urbanek, J., Jiang, H., & Kaltenbach, M. (2011). Nudge to nobesity I: Minor changes in accessibility decrease food intake. *Judgment and Decision Making, 6*(4), 323–332.

Rezai, L., Chin, J., Casares-Li, R., He, F., Bassett-Gunter, R., & Burns, C. (2019). Can message-tailoring based on Regulatory Fit Theory improve the efficacy of persuasive physical activity systems? *Information, 10*(11), 347.

Schwarzer, R. (1999). Self-regulatory processes in the adoption and maintenance of health behaviors. *Journal of Health Psychology, 4*(2), 115–127.

Schwarzer, R. (2001). Social-cognitive factors in changing health-related behaviors. *Current Directions in Psychological Science, 10*(2), 47–51.

Schwarzer, R., Lippke, S., & Luszczynska, A. (2011). Mechanisms of health behavior change in persons with chronic illness or disability: The Health Action Process Approach (HAPA). *Rehabilitation Psychology, 56*(3), 161–170.

Schwarzer, R., & Renner, B. (2000). Social-cognitive predictors of health behavior: Action self-efficacy and coping self-efficacy. *Health Psychology, 19*(5), 487–495.

Sniehotta, F. F., Scholz, U., & Schwarzer, R. (2005). Bridging the intention–behaviour gap: Planning, self-efficacy, and action control in the adoption and maintenance of physical exercise. *Psychology & Health, 20*(2), 143–160.

Spencer, L., Pagell, F., & Adams, T. (2005). Applying the Transtheoretical Model to cancer screening behavior. *American Journal of Health Behavior, 29*(1), 36–56.

Spencer, L., Pagell, F., Hallion, M. E., & Adams, T. B. (2002). Applying the Transtheoretical Model to tobacco cessation and prevention: A review of literature. *American Journal of Health Promotion, 17*(1), 7–71.

St. Maurice, J., & Burns, C. (2015). Using comparative cognitive work analysis to identify design priorities in complex socio-technical systems. *Proceedings of the International Symposium on Human Factors and Ergonomics in Health Care, 4*(1), 118–123.

St. Maurice, J., Burns, C., & Wolting, J. (2018). Applying persuasive design techniques to influence data-entry behaviors in primary care: Repeated measures evaluation using statistical process control. *Journal of Medical Internet Research Human Factors, 5*(4), e28.

Stacey, F. G., James, E. L., Chapman, K., Courneya, K. S., & Lubans, D. R. (2015). A systematic review and meta-analysis of social cognitive theory-based physical activity and/or nutrition behavior change interventions for cancer survivors. *Journal of Cancer Survivorship, 9*(2), 305–338.

Stamatakis, E., Hillsdon, M., & Primatesta, P. (2007). Domestic physical activity in relationship to multiple CVD risk factors. *American Journal of Preventive Medicine, 32*(4), 320–327.e3.

Sun, F., Norman, I. J., & While, A. E. (2013). Physical activity in older people: A systematic review. *BioMed Central Public Health, 13*(1), 449.

Sutton, S. (2001). Back to the drawing board? A review of applications of the transtheoretical model to substance use. *Addiction, 96*(1), 175–186.

Thaler, R., & Sunstein, C. R. (2009). *Nudge: Improving Decisions about Health, Wealth and Happiness*. Penguin Books Limited, New York.

Topa, & Moriano Leon. (2010). Theory of planned behavior and smoking: Meta-analysis and SEM model. *Substance Abuse and Rehabilitation, 1*, 23-33.

Vicente, K. J. (1999). *Cognitive Work Analysis: Toward Safe, Productive, and Healthy Computer-Based Work*. Mahwah, NJ: CRC Press.

Weinstein, N. D., Kwitel, A., McCaul, K. D., Magnan, R. E., Gerrard, M., & Gibbons, F. X. (2007). Risk perceptions: Assessment and relationship to influenza vaccination. *Health Psychology, 26*(2), 146–151.

Wurtele, S. K., & Maddux, J. E. (1987). Relative contributions of protection motivation theory components in predicting exercise intentions and behavior. *Health Psychology, 6*(5), 453–466.

Young, M. D., Plotnikoff, R. C., Collins, C. E., Callister, R., & Morgan, P. J. (2014). Social cognitive theory and physical activity: A systematic review and meta-analysis: Social cognitive theory and physical activity. *Obesity Reviews, 15*(12), 983–995.

Zhang, C.-Q., Zhang, R., Schwarzer, R., & Hagger, M. S. (2019). A meta-analysis of the health action process approach. *Health Psychology, 38*(7), 623–637.

# Section IV

## Conclusion

# 12 Key Takeaways for Applying Patient Ergonomics across Settings and Populations

*Rupa S. Valdez*
University of Virginia

*Richard J. Holden*
Indiana University School of Medicine

## CONTENTS

The practice of human factors and ergonomics (HFE) in health care may be considered a mature discipline with over 50 years of scholarship dedicated to this intersection. What began as a handful of publications in the middle of the last century (Chapanis & Safrin, 1960; Hindle, 1968; Rappaport, 1970) has since grown into a large, multidisciplinary community of practice. These days, the Health Care Technical Group of the U.S. Human Factors and Ergonomics Society is one of the most robust and active within the organization. Moreover, health care is the focus of the society's second largest annual meeting, the International Symposium on Human Factors and Ergonomics in Health Care (Health Care Symposium).

Traditionally, the practice of HFE in health care has focused predominately on institutional settings of care and the work of healthcare professionals in these settings. In other words, HFE professionals have historically sought to improve the work performance of physicians, nurses, pharmacists, and similar paid, trained staff in clinical and hospital spaces. As the field has gained traction, smaller communities of practice have emerged under this larger umbrella. This can be seen in the structure of the Health Care Symposium, which this previous year was divided into multiple tracks, including healthcare environments, consumer and clinical health care information technology (IT), patient safety research and initiatives, and medical- and drug-delivery devices. Further, as demonstrated through panels at recent conferences, less formalized communities of practice have emerged on certain settings (emergency department, intensive care unit) (Maguire et al., 2019; Wang et al., 2019) and populations (hospital patients receiving palliative care, patients with breast cancer) (Ebnali et al., 2019; Patterson et al., 2019).

Through this handbook, we attempted to encourage both an overall community of practice in patient ergonomics and the development of smaller communities of practice focused on specific settings and populations. Volume I in this handbook brings together the general theories, methods, and approaches that form the foundation for all researchers and practitioners engaging in patient ergonomics. Volume II builds upon this broader foundation by exploring the ways in which patient ergonomics must be and has been adapted to particular contexts. Such smaller communities of practice either have been established, as in the case of older adults (Czaja et al., 2019; Mitzner et al., 2009) or culturally informed consumer health IT (Holden & Valdez, 2019; Montague et al., 2013, 2014; Zayas-Cabán & Marquard, 2009), or are emerging, for example, focusing on marginalized communities (Valdez et al., 2019) and children with medical complexities (Werner et al., 2020). As this growth continues, we anticipate patient ergonomics to be more attentive to the type of people performing work and the settings in which they perform such work.

## 12.1  EIGHT IDEAS TO KEEP IN MIND ABOUT PATIENT ERGONOMICS ACROSS CONTEXTS

Although each chapter in Volume II explores a particular context and draws implications for patient ergonomics in that space, common themes emerge across chapters. These themes may be thought of as key points to consider when practicing patient ergonomics in these contexts and other contexts not explicitly covered in this volume.

### 12.1.1  PATIENT WORK IS UBIQUITOUS

As a collective, the chapters in this volume emphasize the range of individuals engaged in patient work and locations in which such work takes place. It would not be an exaggeration to say that everyone engages in some form of patient work. Even individuals not currently living with a chronic health condition or experiencing an acute health-related event engage in patient work, sometimes automatically such as when choosing what foods to select from a range of options (see Chapter 11). Home and community settings are central to patient work as much of this work occurs in the intervals between interactions with health professionals (e.g. Chapters 4 and 5). Beyond this, however, patient work also takes place in settings that are typically thought of as spaces for professional work (see Chapter 2) and settings not predominately associated with health care (see Chapter 6).

### 12.1.2 Patient Work Is Shaped by Context

Although certain tasks and processes associated with patient work may be seen across contexts (e.g. managing medication, seeking information), the particular ways in which they are performed vary significantly by context. As a result, the ways in which a particular task or process must be supported are unlikely to be uniform across settings and populations. For example, information seeking is an aspect of patient work salient in emergency departments, community pharmacies, and online health communities, among others (see Chapters 2, 5, and 6 respectively). Yet, in each setting, the ways in which concepts such as trust, cognitive workload, information chaos, and situation awareness must be considered differ. Similarly, supporting medication management in different populations may require attention to varying needs. Managing medications for a chronically ill young child or older adult, for example, may require particular consideration of the role of one or more informal caregivers and the coordination of multiple medication regimens (Chapters 8 and 9). In contrast, medication management for a relatively healthy young adult who is a non-English speaker may require more attention to questions of literacy (Chapter 10).

### 12.1.3 Patient Work Is Not Experienced Equally

Although patient work is seen across settings and populations, the engagement of such efforts is not equitably experienced. The most obvious distinction may be between individuals who are generally healthy and those who live with chronic health conditions. Individuals who are generally well and predominately engage in patient work as a health-seeking behavior may spend limited amounts of time on health-related activities. In contrast, those managing chronic health conditions may need to engage in such activities on an ongoing basis. Often less attended to, though, is the differential impact across populations who experience health disparities. For such populations, a similar task may require additional patient work in comparison to a more privileged population. For example, reading and making sense of an after-visit summary may be more difficult for an individual with low literacy or low English proficiency (see Chapter 10). Similarly, adhering to an agreed-upon diet may be more challenging for an individual with a limited budget and unreliable access to nutritious foods.

### 12.1.4 Patient Work Is Intertwined with the Work of Others

Although the term patient work may often evoke the image of an individual performing work in isolation (Yin et al., 2020), in reality, patient work may be deeply intertwined with the work of others. In some cases, others may consist of informal caregivers who play a consistent and significant role such as in the case of young children and older adults (see Chapters 8 and 9). In other cases, the individuals engaged in patient work may also include other people in the patient's social networks, spanning multiple family members, friends, and community members (Skeels et al., 2010; Valdez & Brennan, 2015). Additionally, patients may perform patient work in concert with other patients, in particular sharing efforts related to information seeking and sensemaking through both offline and online support groups (see Chapter 6). Such mutual engagement may also take the form of collective events in which patients encourage each other to pursue a given health-related goal (see Chapter 7). Finally, patient work may occur in tandem with professional work, a form of patient work we call "collaborative" (Holden et al., 2013). The range of professionals with whom patients collaborate varies greatly and is shaped both by the patients' needs and setting of interaction. Together this intertwinement of work and workers can be referred to as the work of collectives (Holden et al., 2013).

### 12.1.5 PATIENT WORK IS A CONTINUUM

Although in this volume, we make distinctions between settings of patient work, in reality, patient work is experienced as a continuum. An individual living with asthma often engages in symptom tracking and medication management in home and community settings. During a severe exacerbation, the same individual must perform behaviors related to patient–professional communication and shared decision-making in a clinical setting. Upon returning home, they may have to coordinate with other family members to modify their routine, preventing another similar occurrence. This simplified example illustrates that, for any given patient, work flows between all settings and integrates different considerations in each. In other words, patient work may be thought of in terms of patient-oriented workflow (Ozkaynak et al., 2017) or a patient journey (Carayon et al., 2020). As such, patient ergonomists must account for transitions between the settings in which patient ergonomics take place (see Chapter 3).

### 12.1.6 PATIENT WORK IS SUPPORTED BY TECHNOLOGY

Although efforts by HFE professionals to support patient work may take many forms, interventions that are founded in technology have been a key focal area. The potential of consumer health information technology (IT) as a means of supporting patient work may be seen across home, community, clinical, and virtual settings (e.g. Chapters 2, 4, 6, 7, and 10). It is imperative, however, for HFE researchers and practitioners to explicitly account for the particular technological needs of a wide range of populations, including those who have been historically underserved. Failure to do so may inadvertently lead to the exacerbation of both the digital divide and persistent health disparities (Gibbons, 2005; Siek et al., 2019). As such, we urge those seeking to support patient work through consumer health IT to purposefully include a wide range of populations in their design efforts (Antonio et al., 2019) and explicitly account for the ways in which sociocultural factors, among others, may shape appropriate design and implementation (Valdez et al., 2012).

### 12.1.7 PATIENT ERGONOMICS DRAWS MEANINGFULLY ON OTHER DISCIPLINES

Although patient ergonomics claims HFE as its home discipline, in reality, it draws on a wide array of disciplines. In addition to integrating theories and methods from related disciplines such as human–computer interaction and applied psychology. It also draws on work from a wide range of health-related disciplines, including nursing (Chapters 2 and 7), pharmacy (Chapter 5), public health (Chapters 4, 10, and 11), primary care (Chapters 6 and 9), behavioral science (Chapter 10), and gerontology (Chapter 9). Furthermore, emerging efforts have sought to learn from disciplines in which participatory and community-engaged approaches are well developed (see Chapters 7, 9, and 10) (Unertl et al., 2016; Valdez & Edmunds, 2019). As the field grows, there is an opportunity for HFE professionals to engage in truly interdisciplinary and transdisciplinary efforts. The integration of other disciplines into HFE practice has been long championed (Moray, 1993, 2000) and has already been demonstrated as essential for the practice of patient ergonomics.

### 12.1.8 PATIENT ERGONOMICS IS AN EMERGENT DISCIPLINE

Although this handbook brings together numerous scholars engaging in the field of patient ergonomics, the field may be best characterized as an emergent discipline. As noted in many literature reviews throughout the chapters of this volume, efforts aimed at applying patient ergonomics across settings and populations remain nascent. Case studies illustrate the essential need for basic research to understand and characterize patient work across contexts. Consequently, many of the examples provided emphasis on the role of qualitative research early in the design process (e.g. Chapters 3, 4, 7, and 10). As the field matures, efforts to systematically capture and communicate patient work across settings and populations will serve as a robust foundation for intervention design and testing.

## 12.2 A CALL TO ACTION

Over half a century ago, the value of HFE theories, methods, and approaches to health care was still in its latent stages. In many ways, patient ergonomics today may be similarly conceptualized. The potential of patient ergonomics to make significant and meaningful contributions not only to patients' health outcomes but also to their broader everyday lives as patients is undeniable. Much work, however, remains to be done to realize this potential, and such a potential relies on the steady growth of a community of practice. In this volume, we explored a range of settings and populations for the application of patient ergonomics, but those we included are far from exhaustive. There are more opportunities than may be named here, but some populations include rural populations, refugees and other immigrants, people with disabilities, family caregivers, and adolescents. Potential additional settings include nursing homes, congregate living spaces, dormitories, homeless shelters, prisons, and airplanes or other transit vehicles. Through this handbook, we have attempted to not only bring together researchers and practitioners but also encourage you, the reader, to lend your expertise to this growing movement. Together, we can transform health and health care for all—now!

## REFERENCES

Antonio, M. G., Petrovskaya, O., & Lau, F. (2019). Is research on patient portals attuned to health equity? A scoping review. *Journal of the American Medical Informatics Association, 26*(8–9), 871–883.

Carayon, P., Wooldridge, A., Hoonakker, P., Hundt, A. S., & Kelly, M. M. (2020). SEIPS 3.0: Human-centered design of the patient journey for patient safety. *Applied Ergonomics, 84*, 103033.

Chapanis, A., & Safrin, M. A. (1960). Of misses and medicine. *Journal of Chronic Diseases, 12*, 403–408.

Czaja, S. J., Boot, W. R., Charness, N., Rogers, W. A., Boot, W. R., Charness, N., & Rogers, W. A. (2019). *Designing for older adults: Principles and creative human factors approaches*, Third Edition. Boca Raton, FL: CRC Press.

Ebnali, M., Shah, M., & Mazloumi, A. (2019). How mHealth apps with higher usability effects on patients with breast cancer? In the *Proceedings of the International Symposium on Human Factors and Ergonomics in Health Care, 8*(1), 81–84.

Gibbons, M. C. (2005). A historical overview of health disparities and the potential of eHealth solutions. *Journal of Medical Internet Research, 7*(5), e50.

Hindle, A. (1968). A systems approach to hospital management. *Operational Research Quarterly, 22*, 39–55.

Holden, R. J., Carayon, P., Gurses, A. P., Hoonakker, P., Hundt, A. S., Ozok, A. A., & Rivera-Rodriguez, A. J. (2013). SEIPS 2.0: A human factors framework for studying and improving the work of healthcare professionals and patients. *Ergonomics, 56*(11), 1–30.

Holden, R. J., & Valdez, R. S. (2019). Beyond disease: Technologies for health promotion. *Proceedings of the International Symposium on Human Factors and Ergonomics in Health Care, 8*(1), 62–66.

Maguire, L. M. D., Vazquez, D. E., Haney, A., Byrd, C., & Sanders, E. B.-N. (2019). Transdisciplinary co-design to envision the needs of the intensive care unit of the future. *Proceedings of the International Symposium on Human Factors and Ergonomics in Health Care, 8*(1), 181–181.

Mitzner, T. L., Beer, J. M., McBride, S. E., Rogers, W. A., & Fisk, A. D. (2009). Older adults' needs for home health care and the potential for human factors interventions. *Proceedings of the Human Factors and Ergonomics Society Annual Meeting, 53*(11), 718–722.

Montague, E., Valdez, R. S., Burns, M., Barnes, L., & Vaughn-Cooke, M. (2014). *Considering culture in the design of health information technology: Lessons learned and experiences.* Presented at the 2014 Human Factors and Ergonomics Society International Annual Meeting.

Montague, E., Winchester, W., Valdez, R. S., Vaughn-Cooke, M., & Perchonok, J. (2013). Considering culture in the design and evaluation of health IT for patients. In the *Proceedings of the 2013 Human Factors and Ergonomics Society International Annual Meeting*, 1088–1092.

Moray, N. (1993). Technosophy and Humane Factors. *Ergonomics in Design, 1*(4), 33–39.

Moray, N. (2000). Culture, politics and ergonomics. *Ergonomics, 43*(7), 858–868.

Ozkaynak, M., Valdez, R., Holden, R. J., & Weiss, J. (2017). Infinicare framework for integrated understanding of health-related activities in clinical and daily-living contexts. *Health Systems, 7*(1), 66–78.

Patterson, E. S., Hritz, C., & Moffatt-Bruce, S. (2019). Reducing alert fatigue for comfort care and palliative care hospital patients. *Proceedings of the International Symposium on Human Factors and Ergonomics in Health Care, 8*(1), 1–3.

Rappaport, M. (1970). Human factors applications in medicine. *Human Factors, 12*(1), 25–35.

Siek, K., Veinot, T., & Mynatt, B. (2019). Research opportunities in sociotechnical interventions for health disparity reduction. *Computing Community Consortium. ArXiv:1908.01035 [Cs]*.

Skeels, M. M., Unruh, K. T., Powell, C., & Pratt, W. (2010). Catalyzing social support for breast cancer patients. *Proceedings of the SIGCHI Conference on Human Factors in Computing Systems*, 173–182.

Unertl, K. M., Schaefbauer, C. L., Campbell, T. R., Senteio, C., Siek, K. A., Bakken, S., & Veinot, T. C. (2016). Integrating community-based participatory research and informatics approaches to improve the engagement and health of underserved populations. *Journal of the American Medical Informatics Association, 23*(1), 60–73.

Valdez, R.S., & Brennan, P. F. (2015). Exploring patients' health information communication practices with social network members as a foundation for consumer health IT design. *International Journal of Medical Informatics, 84*(5), 363–374.

Valdez, R.S., & Edmunds, D. (2019). Community-based research and action in human factors: A dialogue across disciplines. In R. Roscoe, E. Chiou, A. Wooldridge (Eds.). *Advancing Diversity, Inclusion, and Social Justice through Human Systems Engineering*. Boca Raton, FL: CRC Press, Taylor and Francis Group.

Valdez, R.S., Gibbons, M. C., Siegel, E. R., Kukafka, R., & Brennan, P. F. (2012). Designing consumer health IT to enhance usability among different racial and ethnic groups within the United States. *Health and Technology, 2*(4), 225–233.

Valdez, R.S., Holden, R. J., Madathil, K., Benda, N., Holden, R. J., Montague, E., & Werner, N. (2019). An exploration of patient ergonomics in historically marginalized communities. *Proceedings of the Human Factors and Ergonomics Society Annual Meeting, 63*(1), 914–918.

Wang, X., Blumenthal, H. J., Hoffman, D., Benda, N., Kim, T., Perry, S., Franklin, E. S., Roth, E. M., Hettinger, A. Z., & Bisantz, A. M. (2019). Patient-related workload prediction in the emergency department: A big data approach. *Proceedings of the International Symposium on Human Factors and Ergonomics in Health Care, 8*(1), 33–36.

Werner, N., Valdez, R. S., Coller, R., Finesilver, S., Lunsford, C., & Barton, H. (2020). *Children with medical complexity: Challenges and opportunities for human factors/ergonomics*. Virtual Human Factor and Ergonomics Society 2020 Annual Meeting.

Yin, K., Jung, J., Coiera, E., Laranjo, L., Blandford, A., Khoja, A., Tai, W.-T., Phillips, D. P., & Lau, A. Y. S. (2020). Patient work and their contexts: Scoping review. *Journal of Medical Internet Research, 22*(6), e16656.

Zayas-Cabán, T., & Marquard, J. L. (2009). A holistic human factors evaluation framework for the design of consumer health informatics interventions. *Proceedings of the Human actors and Ergonomics Society Annual Meeting, 53*(16), 1003–1007.

# Index

Note: **Bold** page numbers refer to tables and *italic* page numbers refer to figures.